ACT® Coach

Science

ACT® Coach, Science
494NA
ISBN: 978-1-62362-102-5

Contributing Writer: Northeast Editing, Inc.
Cover Image: ©Thinkstock

Triumph Learning® 136 Madison Avenue, 7th Floor, New York, NY 10016

DEAR STUDENT,

Welcome to *ACT® Coach, Science*—your learning path to success!

The ACT® Science Test is designed to test your reasoning skills in the context of biology, physics, chemistry, Earth science, and space science. The creators of the ACT® can draw on over 40 science topics—ranging from atomic structure to taxonomy—when developing passages and questions for the test. We believe that success on the ACT® Science Test begins with a mastery of these topics.

When you understand key science concepts, you know what kind of information to look for as you read a passage on the ACT®. You can quickly identify what a question is asking and how to find the answer. Most important, you won't waste precious minutes sorting out the details of a complex topic, such as photosynthesis or the periodic table. This book will help you review the science content you need to know for test day as you sharpen your science reasoning skills.

ACT® Coach, Science is organized into chapters and lessons, and includes a Pretest and a Posttest. Chapter 1 focuses specifically on the science reasoning skills that you'll use on the ACT®; Chapters 2 through 10 provide a review of science content. You can check your understanding by answering the questions at the end of each lesson. The chapter reviews and practice tests contain questions like those on the ACT®. Answering these ACT®-based questions will allow you to assess your reasoning skills and target the science topics you need to review.

We wish you lots of success on the ACT® and are glad Triumph Learning can be a part of it!

Sincerely,

THE TRIUMPH LEARNING TEAM

Contents

Chapter 1

Scientific Inquiry

The Practice of Science

Key Words • science • scientific inquiry • hypothesis • prediction • experiment • procedure • analyze • conclusion • laboratory report • replicate

Getting the Idea

The word *science* comes from a Latin word that means "knowledge." In its broadest sense, **science** refers to the study of anything related to the natural world. The specific methods and techniques used to study different aspects of the natural world can vary. For example, field ecologists study animals in the wild, while experimental physicists build machines to study particles that are not normally found in nature. However, the discovery of all scientific knowledge is guided by the same basic principles.

The Inquiry Process

The discovery of scientific knowledge is driven by scientific inquiry. **Scientific inquiry** involves posing a question and then using a variety of scientific techniques to find the answer to that question.

Most questions that drive scientific inquiry come from observations. Imagine you are watching a newscast about winter weather in a northern state. You see trucks spreading salt on highways to melt snow. You wonder, "If salt decreases the temperature at which ice melts, how does salt affect the boiling point of water?" You are asking a question that can be studied through further observation, testing, and analysis. In fact, this question has been studied by chemists.

Formulating a hypothesis and testing it with an investigation is often part of scientific inquiry. A **hypothesis** (pl. *hypotheses*) is a possible answer to a scientific question. It can be a **prediction** of what will happen if you alter something in a certain way. A hypothesis must be testable. In other words, there must be some way to show whether the hypothesis is supported. (A hypothesis can be testable even if the technology to test it does not currently exist. A hypothesis may be made but not tested until many years later, when new techniques and equipment are available.)

Scientists develop hypotheses through logical reasoning, direct observations, and a knowledge and understanding of basic science. Reading scientific literature is crucial to understanding the science leading to a hypothesis. Sources include scientific journals and the published research results of other scientists.

Suppose you read the scientific literature and find that salt lowers the freezing point of water. You might then form this hypothesis: Adding salt to water will lower the boiling point of the water.

After forming a hypothesis, a scientist develops a test for the hypothesis. This test is called an **experiment**. When you design an experiment, you plan the specific steps you will follow. A **procedure** is the written step-by-step plan for an experiment. The procedure includes the tools and materials that will be needed to carry out the experiment and states how those tools and materials will be used to gather information.

In your experiment on how salt affects the boiling point of water, your procedure might look like the one shown here:

1. Label five 100-mL beakers as **no salt**, **10 mg**, **20 mg**, **30 mg** and **40 mg**.
2. Add 50 mL of water to each beaker.
3. Use a balance to measure out 10 mg, 20 mg, 30 mg, and 40 mg of salt. Place each salt sample into the beaker with the matching label.
4. Use a spoon to stir the contents of each beaker to dissolve as much of the salt as possible.
5. Place each beaker on a hot plate. Heat each beaker until its water begins to boil. Use a thermometer to measure the boiling point of the water and record the measurement.

Recording Experimental Results

Scientists keep a written record of the experimental procedures they perform. This record allows other scientists to review their work and repeat the experiment themselves.

Scientists create a written record by taking detailed notes during their investigations. These notes include all information derived from their research, observations, measurements, and experiments. The scientists use their notes to **analyze**, or study and interpret, this information. The analysis allows a scientist to form a conclusion about the results of a scientific investigation. A **conclusion** explains whether the observations support the hypothesis. You will learn more about drawing conclusions in Lesson 2.

All this information is then used to create a laboratory report. A **laboratory report** is a written account of the purpose, procedure, results, and conclusions of an experiment. One goal of a laboratory report is to show others how to repeat the work.

Communication in Science

Sharing information is an essential part of science. By communicating with each other, scientists build on what is already known about the natural world. Scientists communicate with each other and with the public by speaking at lectures and press conferences or in interviews. Scientists also publish their research in *scientific journals*—magazines used for communicating scientific findings to other scientists. When scientists share information about their research, they need to explain the goal of their work, how the research was done, and their conclusions. They must report their results honestly and objectively.

In science, a conclusion will not be accepted as accurate unless other people can repeat the procedures and obtain similar results—that is, until they can **replicate** the research. When other scientists replicate a research finding, they can be more confident about discoveries and conclusions. Conclusions are more likely to be correct when research is replicated and the same results are obtained. A hypothesis that is verified by many different scientists is likely to become accepted. However, scientists may interpret the same results in different ways. This can lead to disagreements about scientific studies. Such disagreements can help scientists ask better questions, form better hypotheses, and develop better procedures.

Discussion Question

Suppose you performed the experiment described in this lesson to test the hypothesis about the boiling point of water. What would you do if the results of the experiment did not support the hypothesis? Would you conclude that the hypothesis was inadequate, incorrect, or untestable?

Lesson Review

1. A scientist observes that members of a species of gray moths tend to land on trees with gray bark. Which of these is a reasonable hypothesis to test, based on these observations?

    A. If there is no rain, predators will attack both moths and trees.

    B. If the air is polluted, it will harm the trees but not the moths.

    C. When a moth lands on a tree, it changes color to blend in with the bark.

    D. When a moth looks at a tree, it can distinguish the color of the bark.

2. If your experimental results do not support your hypothesis, you should

    A. change your data to support the conclusion you would like.

    B. report your data and conclusion honestly.

    C. report your hypothesis but not your data.

    D. change your hypothesis to match the data.

3. Which is the correct order in which the terms below are applied in a scientific investigation?

    A. hypothesis, procedure, experiment, results, analysis, conclusion

    B. procedure, experiment, hypothesis, analysis, conclusion, results

    C. hypothesis, procedure, experiment, analysis, results, conclusion

    D. procedure, hypothesis, experiment, results, conclusion, analysis

Planning and Conducting an Investigation

Key Words • observation • variable • constant • independent variable • dependent variable • control group • experimental group • trial • data • conclusion • replicate

Getting the Idea

Recall from Lesson 1 that scientific inquiry is a process of asking meaningful questions and seeking answers to those questions. Experiments are an important way scientists try to answer questions.

Tools for Observation and Measurement

Recall from Lesson 1 that scientists often ask a question after making observations. An **observation** is information gathered through the senses. A color, a texture, and a smell are all observations. However, there are many things in the natural world that we cannot observe directly through our senses. For example, many types of electromagnetic radiation are invisible to us but may be observed using X-ray film, an infrared camera, or a radio receiver. A microscope is a tool a scientist can use to view things that are too small to be seen with the unaided eye. Scientists use tools to extend the senses and better observe the natural world. Some other tools scientists may use include graduated cylinders, spring scales, thermometers, balances, metersticks, metric rulers, and stop watches. Scientists select appropriate tools and measuring devices based on the observations they wish to make.

Designing and Conducting Experiments

Recall that an experiment is a test of a *hypothesis*. A hypothesis is often a statement or prediction about how one factor affects another. For example, a hypothesis might be that adding salt to water will lower the boiling point. As discussed in Lesson 1, an experiment might test this hypothesis by adding different amounts of salt to water and determining the temperature at which boiling occurs. Several factors might affect the outcome of this experiment: the volume of water, the amount of salt that was added, and the pressure of the atmosphere. Any factor that can affect the outcome of an experiment is called a **variable**.

In the experiment described in Lesson 1, some factors were deliberately varied (for example, the amount of salt differed for each beaker). Other factors, such as the volume of water, were deliberately kept the same for all the conditions tested. A factor that is kept the same is called a **constant**.

In contrast, some factors must vary in order for an experiment to work. To determine how adding salt to water affects its boiling point, different amounts of salt must be tested. A variable that is deliberately changed during the experiment is an **independent variable**.

When the beakers of water with different amounts of added salt are heated, the boiling temperatures are measured and recorded. The purpose of the experiment is to determine whether and how the boiling temperature changes in response to the independent variable. The factor that is measured in an experiment and that changes in response to the independent variable is the **dependent variable**. The boiling point is expected to depend on and change in response to the amount of salt added to the water.

To find out whether adding salt raises or lowers the boiling point of water, it is necessary to compare the salt water to water with no added salt. The boiling point of the plain water serves as a baseline to which the experimental results are compared. A good experiment includes a **control group**, or control setup. The beaker with the plain water is the control setup in this experiment. Because the amount of salt is the variable being tested (the independent variable), the **experimental group** or setup contains the four beakers to which different amounts of salt have been added. All other variables in the experimental setup are identical to those in the control. Including a control setup allows scientists to trust that differences in the results of the two groups are caused by the variable being tested—the independent variable.

After the boiling-point experiment has been carried out and the results have been recorded, a scientist may decide to do the entire experiment again, using the same conditions. Each repetition of an experiment is called a **trial**. By doing multiple trials and comparing the results, a scientist can be more confident about the results. Confidence in results of an experiment is discussed in more detail later in this lesson.

Drawing Conclusions from Data

In the boiling-point experiment, the temperature at which the water in each beaker boils is measured and recorded. Recorded measurements or observations are called **data** (sing. *datum*). Once data are collected, they must be analyzed, or interpreted, and a conclusion can be drawn. A **conclusion** states whether the data support the hypothesis and what relationship exists between the variables. In some cases, the conclusion may say that the data do not support a hypothesis. When this happens, a scientist may repeat the experiment to check the accuracy of the results. The scientist may also change the experimental design. When the data still do not support a hypothesis, a scientist may state a new hypothesis and conduct more experiments.

Replicating Results

The process of scientific inquiry does not end when a conclusion supports a hypothesis. Scientists may repeat their own experiment, but other scientists will also study the original investigation carefully to make sure that the results and conclusions are valid. These scientists may also repeat the experiment in their own laboratories, using their own materials and equipment, to try to obtain the same results. In other words, they will try to **replicate** the original results.

Replicating a result helps scientists be confident that the results were not due to an error or chance. (Errors are discussed in Lesson 4.) Scientists place more confidence in discoveries and conclusions if other scientists have verified the results. Replication of results also helps ensure that the process of science is open and honest. Data are more likely to be correct when research is repeated and the same outcome is obtained. However, remember that scientists may interpret the same data in different ways. Debates about scientific studies are helpful in guiding scientists in further research so they can increase our understanding of the natural world.

Discussion Question

A group of scientists tries to replicate another scientist's results and fails to do so. What might this mean? A second group manages to replicate the first scientist's results but comes to a different conclusion. How is this possible? How does replicating results keep the process of science honest?

Lesson Review

1. A student wants to test the hypothesis that plants need soil to grow. Which is the independent variable in the experiment?

   A. air temperature

   B. amount of light

   C. presence of soil

   D. addition of water

2. Which of the following does an experiment test?

   A. constant

   B. hypothesis

   C. conclusion

   D. observation

3. What is the purpose of replicating an experiment?

   A. It ensures that the results support the hypothesis.

   B. It ensures that the results were reported accurately.

   C. It ensures that the results were interpreted correctly.

   D. It ensures that the results are consistent with current explanations.

4. What is the purpose of including a control group in an experiment?

   A. to ensure that the results are not due to chance

   B. to provide a baseline for comparing the dependent variable

   C. to make the effect of the independent variable appear stronger

   D. to increase the number of factors that vary among groups or setups

Organizing and Analyzing Data

Key Words • qualitative data • quantitative data • data table • formula • line graph • circle graph • bar graph • mean • median • mode

Getting the Idea

Drawing conclusions from data is easier when data are organized clearly. To organize their data, scientists often use organizational tools like those shown in this lesson. These visual displays help scientists recognize patterns or trends in the data and determine the types of relationships that exist among variables.

Types of Data

As you conduct scientific investigations, you will collect data. Information described in words, such as color, texture, and shape, or words such as *hot* or *large*, is **qualitative data**. Information given in numbers is **quantitative data**. Records of temperature, speed, mass, pH, volume, and time are examples of quantitative data.

Examples of Qualitative and Quantitative Data

Qualitative Data	Quantitative Data
Bubbles appeared in the solution.	The temperature of the solution increased to 86°C.
The plants had purple flowers.	The mean number of flowers per plant was 20.
The cell contained chloroplasts.	The diameter of the cell was 50 micrometers.
The rock sample was glassy.	The rock sample had a mass of 125 grams.

After collecting data, scientists organize, display, and analyze the data using data tables and graphs. The type of data you have will suggest the best way to organize them.

Data Tables

A **data table** organizes related data into rows and columns, with the independent variable in the first column and one or more dependent variables in columns to the right. When you use a data table to organize quantitative data, organizing the data in numerical order is often helpful. Doing this can help you recognize patterns in the data or find a **formula**, or mathematical sentence, that relates the variables.

For example, both data tables below show the same set of paired data values. Each length measurement is paired with a measurement of mass (the amount of matter in an object). However, the organization of the data in the second data table makes it easier to see that as length increases, mass also increases.

Table 1: Length and Mass of Objects

Length (cm)	Mass (g)
14	27
8	15
12	23
11	22
9	18

Table 2: Length and Mass of Objects

Length (cm)	Mass (g)
8	15
9	18
11	22
12	23
14	27

Organizing Data in Graphs

Data that are organized well are easier to interpret. Scientists often use graphs to organize and show quantitative data, because graphs can display a lot of data in a small space. Graphs also make it easier to see patterns or trends in the data. There are several types of graphs, including line graphs, circle graphs, and bar graphs. Each type is best for displaying different types of data.

A **line graph** uses points or lines to show relationships between variables. Line graphs are the best way to show continuous quantitative data, such as time, temperature, or speed. Line graphs are often used to show changes in variables over time. You can see an example of a line graph below. Usually, the independent variable—such as age or time—is shown on the horizontal axis, or *x*-axis. The dependent variable is shown on the vertical axis, or *y*-axis. Each axis has a clear label that includes units. The axes should be scaled so that all data values can be displayed on the graph.

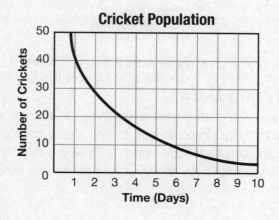

A **circle graph**, or pie graph, shows how parts relate to a whole. Data in a circle graph are given in either fractions or percentages.

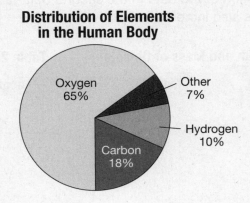

Distribution of Elements in the Human Body

- Oxygen 65%
- Other 7%
- Hydrogen 10%
- Carbon 18%

A **bar graph** compares data using bars of different heights or lengths. Usually, the bars represent noncontinuous, qualitative data, or data that fall into distinct categories (such as eye colors, symptoms, or different minerals in a rock), on one axis. The other axis shows continuous, quantitative data. A double or multiple bar graph uses bars of different colors to compare two or more sets of related data. The graph's key tells you what each color bar represents.

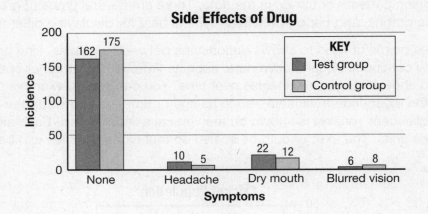

Side Effects of Drug

KEY
- Test group
- Control group

Symptoms	Test group	Control group
None	162	175
Headache	10	5
Dry mouth	22	12
Blurred vision	6	8

No matter which type of graph you use, make sure it has a title and is clearly labeled.

Comparing and Analyzing Data

It is easier to compare and analyze data that are organized in a data table or graph. When scientists analyze data, they look for patterns and trends in the data and use these patterns to draw conclusions. The purpose of an experiment is to test a hypothesis about how two or more variables are related. Analyzing data allows scientists to see how the variables relate to each other.

The dependent and independent variables may be related in different ways. Variables have a *direct variation* when one variable increases as the other variable increases, or when one variable decreases as the other decreases. This change in the same direction is also called a *direct relationship*. The graph below shows a direct relationship between temperature and volume. As the temperature of the gas increases, so does the volume. In other cases, one variable decreases when another increases, showing an *inverse variation*. This change in opposite directions is also called an *inverse relationship*, as shown in the line graph on page 15. That graph illustrates that the number of crickets decreases as the time, in days, increases.

Volume of a Gas at Constant Pressure

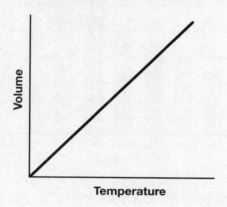

Sometimes, data may show that variables have no relationship with each other. This result appears on a graph as either a flat line or randomly scattered points. Sometimes a data point falls significantly outside the pattern of other data points. Such a result is called an *outlier*. It is important to figure out why an outlier occurs. It may change the interpretation of the data.

Describing Data with Statistics

A data table or graph can display a large amount of information. Sometimes, you want to communicate something important about your data more briefly. A *statistic* is a number that describes or makes a prediction about a set of data. The **mean**, or *average*, is a statistic that is the result of adding together all the values in a data set and dividing the sum by the number of values in the data set. The **median** is the middle value in a data set when all the values are arranged from least to greatest. Half of the values in the set fall above the median, and half fall below it. (If a data set contains an even number of values, the median is the mean of the two middle values.) Another statistic is the **mode**, which describes the most frequently occurring value in a data set. In addition, the *range* of a set of values is the difference between the largest and smallest values in the data set.

Each type of statistic may be useful, depending on what you want to communicate about a set of data. For example, suppose a sociologist wants to describe the family income in a city that includes both wealthy and working-class families. Because of the high-earning families, the mean income is higher than what 50 percent of the families earn. Describing the median income is more informative because it shows that half of the families earn less than the median, and half earn more.

Extrapolating and Interpolating from Data

Sometimes, organizing data allows you to make a prediction. An *extrapolation* is a prediction that can be tested. Based on the graph below, you could reasonably predict that more fertilizer was applied in 2010 than in 2000. You might even predict that about 65 metric tons of fertilizer was applied in 2010, and you can test this prediction by finding the data for 2010.

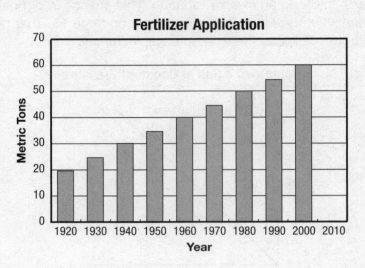

Similarly, even though the graph does not show data for 1975, you might infer that 47 metric tons of fertilizer was applied that year. Making a prediction about a value between two data points is called *interpolation*.

Discussion Question

The data table below shows the results of the boiling-point experiment.

Salt added (mg)	0	10	20	40
Temperature at boiling (°C)	100.4	102.0	103.2	107.1

How could these data be graphed? What conclusion can you draw about the relationship between the amount of salt in the water and the change in boiling point?

Lesson Review

1. Which type of graph would **best** display the data shown in this data table?

Category of Bird	Number Observed	Percentage
Perching	14	56%
Wading	7	28%
Other	4	16%
Total	25	100%

   A. line graph

   B. circle graph

   C. bar graph

   D. histogram

2. Which of the following types of observation is qualitative rather than quantitative?

   A. color

   B. weight

   C. pH level

   D. temperature

3. There is an inverse relationship between the number of people in a population receiving the flu vaccine and the number of flu cases. Based on this information, which of the graphs below is **not** correct?

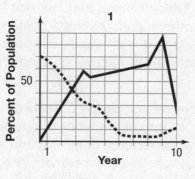

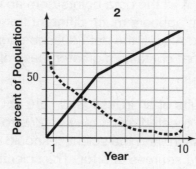

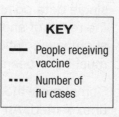

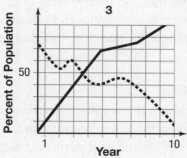

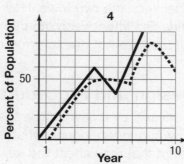

   A. Graph 1

   B. Graph 2

   C. Graph 3

   D. Graph 4

Identifying and Preventing Errors

Key Words • precision • accuracy • significant figures • conclusion • bias

Getting the Idea

Scientists draw conclusions from data obtained from conducting experiments. However, if the data or observations resulting from an experiment are incorrect, any conclusions based on those data will not be valid. This is why it is important to understand the sources of error and how to reduce the number of errors.

Sources of Error

As they conduct experiments, scientists record their procedures, observations, and results using journals and computers. Keeping records allows scientists to check their methods and data for accuracy and identify any possible sources of error. Scientists can make several types of errors in a scientific investigation. These types of errors include procedural errors, measurement errors, calculation errors, and errors in interpretation.

Detecting Errors

How can scientists tell whether their results contain errors? Some clues may indicate errors. For example, if all the data points from an experiment follow a trend except for a single data point that appears much different from the others, then that data point may be the result of an error. Also, if the data describe something that is physically impossible, such as a solution that contains a greater mass of dissolved salt than water, then an error must have been made.

Sometimes, the results of an investigation are not impossible but simply unlikely or unexpected. An unexpected result may be due to one or more of the types of errors discussed in this lesson, and the scientist should review the records of the experiment to try to find possible sources of error. The scientist may repeat the experiment and compare the results between the two trials. However, unexpected results may also occur because the variables affect each other in a way that the scientist did not predict. Unexpected results, if they are not due to error, can lead to new findings, insights, and scientific theories.

Experimental Design and Procedural Errors

A *procedural error* is caused by a flaw in how the experiment is designed. This can include choosing the wrong independent variable, selecting the wrong equipment, not keeping factors constant that may affect the results, or not including a control group or control setup.

Suppose a student wants to determine what effect pH has on the growth of three different types of seeds, using the following setup:

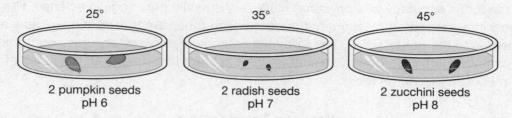

25°	35°	45°
2 pumpkin seeds pH 6	2 radish seeds pH 7	2 zucchini seeds pH 8

The student intends to test two variables: seed type and pH. It is possible to test these two independent variables at the same time. However, to do so correctly, the experiment would need three separate groups or conditions, each containing only one type of seed. In this case, each type of seed would be placed in different containers with solutions of varying pH. All other variables (temperature, container type, and number of seeds) would need to be held constant. In the student's setup, too many factors are allowed to vary. Temperature is not held constant for all three samples, and each sample varies in both pH and type of seed.

Using an incorrect sample size or selection may also be a source of procedural error. Suppose a student wants to know whether most dogs have short ears or long ears, and examines the dogs in the illustrations below.

Observing only the dogs in the illustrations, the student would conclude that half of all dogs have short ears and half have long ears. Of course, this may be an incorrect conclusion. The sample of dogs is not large enough to allow for a valid conclusion either way.

Measurement and Instrument Errors

Inaccurate measurements can also introduce errors into an investigation. *Measurement errors* are mistakes in selecting, using, or reading measurement tools. For example, if you mistakenly read the volume of water contained in a graduated cylinder at the top of the edges of the liquid, rather than at the bottom of the meniscus, all of your volume measurements will be incorrect. In the example shown in the illustration, each measurement would be off by nearly 1 mL.

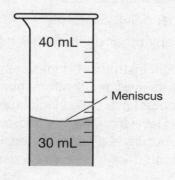

Accuracy and Precision

Scientists try to produce measurements that are both as precise and as accurate as possible. However, the terms *accuracy* and *precision* have very specific meanings in science. **Precision** refers to how close repeated measurements are to each other. **Accuracy** is how close a measurement is to the actual value. The following example compares accuracy and precision. The table contains data recorded by two students. Each student measured the mass of the same sample of muscle tissue three times.

Mass of a Tissue Sample

Student 1	Student 2
0.019 kg	0.016 kg
0.019 kg	0.020 kg
0.019 kg	0.016 kg

Student 1's measurements are more precise because they are closer to each other. However, because the actual mass of the sample was 0.015 kg, the second student's measurements are more accurate. High precision cannot guarantee that a measurement is correct. It only means that there is very little difference between measurements. Suppose you measured the height of a plant repeatedly with a misprinted meterstick. Your measurements would be consistent (precise), but they would not indicate the true height of the plant (they would be inaccurate).

The precision of a measurement is limited by the precision of the measuring instrument. Consider the graduated cylinder on the previous page. The smallest markings on the cylinder are one milliliter apart. If the meniscus falls between milliliters, the measurement can be estimated to one-tenth of a milliliter (for example, 32.2 mL). This is the most precise measurement possible with this instrument. In contrast, a graduated cylinder with its smallest markings one-tenth of a milliliter apart would be more precise, allowing measurements to be estimated to one-hundredth of a milliliter.

Precision is indicated by the number of significant figures recorded in a measurement. **Significant figures** are the meaningful, reliable numbers in a measurement. For example, a measurement of 14.2 g is said to have three significant figures. Significant figures include the following:

- whole-number digits other than zero (537)
- final zeros after a decimal point (5.370 m)
- zeros located between any other digits (503.7 m)

Choosing an appropriate measurement instrument is important. Scientists usually try to use the most precise and accurate instruments available. Instruments must also be appropriate in other ways. For example, chemists use compounds called indicators to determine changes in pH. The indicator changes color when the pH level increases or decreases past a certain point. However, the point at which the color change occurs is different for each type of indicator. Choosing the wrong indicator could lead a chemist to miss a pH change or record the wrong pH.

Calculation Errors

Correct calculations are also vital. *Calculation errors* are a common source of incorrect results. Such errors have two sources: simple mathematical errors and errors in the use of formulas. For example, suppose you incorrectly add data from multiple trials in an experiment to calculate an average. This is a mathematical error that will result in an incorrect final calculation.

Many calculations in science involve the use of formulas. For example, the density of a substance can be determined using this formula:

$$D = \frac{m}{V}$$

In this formula, *D* stands for density, *m* represents mass, and *V* represents volume. To determine the density of a specific substance, substitute the values for *m* and *V* that you know into the formula, and make the calculation.

Example: A metal bar has a mass of 447 g and a volume of 53 cm^3. What is its density?

$$D = \frac{m}{V}$$

$$D = \frac{447 \text{ g}}{53 \text{ cm}^3}$$

$$D = 8.43 \text{ g/cm}^3$$

When calculations involve the use of formulas, it is important to check to make sure you are substituting the correct values into the formula in the proper places. Once you have done so, you can simply do the math. Using a calculator is one way to minimize mathematical errors. It is also a good idea to double-check all measurements and calculations to verify your results.

Calculations based on measurements are limited to the smallest number of significant figures present in any of the starting measurements.

Errors in the Interpretation of Results

At the end of an investigation, scientists interpret their data to form a conclusion. Recall that a **conclusion** states whether the results support the hypothesis. A conclusion explains what the data reveal about the question posed in a scientific investigation. Before scientists report their conclusions, they evaluate whether the conclusion is reasonable. This involves reviewing the methods used during the investigation and checking the data gathered against available information. To be reasonable, a conclusion must be supported by the data gathered during the investigation.

Errors in interpretation are reduced by analyzing accurate data and forming reasonable, supported conclusions.

Throughout an investigation, scientists must keep data accurate so that they may draw a reasonable conclusion. One way to do this is to record observations as soon as they are made. Scientists should also keep data accurate by double-checking measurements and calculations and conducting multiple trials of an experiment.

Although scientists usually agree on the importance of keeping good records, they often disagree on the actual interpretation of evidence. Sometimes different explanations can be given for the same set of data. In addition to simple error, these differing explanations can be caused by each investigator's individual perspective, or bias. **Bias** is a personal prejudice, unfair preference, or slanted point of view. For example, a drug company may plan to test a new vaccine developed for the prevention of a particular virus. Since the company hopes to find the vaccine effective, some might argue that scientists working for the company are likely to interpret the results in a positive way.

Discussion Question

Imagine a scenario in which a scientist does not use adequate records and precise equipment in the laboratory. What might the consequences be? How might research and development be affected?

Lesson Review

1. The drawing shows a liquid in a graduated cylinder.

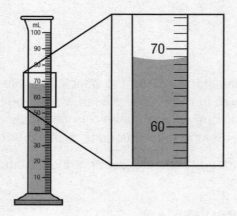

Which of the following **best** represents the volume of the liquid?

A. 69.8 mL

B. 67 mL

C. 68.5 mL

D. 68 mL

2. A student investigated whether salt raises the boiling point of water. He put 2 L of water at 20°C and 200 mL of salt in a pot, heated the solution over a flame, and measured the temperature when the water reached a rolling boil. He repeated the experiment three times and recorded the same result each time. He concluded that salt raises the boiling point of water by 5°C. Where was the error in his experimental design?

    A. He did not boil a pot of water without salt.

    B. He did not conduct the trials at the same time.

    C. He waited until the water reached a rolling boil.

    D. He should have repeated the measurement several more times.

3. Use the formula

    $$D = \frac{m}{V}$$

    to calculate the density of a piece of metal that has a volume of 5.32 cm³ and a mass of 52.0 g. Use the correct number of significant figures in your response.

    A. 0.1 g/cm³

    B. 9.77 g/cm³

    C. 9.8 g/cm³

    D. 10 g/cm³

4. The table shows repeated measurements by laboratory partners of the volume of oxygen released by a plant. Using a more accurate technique, their teacher measured the volume of oxygen released as 0.208 mL.

Attempt 1	0.205 mL
Attempt 2	0.211 mL
Attempt 3	0.206 mL

    Which statement **best** describes the students' measurements?

    A. They are precise but not accurate.

    B. They are accurate but not precise.

    C. They are both precise and accurate.

    D. They are neither precise nor accurate.

Safety and Ethics in Science

Key Words • field study • culture • scientific ethics

Getting the Idea

Scientists in any field, from students to experienced professionals, must follow guidelines to prevent injury to themselves and others. Biologists must follow additional rules when working with living organisms. All scientists must consider the effects of their work on humans and on other living things.

General Laboratory Safety Guidelines

Laboratory work requires the use of special equipment, chemicals, and biological materials. Some of these materials can be dangerous if used incorrectly. The guidelines below will help keep you safe in the lab.

Supervision	<ul><li>Never work in a laboratory unless a teacher is present.</li><li>Never carry out a lab investigation without teacher approval.</li><li>Report injuries, damaged equipment, spills, or other potential hazards to your teacher immediately.</li></ul>
Behavior and Conduct 	<ul><li>Review the safety rules and safety symbols covered in your textbook and posted in your laboratory.</li><li>Read all instructions carefully before starting an investigation. If you are unsure of an instruction, ask your teacher for guidance.</li><li>If you design an investigation, get your teacher's approval before carrying it out.</li><li>Use only the materials and equipment listed for your investigation.</li><li>Know the locations and proper use of all emergency equipment, including fire alarms, fire extinguishers, fire blankets, fume hoods, emergency showers, eye wash stations, and first aid kits.</li><li>Never fool around in the laboratory.</li><li>Keep your work area neat and organized</li><li>Examine all equipment before using it. Look for chips and cracks in glassware and frayed or broken cords on electrical equipment.</li><li>Never bring food or drink into the lab.</li><li>Clean up your work area after an investigation, following your teacher's instructions on how to dispose of used and unused materials.</li><li>Turn off and disconnect all electrical devices when the investigation is completed.</li><li>Return all equipment to its storage area.</li><li>Wash your hands thoroughly at the end of an investigation.</li></ul>

Attire		<ul><li>Always wear a lab coat or an apron when working in the lab.</li><li>Wear safety glasses or goggles with side shields when working with or near chemicals, flames, or fumes.</li><li>Do not wear loose clothing, sandals, or open-toed shoes.</li><li>Wear protective plastic or rubber gloves when handling chemicals or biological specimens. Wear heat-resistant gloves when handling hot objects.</li></ul>

Handling Living Organisms

Some investigations may involve working with living organisms, either inside or outside the laboratory. An investigation outside the lab is called a **field study**. Below are guidelines for working with organisms either inside the laboratory or as part of a field study. These guidelines help protect both you and the organisms being studied.

- Tell your teacher if you are allergic to any plants, animals, molds, latex, foods, or other substances. If you have allergies, avoid substances that trigger an allergic reaction.

- Always treat animals and other living organisms humanely.

- Never touch a living organism unless you are told to do so. If you are injured when handling a living organism, tell your teacher immediately.

- Some biological materials can injure you or cause disease if touched or ingested. Wear protective plastic or rubber gloves when handling organisms or biological materials. Never taste any biological material.

- You may use petri dishes to grow **cultures**—cells, tissues, or microorganisms maintained under laboratory conditions. Be sure to seal all culture dishes you use. Never open a sealed container, such as a culture dish containing bacteria or a plastic bag containing mold, unless you are instructed to do so.

- Learn to recognize and avoid poisonous plants such as poison ivy, poison oak, and poison sumac.

- If you are working outdoors, dress appropriately. Wear long pants, a long-sleeved shirt, and a hat when working in wooded areas. Wear insect repellent in areas where insects are likely to be a problem. Wear good walking shoes or boots.

- If you are working in an open area, apply sunscreen to exposed skin. A hat and sunglasses can also protect you from the sun's harmful UV rays.

- Wash your hands thoroughly after handling any organism.

Working Safely with Glassware and Sharp Objects

Many lab accidents involve broken glass. You can reduce the risk by using glassware properly, working carefully, and keeping your work area neat. Notify your teacher at once if you break glassware. Do not clean up the broken glass unless your teacher tells you to do so. Keep in mind that any materials spilled from broken glassware should be cleaned up in an appropriate way. When reporting broken glassware, tell your teacher what, if anything, it contained.

Many investigations will require you to work with sharp objects such as scissors, knives, scalpels, pins, or probes. Always handle these objects carefully to avoid being cut. Whenever you cut something, cut in a direction away from your body.

Working Safely with Heat and Chemicals

The guidelines below will help you work safely with heat, chemicals, and biological materials.

Heating Safety	Safety with Materials and Equipment
■ Wear safety goggles when heating any substance. ■ Tie back or secure long hair or loose clothing when you use a Bunsen burner or open flame.  ■ Never heat a substance in a closed or sealed container, including a test tube with a stopper. ■ When heating test tubes, tilt or point them away from yourself and others.  ■ Never heat any substance unless you are instructed to do so. Use only the type of heating device (Bunsen burner, hot plate, etc.) you are instructed to use. ■ Protect your hands from burns by using heat-resistant gloves or tongs when handling hot containers. 	■ Carry microscopes with one hand on the arm and the other below the base. ■ Wear safety goggles and a lab coat or apron when handling chemicals or biological materials. ■ Read labels to become aware of poison symbols or other warnings. ■ Never mix any chemicals or biological materials unless you are told to do so. ■ Never touch or taste any chemical or biological materials. ■ Never smell a chemical or biological sample unless you are instructed to do so. ■ If you need to smell a sample in a container, hold the container away from your face and waft the vapors toward your nose.  ■ Rinse your eyes immediately if you get any foreign matter in or near them. Notify your teacher.  ■ Work only in well-ventilated areas. ■ Never return unused chemicals or biological materials to their original containers. Ask your teacher how to dispose of unused materials. ■ To avoid spills, always label empty containers before adding chemicals to them. ■ Reset triple beam balances to the zero mark when you are finished.

Lab Cleanup

You can help make the laboratory safer by keeping it neat. Always clean up at the end of an investigation. Destroy bacterial cultures when the investigation is completed to avoid contaminating areas within or outside of the lab. Your instructor will review the appropriate method of decontamination for each biological material you use.

To conserve resources, use only as much as you need for your investigation. Some materials can be reused in later investigations. Others, including most plastics and paper, can be recycled. Your teacher can tell you where to put recyclable materials and trash.

Ethical Responsibilities of Scientists

Some scientific research has the potential to cause harm to people or other living things. Harm may occur when scientists conduct experiments with people or animals as subjects. Harm may also result when an experiment has the potential to affect people, other organisms, or ecosystems. Scientific investigations that have the potential to cause harm raise questions of **scientific ethics**—principles of conduct that scientists should follow.

It is important to identify when ethics must be considered in science. Some types of research require more ethical considerations than others. Scientists must consider ethics whenever an experiment or procedure involves directly testing humans. Two examples of this include testing transmission of the AIDS virus and testing the effects of a new herbicide on humans.

Ethics must also be considered when experimenting on animals. Most animals can feel pain. Also, many animals may suffer from being confined in small spaces. On the other hand, scientists measuring the iron content in a municipal water supply would not raise such ethical questions because no humans or animals would be involved in that investigation.

Even scientists can disagree about some ethical questions. Medical scientists may disagree about whether severely ill patients should be enrolled in experiments to test new drugs and treatments. Some scientists think that it is not ethical to experiment on animals, or scientists may choose not to experiment on animals with backbones (vertebrates), which are more similar to humans. Other scientists may reason that an animal's life in the laboratory is safer, longer, and more comfortable than the life of a similar animal in the wild, where it must find food, seek shelter from severe weather, and avoid predators.

Although there are no definite answers to questions of scientific ethics, scientists try to conduct research ethically by following several guidelines. One guideline is that scientists must obtain *informed consent* from the people participating in an experiment. The scientists must explain to the participants all of the risks and benefits involved and exactly what will be done to them. Once people are informed about the experiment, they can give their consent to participate or decide not to.

Another guideline in scientific ethics is to minimize the pain and harm caused to any animals used in research. Although they may be fed or injected with drugs, the animals must be treated humanely. They must be kept in safe, clean conditions with adequate food and water. They must also be exposed to periods of light and darkness, as they would be in nature.

Monitoring the Impact on the Environment

Scientists also help people determine whether certain projects are being carried out in the least damaging manner, and whether some projects should be carried out at all. Large-scale projects, such as dams or power plants, often require an Environmental Impact Statement (EIS) to be filed with the federal government. An EIS is a document that describes both the positive and the negative effects of the proposed project on the environment. An EIS also describes potential alternative projects that can be carried out with less impact.

The scientists and technical people who do this work are specially trained. The table below describes some of the careers associated with environmental monitoring.

Careers Associated with Monitoring the Environment

Field	Description of Career
Chemical engineering	Understanding how physical and life sciences can be applied to produce both materials and energy
Environmental engineering	Applying science to improve and monitor the natural environment and to minimize and eliminate pollution
Environmental science	Studying the environment and proposing solutions to environmental problems
Forestry	Managing, conserving, and creating forests, which are an important source of habitats as well as natural resources
Fisheries science	Studying and monitoring fisheries, which consist of the natural fish populations, the people who harvest and depend on those populations, and the methods that they use. Fisheries scientists try to maintain healthy, stable fisheries so that people can continue to harvest this natural resource.

Discussion Question

A group of scientists identifies and sequences a version of a gene that causes some types of cancer. What are some of the ethical considerations involved in making this discovery? What are some of the ethical considerations involved with developing a test to screen for this gene?

Lesson Review

1. Which of the following is **not** a safety precaution that should be used when working with cultures in petri dishes?

    A. Seal all dishes you use.

    B. Never open a sealed container unless instructed.

    C. Destroy all cultures before disposing of plastic petri dishes.

    D. Use the same probe to move cultures between all dishes.

2. You are using a scalpel in a dissection. Which safety guideline should you follow?

    A. Cut toward your body.

    B. Cut away from your body.

    C. Wear heat-resistant gloves.

    D. Hold the specimen with tongs.

3. Which of the following types of research requires the **greatest** amount of ethical consideration?

    A. testing the effects of a new cancer drug on laboratory animals

    B. determining the impact of a proposed dam on the surrounding ecosystem

    C. modifying the organs used in transplants to make them less likely to be rejected

    D. developing a crop that is genetically engineered to grow in the presence of a weed killer

Chapter 1 Review

A series of experiments performed by scientists in the seventeenth through nineteenth centuries gradually disproved the idea that living things could form from once-living matter. This idea was called *spontaneous generation*.

Experiment 1

In 1668, Francisco Redi published an experiment on the generation of flies from rotting meat. Redi placed pieces of veal in glass jars. He sealed the tops of one group of jars, covered the tops of a second group with a mesh material, and left the third group uncovered. He then recorded the numbers of fly larvae and flies on or in the jars. Redi's experiment has been replicated by modern scientists. The results of one of these replications are shown in Figure 1.

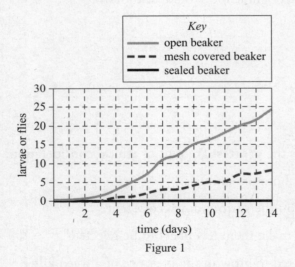

Figure 1

Experiment 2

In 1745, John Needham tested the hypothesis that meat may still contain a vital force capable of generating smaller organisms, such as microbes. He created a meat broth, poured the broth into flasks, and boiled them. After the broth cooled, he sealed the flasks. Another group of flasks was treated in the same way, but not boiled. The broth in all the flasks became cloudy after several days, indicating that microorganisms were present. Needham concluded that the vital force contained in the original meat was not destroyed by boiling, and that it could generate microorganisms.

Experiment 3

In 1768, Lazzaro Spallanzani replicated Needham's experiment, with modifications. He repeated Needham's procedure, but he sealed the flasks before boiling the broth. He also removed the air from the sealed flasks to prevent pressure from building and damaging the glass. Using a microscope, Spallanzani observed microorganisms in the unsealed flasks. However, the broth in the sealed flasks showed no signs of life.

Experiment 4

In 1859, French scientist Louis Pasteur replicated Needham's and Spallanzani's experiments. He used a special type of flask with a long, bent neck designed to allow the entry of air. However, any microorganisms that enter the flask become trapped in the bend of the neck.

Pasteur filled the bent-neck flasks with meat broth, which he then boiled. After boiling, Pasteur removed the necks from one group of flasks and left the other group intact (Figure 2). Pasteur observed that the broth in the broken-neck flasks became cloudy, while the broth in the intact flasks remained clear.

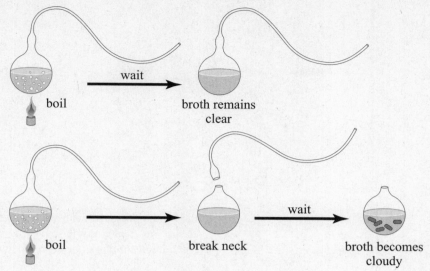

Figure 2

1. In the replication of Experiment 1, how many more fly larvae were present in the open beaker than in the mesh-covered beaker, after ten days?

   A. Approximately 5
   B. Approximately 10
   C. Approximately 15
   D. Approximately 20

2. Although Spallanzani concluded that his experiment disproved spontaneous generation, other scientists did not agree with this conclusion. Which of the following is a valid criticism of Spallanzani's conclusion?

   F. Heat can destroy the vital force that generates living things.
   G. Boiled broth needs to remain sterile to preserve the vital force.
   H. Microorganisms cannot grow in the broth when no air is present.
   J. Boiled broth becomes cloudy due to microorganisms present in the air.

3. Based on the results of Experiment 1, which of the following is an appropriate conclusion?

   A. The fly larvae source is outside of the jars.
   B. Sealing meat in a jar slows the rotting process.
   C. Flies are attracted by the sight of rotting meat.
   D. Larvae require a source of air to change into flies.

4. Why did Experiment 2 fail to disprove the theory of spontaneous generation?

   F. It used meat broth instead of untreated raw meat.
   G. It destroyed the nutrients present in the meat broth.
   H. It allowed the presence of air in the flasks with the meat broth.
   J. It included a source of new organisms other than the meat broth.

5. In Experiment 4, what was the purpose of removing the necks from some of the boiled flasks?

   A. It allowed air to enter the flasks.
   B. It delayed the growth of microbes.
   C. It provided a baseline for comparison.
   D. It preserved the nutrients in the broth.

Chapter 2 Matter

Atoms and Elements

Key Words • matter • atom • element • proton • neutron • electron • nucleus • mass number • isotopes • average atomic mass • electron cloud • energy level • charge • ion • chemical symbol • atomic number

Getting the Idea

Chemistry is the branch of science concerned with what matter is made of and how it changes. **Matter** is anything that has mass and volume. You and everything around you—this book, your chair, the air you breathe—are matter.

The Building Blocks of Matter: Atoms and Elements

Atoms are the basic building blocks of most of the matter around us. However, individual atoms are much too small to be seen with the unaided eye or even with a light microscope. Each kind of atom is an element.

A *pure substance* is matter that has the same composition throughout. An **element** is a pure substance that cannot be broken down into a simpler substance by ordinary chemical means. Examples of elements include iron, copper, hydrogen, and carbon. An atom is the smallest particle of an element that has all the properties of that element. Each element consists of one type of atom, and the atoms of each element are different. Some substances, such as pure gold or helium gas, are made up of atoms of a single element. Other substances, such as water or carbon dioxide, consist of combinations of atoms bonded together in a specific arrangement. These compounds are discussed in Lesson 8.

The Structure of the Atom

Atoms are made up of smaller, subatomic particles. The three main types of subatomic particles are protons, neutrons, and electrons, and these differ in mass and charge. These particles are in turn made up of smaller particles called *quarks*, which can only be detected using special equipment. The main subatomic particles and their properties are summarized in the table below. The unit of mass for subatomic particles is the atomic mass unit (amu). Protons and neutrons each have a mass of 1 amu, but electrons have so little mass that they are assigned 0 amu.

Subatomic Particles

Particle	Charge	Mass (amu)	Location in Atom
Proton	Positive	1	Nucleus
Neutron	Neutral	1	Nucleus
Electron	Negative	0	Electron cloud

Each type of subatomic particle is located in a specific region of the atom. The **nucleus**, which is made up of positively charged protons and electrically neutral neutrons, is the dense center of the atom. Because protons and neutrons each have far more mass than electrons, almost all the atom's mass is located in the tiny, dense nucleus.

An atom's **mass number** is equal to the number of protons plus the number of neutrons in the atom. All atoms of a given element have the same number of protons. However, atoms of the same element can have different numbers of neutrons. These atoms are called **isotopes**. Isotopes of an element have the same atomic number but different mass numbers.

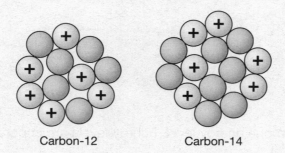

Carbon-12   Carbon-14

The isotopes of an element are indicated by writing the mass number after the element's name—for example, carbon-12. The diagram above shows the nuclei of two carbon isotopes. The nucleus of carbon-12 has 6 protons and 6 neutrons, while the nucleus of carbon-14 has 6 protons and 8 neutrons. Although one atom has more mass than the other, both are carbon atoms because they have 6 protons. Having more or fewer neutrons changes the atom's mass but not its identity. You will learn more about isotopes in the next lesson.

The different isotopes of an element determine the element's average atomic mass. Just as an exam average is made up of the average of all the exam scores earned in a marking period, the **average atomic mass** of an element is the average mass of all the isotopes of the element that are found in nature. Isotopes that are more common are counted more often in the average (just as a test score that was earned on three different exams would be counted three times).

Electrons and Energy Levels

Electrons are subatomic particles with very little mass and a negative charge. Electrons exist in a region outside the nucleus called the **electron cloud**.

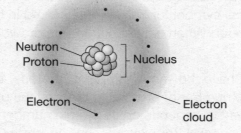

Neutron
Proton
Nucleus
Electron
Electron cloud

Within the electron cloud, electrons are in constant motion in areas called energy levels. An **energy level** is a region in which electrons having similar amounts of energy are likely to be located. (Energy can be thought of as the ability to make matter move or change. It is explained in more detail in Chapter 3.) Electrons can absorb and release energy. When they do so, their location in the atom changes. If an electron gains energy, it moves farther from the nucleus. If an electron loses energy, it moves closer to the nucleus.

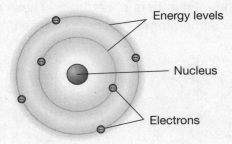

Most atoms have more than one energy level. Energy levels are important in bonding, which is discussed in Lesson 8.

Neutral Atoms and Charged Ions

Protons have a positive charge, and electrons have a negative charge. **Charge** is a property of matter that causes it to experience a force when it is near other charged matter. Charge can be positive or negative. Opposite charges attract each other. Like charges repel each other. An atom is held together by the attraction between the positively charged nucleus and the negatively charged electrons.

In a single atom, the charges of the protons and neutrons combine. An atom with 6 protons in its nucleus (for a charge of +6) and 6 electrons in its electron cloud (for a charge of −6) has a net or total charge of zero (+6 + [−6] = 0). Therefore, it is considered a neutral atom.

In contrast, an **ion** is an atom with a net positive or negative charge. This may be because it has more electrons than protons (for a net negative charge), or because it has more protons than electrons (for a net positive charge). Ions are discussed in more detail in Lessons 8 and 9.

Unique Characteristics of Elements

Atoms of elements are represented by a **chemical symbol**, a one- or two-letter abbreviation. For example, the letter O represents the element oxygen, and the letter H represents the element hydrogen. The chemical symbol for helium, a gas used in balloons, is He. All chemical symbols begin with a capital letter. When a symbol consists of two letters, only the first letter is capitalized.

All atoms of the same element have the same number of protons, and each element has a unique number of protons. The number of protons in the nucleus of an atom is called the **atomic number**. An atom's identity depends on its atomic number, and no two elements have the same atomic number. Chlorine (Cl), for example, has 17 protons and an atomic number of 17. Sodium (Na) has 11 protons and an atomic number of 11.

Discussion Question

The most abundant isotope of oxygen is oxygen-16. Oxygen-16 has an atomic number of 8 and an atomic mass of 16 amu. The isotope oxygen-17 has an atomic number of 8 and an atomic mass of 17 amu. Based on this information, how many protons, neutrons, and electrons are present in one atom of oxygen-16 and in one atom of oxygen-17? Explain your answer.

Lesson Review

1. An atom of neon (Ne) has 10 protons, 10 neutrons, and 10 electrons. What is the mass number of neon?

   A. 0 amu

   B. 10 amu

   C. 20 amu

   D. 30 amu

2. Hydrogen-1 and hydrogen-2 are isotopes. Which statement describes how hydrogen-1 and hydrogen-2 differ?

   A. Hydrogen-2 has more protons than hydrogen-1.

   B. Hydrogen-2 has more electrons than hydrogen-1.

   C. Hydrogen-2 has a higher mass number than hydrogen-1.

   D. Hydrogen-2 has a higher atomic number than hydrogen-1.

3. Which process can change a neutral atom into an ion of the same element?

   A. gain or loss of a proton

   B. gain or loss of an electron

   C. gain or loss of a neutron

   D. gain or loss of a nucleus

4. Which of the following is the smallest particle of an element that has all the properties of the element?

   A. atom

   B. proton

   C. neutron

   D. electron

The Periodic Table

Key Words • periodic table • period • group • family • valence electron • periodicity • alkali metal • reactive • alkaline earth metal • transition metal • metalloid • nonmetal • halogen • noble gas • inert • rare earth element • radioactivity

Getting the Idea

There are more than 100 known elements. Atoms of these elements join in different ways to form other kinds of matter. While some elements combine easily, others tend not to combine at all. To better understand elements, scientists have organized them in the **periodic table**.

The Structure of the Periodic Table

Look at the key on the next page showing the box for silicon (Si). It contains the name and symbol for this element. The box also shows two important numbers: the atomic number and the average atomic mass. In the periodic table, the elements are arranged in order of increasing atomic number, which is unique to each element. Silicon's atomic number is 14, meaning that a silicon atom contains 14 protons. The second number, the average atomic mass, is usually not a whole number because it is the average of the masses of the naturally occurring isotopes of an element. Silicon's average atomic mass is 28.066.

The positions of elements in the periodic table give information about their physical and chemical properties and how they relate to the atomic structure. A horizontal row of elements in the periodic table is called a **period**. The periodic table has seven periods. Atoms (and ions) tend to increase in mass from left to right within a period. Elements in a vertical column of the periodic table form a **group**. A group is also called a **family** because the elements share physical and chemical properties and tend to behave in similar ways in chemical reactions. Atoms (and ions) tend to increase in mass from top to bottom within a group. As you read, locate the information described on the periodic table.

Recall from Lesson 6 that electrons are found in different energy levels around the nucleus. Elements in the same period have the same number of energy levels. The number of energy levels increases from top to bottom within all groups. In contrast, elements in the same group have the same number of valence electrons. **Valence electrons** are electrons located in the outermost energy level of an atom. The number of valence electrons increases from left to right across periods. This repeating pattern in the physical properties of atoms and ions is called **periodicity**.

The Periodic Table

Mass numbers in parentheses are those of the most stable or most common isotopes.

Key:
- Atomic number — 14
- Symbol — **Si**
- Atomic mass — 28.086
- Name — Silicon

Group	1 IA	2 IIA	3 IIIB	4 IVB	5 VB	6 VIB	7 VIIB	8	9 VIII	10	11 IB	12 IIB	13 IIIA	14 IVA	15 VA	16 VIA	17 VIIA	18 VIIIA
1	1 H 1.008 Hydrogen																	2 He 4.003 Helium
2	3 Li 6.941 Lithium	4 Be 9.012 Beryllium											5 B 10.811 Boron	6 C 12.011 Carbon	7 N 14.007 Nitrogen	8 O 15.999 Oxygen	9 F 18.998 Fluorine	10 Ne 20.179 Neon
3	11 Na 22.989 Sodium	12 Mg 24.305 Magnesium											13 Al 26.982 Aluminum	14 Si 28.086 Silicon	15 P 30.974 Phosphorus	16 S 32.066 Sulfur	17 Cl 35.453 Chlorine	18 Ar 39.948 Argon
4	19 K 39.098 Potassium	20 Ca 40.078 Calcium	21 Sc 44.956 Scandium	22 Ti 47.867 Titanium	23 V 50.943 Vanadium	24 Cr 51.996 Chromium	25 Mn 54.938 Manganese	26 Fe 55.845 Iron	27 Co 58.933 Cobalt	28 Ni 58.693 Nickel	29 Cu 63.546 Copper	30 Zn 65.390 Zinc	31 Ga 69.723 Gallium	32 Ge 72.610 Germanium	33 As 74.922 Arsenic	34 Se 78.960 Selenium	35 Br 79.904 Bromine	36 Kr 83.800 Krypton
5	37 Rb 85.468 Rubidium	38 Sr 87.620 Strontium	39 Y 88.906 Yttrium	40 Zr 91.224 Zirconium	41 Nb 92.906 Niobium	42 Mo 95.940 Molybdenum	43 Tc (97.907) Technetium	44 Ru 101.070 Ruthenium	45 Rh 102.906 Rhodium	46 Pd 106.42 Palladium	47 Ag 107.868 Silver	48 Cd 112.411 Cadmium	49 In 114.818 Indium	50 Sn 118.710 Tin	51 Sb 121.760 Antimony	52 Te 127.60 Tellurium	53 I 126.905 Iodine	54 Xe 131.293 Xenon
6	55 Cs 132.906 Cesium	56 Ba 137.327 Barium	57 La 138.906 Lanthanum	72 Hf 178.490 Hafnium	73 Ta 180.948 Tantalum	74 W 183.84 Tungsten	75 Re 186.207 Rhenium	76 Os 190.230 Osmium	77 Ir 192.217 Iridium	78 Pt 195.084 Platinum	79 Au 196.967 Gold	80 Hg 200.590 Mercury	81 Tl 204.383 Thallium	82 Pb 207.200 Lead	83 Bi 208.980 Bismuth	84 Po (208.982) Polonium	85 At (209.987) Astatine	86 Rn (222.018) Radon
7	87 Fr (223.019) Francium	88 Ra (226.025) Radium	89 Ac (227.028) Actinium	104 Rf (263.113) Rutherfordium	105 Db (262.114) Dubnium	106 Sg (266.122) Seaborgium	107 Bh (264.125) Bohrium	108 Hs (269.134) Hassium	109 Mt (268.139) Meitnerium	110 Ds (272.146) Darmstadtium	111 Rg (272.154) Roentgenium	112 Uub (277)	113 Uut (284)	114 Uuq (289)	115 Uup (288)	116 Uuh (292)		118 Uuo (294)

Lanthanide Series

58 Ce 140.116 Cerium	59 Pr 140.908 Praseodymium	60 Nd 144.242 Neodymium	61 Pm (144.913) Promethium	62 Sm 150.360 Samarium	63 Eu 151.964 Europium	64 Gd 157.250 Gadolinium	65 Tb 158.925 Terbium	66 Dy 162.500 Dysprosium	67 Ho 164.930 Holmium	68 Er 167.259 Erbium	69 Tm 168.934 Thulium	70 Yb 173.040 Ytterbium	71 Lu 174.967 Lutetium

Actinide Series

90 Th 232.038 Thorium	91 Pa 231.036 Protactinium	92 U 238.029 Uranium	93 Np (237.048) Neptunium	94 Pu (244.064) Plutonium	95 Am (243.061) Americium	96 Cm (247.070) Curium	97 Bk (247.070) Berkelium	98 Cf (251.079) Californium	99 Es (252.083) Einsteinium	100 Fm (257.095) Fermium	101 Md (258.098) Mendelevium	102 No (259.101) Nobelium	103 Lr (262.110) Lawrencium

Groups of Elements

The groups in the periodic table are numbered 1–18. Some of the groups, or families, also have common names that you should know. The groups on the left side of the periodic table are the metals: the alkali metals, alkaline earth metals, and transition metals. Metals contain few electrons in their valence energy shells, or levels, and are likely to give up their valence electrons in reactions. With the exception of hydrogen, metals make up Groups 1–12. (Hydrogen is in Group 1, but because it has unusual properties, it is not classified with any other element.) Many elements in Group 13 and a few elements in Groups 14 and 15 are also metals.

The Group 1 elements are called **alkali metals**. Alkali metals are very **reactive**, meaning that they tend to combine with other elements to form compounds. (Compounds are discussed in Lesson 8.) Alkali metals have a single valence electron. Sodium (Na) is an alkali metal. It commonly binds with chlorine (Cl) to form sodium chloride, or table salt. The Group 2 elements are the **alkaline earth metals**, which have two valence electrons. Like alkali metals, they are also very reactive. Calcium (Ca) is an alkaline earth metal.

Groups 3–12 in the periodic table contain the **transition metals**, such as silver (Ag), gold (Au), mercury (Hg), and iron (Fe). These can often be found as pure elements because they are less reactive than the Group 1 and Group 2 metals. Transition metals have the physical properties commonly associated with metals: *metals* are generally shiny, malleable (can be hammered into thin sheets), ductile (can be drawn into thin wires), solid at room temperature (except for mercury, which is a liquid), and good conductors of heat and electricity.

The stair-step line dividing the metals on the left from the nonmetals on the right starts in Group 13, the *boron family*. Most of the elements on either side of this line are called **metalloids** and have properties between those of metals and nonmetals. (Aluminum is a metal, not a metalloid.) **Nonmetals** are generally dull in appearance, brittle, and poor conductors of heat and electricity. Many nonmetals are gases at room temperature, including oxygen and nitrogen. Nonmetals are found on the right side of the periodic table, in Groups 13–18. Nonmetal atoms have three or more electrons in their valence levels and, in contrast to metals, tend to share or gain electrons. Atoms in the *carbon family* (Group 14) have four valence electrons. Carbon (C) is one of the most important elements in living things. Life on Earth is sometimes called carbon-based because living things largely consist of carbon.

Elements in Group 15, the *nitrogen family*, also play essential roles in organisms. Nitrogen (N) makes up proteins, and phosphorous (P) is found in many biological molecules, including ATP (discussed in Chapter 5). Arsenic (As), a metalloid in the nitrogen family, has physical and chemical properties similar to nitrogen or phosphorous. These properties allow arsenic to react in similar ways in the body, which makes it harmful.

Group 16 is the *oxygen family*, which has six valence electrons. Oxygen (O) is essential to life in the form of oxygen gas (O_2). Oxygen also makes up a large portion of Earth's crust as a component of minerals, which are described in Chapter 9.

Group 17 elements are the **halogens**, which have seven valence electrons. Halogens are highly reactive, but unlike metals, halogens tend to gain electrons in reactions. Chlorine (Cl) is a common example of a halogen. Another example of periodicity is that Group 17 elements are less reactive moving down the group. Finally, Group 18 elements are the **noble gases**, so called because they tend not to react at all with other elements. In other words, they are **inert**. Helium (He) and neon (Ne) are noble gases.

Rare Earth Elements and Radioactivity

Elements in the lanthanide series (elements 57–71) plus scandium and itrium are the **rare earth elements**. They are fairly abundant in Earth's crust, but they are seldom found in large quantities in any one location. They have many uses, especially in technology.

Some elements are radioactive. **Radioactivity** is the spontaneous release of particles and/or energy from the nucleus of an atom. Recall that isotopes are different forms of an element. *Stable isotopes* do not emit particles or energy—they are not radioactive. *Unstable isotopes* do emit radiation. All the elements with atomic numbers greater than 82 have unstable, radioactive isotopes. The transition metal technitium is also somewhat radioactive.

The elements that follow uranium in the periodic table are called the transuranic elements. These elements are not normally found in nature, although some have been detected in very small amounts. Scientists have created these elements in particle accelerators and nuclear reactors.

An unstable nucleus can decay in many ways. Two common types of nuclear decay are alpha decay and beta decay, which change the number of protons in the nucleus, turning the element into a different element. Alpha decay occurs because there are too many protons in the nucleus. The nucleus spontaneously emits an *alpha particle*, which consists of two protons and two neutrons (it is identical to a helium nucleus). The mass number of the unstable nucleus decreases by four (the amu of 2 protons + 2 neutrons), but its atomic number decreases by two. The alpha decay of uranium-238 is shown below on the left.

Alpha Decay   **Beta Decay**

$$^{238}_{92}U \longrightarrow \,^{234}_{90}Th \,+\, ^{4}_{2}He \qquad\qquad ^{14}_{6}C \longrightarrow \,^{14}_{7}N \,+\, ^{0}_{-1}e$$

alpha particle   beta particle

Beta decay occurs when the neutron-to-proton ratio is too great in the nucleus. This causes instability. A neutron then becomes a proton by emitting an electron (beta particle). The mass number of the unstable nucleus stays the same, while the atomic number increases by one. The beta decay of carbon-14 is shown above on the right.

Discussion Question

Fluorine is located in Period 2 and Group 17. Magnesium is located in Period 3 and Group 2. How can you use this information to determine which element has more valence electrons? protons? neutrons? energy levels?

Lesson Review

1. The periodic table listing for potassium is shown.

19
K
Potassium
39.098

Which of the following lists the average atomic mass, atomic number, and number of electrons for this element?

A. average atomic mass: 19; atomic number: 39.098; electrons: 39

B. average atomic mass: 19; atomic number: 39.098; electrons: 19

C. average atomic mass: 39.098; atomic number: 39; electrons: 19

D. average atomic mass: 39.098; atomic number: 19; electrons: 19

2. Francium is an element in Group 1 and Period 7. How many valence electrons does an atom of francium contain?

A. 1   C. 7

B. 6   D. 8

3. Look at the periodic table at the beginning of the lesson. Based on their positions in the periodic table, which of these pairs of elements are both metals?

A. silicon (Si) and lead (Pb)   C. nitrogen (N) and oxygen (O)

B. gold (Au) and xenon (Xe)   D. sodium (Na) and vanadium (V)

4. Refer to the periodic table in the lesson to answer the following: An atom of the isotope cesium-137 undergoes beta decay. Which element or isotope forms as a result?

A. barium-137   C. iodine-133

B. cesium-135   D. xenon-137

5. Which element does **not** occur in nature?

A. xenon (Xe)   C. protactinium (Pr)

B. iridium (Ir)   D. mendelevium (Md)

Chemical Bonding

Key Words • compound • mixture • molecule • chemical formula • chemical bond • ionic bond • ion
• covalent bond • metallic bond

Getting the Idea

As you saw in your study of the periodic table, scientists have discovered more than
100 different elements. These elements, either singly or in combination, make up other
kinds of matter. Most matter exists as combinations of elements called compounds.
Compounds form when attractive forces join atoms of different elements.

Compounds and Molecules

Most matter exists as compounds rather than separate elements. A **compound** is a pure
substance that forms when two or more elements join chemically. The original elements
do not retain their individual physical and chemical properties. For example, sodium is a
metal that explodes when combined with water, and chlorine is a gas that is toxic to most
organisms. These elements combine to form sodium chloride, the edible white solid you
know as table salt.

A **mixture** is matter made up of two or more substances that are combined physically.
They do not join chemically, so they keep their own properties. For example, in a mixture
of salt and sugar, some of the crystals will taste sweet, and some will taste salty. The
amounts of each substance can vary. A mixture of salt and sugar can contain any
amount of each. By contrast, the elements that make up a compound are always found
in specific ratios. For example, when sodium and chlorine atoms combine to make salt,
they combine in a 1:1 ratio (there is one sodium atom for every chlorine atom). Also unlike
mixtures, the substances that make up a compound cannot be separated by physical
means.

A **molecule** is the smallest unit of a compound that has all the properties of the
compound. Because elements combine in specific ratios to form compounds, each
molecule of a compound has a definite composition. Water is a compound you encounter
each day. It is a compound of hydrogen and oxygen. To form a molecule of water, the
elements oxygen and hydrogen must combine in a specific way—two atoms of hydrogen
must join with one atom of oxygen. If hydrogen and oxygen combine in any other ratio,
they form a different compound.

Some elements exist naturally as *diatomic molecules*—molecules made up of two atoms
of the same element. These include hydrogen gas (H_2) and oxygen gas (O_2).

Like elements, compounds can be represented by symbols. A **chemical formula** is an abbreviation that uses chemical symbols and subscripts to show the number of atoms of each element in a molecule of a compound. The chemical formula for water is H_2O. The subscript 2 in this formula shows how many atoms of hydrogen are in the molecule. The absence of a subscript indicates that only one atom of the element is present. Chemical formulas are discussed further in Lesson 10.

Chemical Bonds

Chemical bonds are the forces that hold atoms together in a compound. They are caused by interactions between the valence electrons of atoms. Recall that valence electrons are the electrons in the outermost energy level of an atom. The way in which atoms rearrange their valence electrons to combine chemically defines the type of chemical bond that forms. Compounds are held together by either ionic bonds or covalent bonds. Metallic bonds, found in solid metals, are also described in this lesson.

The number of valence electrons affects how an atom will bond and how many bonds it will form. Atoms are most stable when their outermost (valence) energy level is completely filled. This usually means that it contains eight electrons, or a *stable octet*. (Note that hydrogen and helium need only two electrons to fill their valence level.) It is helpful to think of bonding as an attempt by atoms to fill their outermost energy level with a stable octet by losing, gaining, or sharing electrons. Also, notice that different elements have different numbers of valence electrons available for bonding interactions. Recall that the number of valence electrons is related to an element's group in the periodic table. Group 1 elements have one valence electron, Group 2 elements have two, and Group 13 elements have three. Elements in Groups 14, 15, 16, and 17 have 4, 5, 6, and 7 electrons, respectively. Group 18 elements, the noble gases, have a stable octet and therefore tend not to form bonds. (The transition metals, Groups 3–12, have varying numbers of electrons available for bonding.)

Ionic Bonds

Ionic bonds form when one atom transfers its valence electrons to the outer energy level of another atom. Atoms with 1, 2, or 3 valence electrons (metals) have a tendency to transfer their electrons to atoms of nonmetal elements that have 7, 6, or 5 valence electrons. Therefore, ionic bonds form between metal atoms and nonmetal atoms. When a metal loses its valence electrons, its outermost energy level vanishes. The next energy level inward becomes the outer energy level. It now has a stable octet of electrons—that is, eight electrons in its outer energy level.

Recall from Lesson 7 that sodium (Na) is located in Group 1 of the periodic table. Group 1 elements are the most reactive metals, readily losing their single valence electron. A neutral sodium atom has 11 protons and 11 electrons. Two of those electrons fill the first energy level; another 8 fill the second energy level. The last lone valence electron is in the third energy level. Because this energy level is not filled, the sodium atom is unstable.

The Group 17 elements are the most reactive nonmetals, readily gaining a valence electron to achieve a stable octet. Atoms of the nonmetal chlorine (Cl) have 7 valence electrons and need only one more to fill the outermost level with a complete octet. When sodium and chlorine are brought together, a sodium atom transfers its outermost electron to a chlorine atom. These elements then combine in a 1:1 ratio to form sodium chloride (NaCl).

After the electron transfer, each atom becomes a charged atom, or **ion**. When electrons are removed from an atom, the excess charge from the protons produces a *positive ion* (Na^+). When an atom gains an electron, there is an excess negative charge. A *negative ion* forms—in this case, a chloride ion (Cl^-). An electron dot diagram of this electron exchange is shown below.

1 electron to give up   Na •

•Cl: 1 electron to get

Sodium gives 1 electron to chlorine   Na • → •Cl:

Sodium becomes a positive ion Na^+

:Cl^-:   Chlorine becomes a negative ion

The oppositely charged ions strongly attract each other, forming ionic bonds. These bonds hold the ions in a rigid, repeating pattern called a *lattice*. (Ions and lattices are described in more detail in Lesson 9.)

Covalent Bonds

Some elements form bonds by sharing valence electrons to gain a more stable electron structure. These are called **covalent bonds**. As with ionic bonds, atoms forming covalent bonds seek to have a total of 8 valence electrons.

Covalent bonds are most likely to form between nonmetals, which have 4, 5, 6, or 7 valence electrons. The diagram below shows how a covalent bond forms between two chlorine atoms, each with 7 valence electrons. The chemical formula for the molecule that results is Cl_2.

:Cl•   ×Cl×   ×Cl×Cl: Each atom shares one valence electron, forming a covalent bond

Sometimes, two different nonmetal atoms combine to form a compound. For example, nitrogen and hydrogen combine to form ammonia (NH_3). A covalent bond forms between the nitrogen atom and each hydrogen atom, as shown.

:N•   +   ×H   +   ×H   +   ×H   →   H NH H   Covalent bonds

Nitrogen atom   Hydrogen atom   Hydrogen atom   Hydrogen atom   Ammonia molecule

Carbon dioxide (CO_2) is a covalent compound formed by a single carbon atom with 4 valence electrons and two oxygen atoms, each having 6 valence electrons. To achieve a stable octet, the carbon atom must share two pairs of electrons with each oxygen atom. This is called a *double bond*, formed when atoms share two pairs of electrons. The electron dot diagram shows how a carbon dioxide molecule forms.

Carbon dioxide

A *triple bond* is formed by the sharing of three pairs of electrons. An example of a molecule with a triple bond is nitrogen gas (N_2), which forms from two nitrogen atoms. (Note that nitrogen gas is not a compound, because it is not made up of more than one element. It is a molecular element.) The formation of the nitrogen gas molecule is shown.

Needs to share
3 electrons = triple bond

Metallic Bonds

Although pure metals are not compounds, it is useful to think about the bonds that hold metal atoms together in a solid. Metal atoms form metallic bonds with each other. **Metallic bonds** are caused by the attraction between positive ions and negative electrons. Recall that metals tend to give up electrons easily. In a solid metal, the atoms become positive ions and are arranged in a regular lattice. The valence electrons from the atoms are shared among the ions, similar to the sharing of electrons in covalent bonds. However, the valence electrons in metals are not bound to any one ion but can move freely between ions. This property of metals allows them to conduct an electric current, as explained in Chapter 3. It also makes them ductile and malleable: you can bend, twist, or hammer sheets of aluminum foil, for example, without shattering it.

Discussion Question

What is the relationship between the number of electrons in an atom's outermost energy level and the type of ion (positive or negative) it becomes when forming ionic bonds?

Lesson Review

1. What type of element typically loses electrons to form an ionic bond?

    A. metal

    B. metalloid

    C. noble gas

    D. nonmetal

2. Which of the following occurs during covalent bonding?

    A. Electrons are shared.

    B. Electrons are lost only.

    C. Electrons are gained only.

    D. Electrons are gained and lost.

Refer to the periodic table in Lesson 7 to answer the following questions.

3. Which pair of elements will form ionic bonds?

    A. zinc (Zn) and mercury (Hg)

    B. nitrogen (N) and bromine (Br)

    C. potassium (K) and calcium (Ca)

    D. magnesium (Mg) and oxygen (O)

4. How can a Group 16 element gain a stable octet?

    A. by losing two valence electrons

    B. by sharing two valence electrons

    C. by gaining four valence electrons

    D. by sharing four valence electrons

5. Methane is a covalent compound of carbon (C) and hydrogen (H). How can carbon and hydrogen share electrons to form a molecule of methane?

    A. A carbon atom shares four valence electrons with a single hydrogen atom.

    B. A carbon atom shares one valence electron with each of four hydrogen atoms.

    C. A carbon atom shares two valence electrons with each of two hydrogen atoms.

    D. A carbon atom shares three valence electrons with each of three hydrogen atoms.

Ions

Key Words • ion • polyatomic ion • electrostatic force • crystal

Getting the Idea

An ion forms when an atom gains or loses electrons. Different types of ions can form in this way. However, each element tends to form a specific type of ion. What patterns determine the type of ion an element will form?

Positive and Negative Ions

Recall that an **ion** is a charged atom. A neutral atom of an element contains equal numbers of protons and electrons. The positive charge of the protons cancels out the negative charge of the electrons, and the atom has a *net* (total or combined) charge of zero. An atom forms an ion when it gains or loses one or more electrons. If an atom loses an electron, the positive charge from the protons will be one greater than the negative charge from the electrons. Its net charge will therefore be +1. (An ion with a positive charge is called a *cation*.) An ion with a charge of +1 is represented by writing the superscript "+" to the right of the chemical symbol for that element. For example, Na^+ is the symbol for a sodium atom that has lost one electron.

What if an atom gains an electron instead? Then, the negative charge from the electrons will be one greater than the positive charge from the protons. Its net charge will be −1. (An ion with a negative charge is called an *anion*.) An ion with a charge of −1 is represented by writing the superscript "−" to the right of the chemical symbol for that element. For example, F^- is the symbol for a fluorine atom that has gained one electron.

Atoms can form ions by gaining or losing more than one electron. For example, calcium (Ca) tends to lose two electrons, taking on a charge of +2. The symbol for this ion includes the number 2 in the superscript before the "+" sign: Ca^{2+}.

Polyatomic Ions

A **polyatomic ion** is a charged, covalently bonded molecule that acts like a single atom in forming ionic bonds with other atoms. The total number of electrons in all the atoms making up the molecule is less than or greater than the total number of protons. This gives the molecule a net positive or negative charge. When forming ionic bonds with atoms of other elements, the polyatomic ion acts in the same way that an ion made from a single atom would. It takes electrons from or donates electrons to the other element.

The Structure of Solid Ionic Compounds

Ionic compounds form when atoms of one element remove electrons from atoms of another element. The result is that both types of atoms become more stable by having a complete octet of electrons in their valence energy levels. However, the atoms also become ions. Because one atom gains electrons and the other loses electrons, their ions have opposite charges.

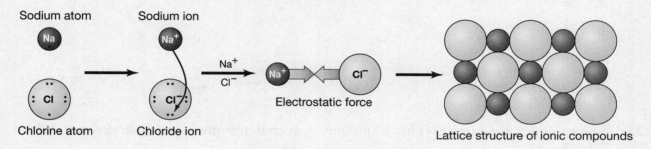

Lattice structure of ionic compounds

Opposite charges attract each other (see Chapter 3). The attractive force between opposite charges is called the **electrostatic force**. This force holds the ions of an ionic compound together tightly in a lattice or regular, repeating three-dimensional array. In the sodium chloride (NaCl) array shown, the sodium ions fill the spaces between the chloride ions. Each sodium ion is an equal distance away from each chloride ion. A solid made up of ions, atoms, or molecules arranged in a regular, repeating pattern is called a **crystal**.

Sodium Chloride Lattice Structure

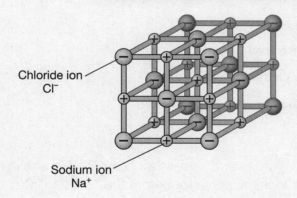

Chloride ion
Cl⁻

Sodium ion
Na⁺

Discussion Question

Can lithium (Li) and potassium (K) form an ionic compound with each other? What about carbon (C) and oxygen (O)? What is required for an ionic compound to form, and why?

1. Strontium (Sr), an element in Group 2, forms positive ions. An atom of strontium has 38 protons and 38 electrons. How many electrons does a strontium ion have?

   A. 36

   B. 37

   C. 39

   D. 40

2. The transition metal iron (Fe) has 26 protons. A neutral iron atom loses three electrons. What is its charge?

   A. −3

   B. −23

   C. +3

   D. +23

3. What is the role of the electrostatic force in an ionic compound?

   A. It attracts ions with like charges to each other.

   B. It adds electrons to the valence level of an atom.

   C. It attracts ions with opposite charges to each other.

   D. It removes electrons from the valence level of an atom.

Chemical Reactions and Equations

Key Words • chemical formula • subscript • chemical reaction • reactant • product • chemical equation • coefficient

Getting the Idea

Compounds undergo chemical changes to form new compounds. How do we know what elements a compound consists of? How do we describe the chemical changes that occur to form new compounds? In this lesson, you will learn how compounds and their changes are described.

Symbols, Formulas, and the Language of Chemistry

Recall that a chemical symbol is a one- or two-letter abbreviation that represents an element. For example, the letter H represents hydrogen. The chemical symbol for iron, a common metal, is Fe. Like elements, the molecules that make up compounds are also represented by symbols. For a covalent compound, the **chemical formula** shows the number of atoms of each element that make up a molecule. For example, the chemical formula for water is H_2O. The small number 2 written to the right and slightly below the symbol for hydrogen (H) is an example of a subscript. A **subscript** shows how many atoms of an element are in a molecule of a substance. The number 1 is not used as a subscript. The absence of a number indicates only one atom of the element.

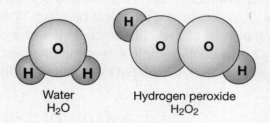

Water
H_2O

Hydrogen peroxide
H_2O_2

Notice that the ratio of hydrogen to oxygen in water is 2:1. When the elements combine chemically to make water, two hydrogen atoms always combine with one oxygen atom. If the ratio of the atoms is changed, the compound they produce also changes. Hydrogen peroxide contains the same elements as water but in a different ratio: in this case, 1:1. A molecule of hydrogen peroxide consists of two atoms of hydrogen and two atoms of oxygen. The chemical formula for this compound is H_2O_2. For an ionic compound, the chemical formula simply shows the ratio of atoms. For example, the compound magnesium chloride has the formula $MgCl_2$. This means that for every magnesium ion, there are two chloride ions. (Ionic compounds do not form molecules.)

Chemical Reactions

When compounds such as H_2O_2 or $MgCl_2$ undergo chemical reactions, they do not remain H_2O_2 or $MgCl_2$. A **chemical reaction** is a change in the arrangements of atoms in substances, yielding one or more new substances. The new substances contain the same numbers and types of atoms as the original substances, but they are arranged differently. For example, carbonic acid (H_2CO_3) forms water and carbon dioxide.

$$H_2CO_3 \rightarrow H_2O + CO_2$$

Notice that the identity of the carbon, oxygen, and hydrogen atoms in the carbonic acid did not change. These atoms were simply combined in new ways to form new substances. In a chemical reaction, the original or starting substances are called the **reactants**. The new substances that are formed are the **products**.

Chemical Equations

Just as chemical symbols and formulas tell us the elements that make up different substances, chemical equations tell us how substances change in a chemical reaction. A **chemical equation** includes the chemical formulas for reactants on the left side of an arrow and the formulas for the products on the right side. A chemical equation for the reaction in which hydrogen peroxide forms the products water and oxygen is shown.

$$H_2O_2 \rightarrow H_2O + O_2$$

The subscripts show that there are 2 atoms of hydrogen and 2 atoms of oxygen in the reactants. Notice that in the products, there are 2 atoms of hydrogen and 3 atoms of oxygen (1 in H_2O and 2 in O_2).

Chemical reactions often involve more than one molecule of a compound. **Coefficients** show the numbers of each type of molecule in a chemical reaction. When a symbol has no coefficient, the reaction involves one molecule of that substance. In the chemical equation below, the number 2 to the left of H_2O_2 is a coefficient. It shows that the reactant consists of two molecules of hydrogen peroxide. The coefficient before H_2O indicates that the reaction produces two molecules of water.

$$2H_2O_2 \rightarrow 2H_2O + O_2$$

Discussion Question

Why are chemical symbols, formulas, and equations useful?

Lesson Review

1. Octane (C_8H_{18}) is a compound in gasoline. How many atoms of carbon are in one molecule of octane?

   A. 8

   B. 10

   C. 18

   D. 26

2. Which of the following pairs of formulas represents the reactants in the chemical reaction described by the equation below?

   $NaCl + AgF \rightarrow NaF + AgCl$

   A. $AgF + NaF$

   B. $NaCl + AgF$

   C. $NaF + AgCl$

   D. $NaCl + AgCl$

3. Which of the following change in a chemical reaction?

   A. bonds between atoms

   B. identities of elements

   C. numbers of atoms

   D. numbers of subatomic particles

Matter and Energy in Chemical Reactions

Key Words • law of conservation of matter • balanced equation • mole • Avogadro's number
exothermic reaction • endothermic reaction • activation energy

Getting the Idea

In a chemical reaction, the atoms in a compound or element are rearranged and joined chemically to form a new substance. The number of each kind of atom remains the same. Since atoms are neither created nor destroyed, you can use chemical formulas to figure out the mass of each substance involved in a reaction and determine how atoms rearrange themselves during a chemical change.

The Law of Conservation of Matter

Recall from Lesson 10 that chemical reactions involve changes in the way in which atoms are grouped, or arranged. The products of a reaction always contain the same kind and number of atoms as the reactants. This important principle is known as the **law of conservation of matter**, which states that during a chemical reaction, matter cannot be created or destroyed but can be rearranged into a different form. The law of conservation of matter makes it possible to calculate the masses of reactants and products.

In order to verify that a chemical equation obeys the law of conservation of matter, the equation must be balanced. In a **balanced equation**, each side of the equation (reactants and products) must have the same number of atoms of each element, because matter is conserved.

Example of an unbalanced equation:

$$H_2 \quad + \quad O_2 \quad \rightarrow \quad H_2O$$

2 H atoms + 2 O atoms ≠ 2 H atoms and 1 O atom

Example of a balanced equation:

$$2H_2 \quad + \quad O_2 \quad \rightarrow \quad 2H_2O$$

4 H atoms + 2 O atoms = 4 H atoms and 2 O atoms

Balancing Chemical Equations

There is a systematic way to balance chemical equations. Follow the steps below to balance a chemical equation. The table shows how to identify and balance an unbalanced equation.

Step 1: Count the number of atoms of each element in the reactants and products.

Step 2: Balance the elements, one at a time, by using coefficients.

- When no coefficient is written, it is assumed to be 1.
- Never balance an equation by changing subscripts.
- Make sure all coefficients are in the lowest possible ratio.

Balancing a Chemical Equation

Scenario	Equation
An experiment shows that sodium atoms and oxygen molecules combine to produce sodium peroxide molecules. The formulas for these substances are Na, O_2, and Na_2O_2.	$Na + O_2 \rightarrow Na_2O_2$
Count the atoms of each element in the reactants (Na and O_2) and product (Na_2O_2). Counting atoms shows that the oxygen atoms remain the same, but the sodium atoms do not. It appears that a sodium atom has been created by the reaction. Since this violates the law of conservation of matter, the equation must be unbalanced.	1 Na atom + 2 O atoms $\neq$ 2 Na atoms + 2 O atoms
To balance an equation, adjust the coefficients so that no atoms are created or destroyed. The formulas cannot be altered, so never change the subscripts. A sodium atom is Na, not Na_2. Balance the sodium atoms by placing the coefficient "2" before the reactant Na.	**2**Na + O_2 $\rightarrow$ Na_2O_2 2 Na atoms + 2 O atoms = 2 Na atoms + 2 O atoms

Balance the following chemical equations:

$$Ag_2S \rightarrow Ag + S_8$$

$$C_3H_8 + O_2 \rightarrow CO_2 + H_2O$$

$$2BF_3 + Li_2SO_3 \rightarrow B_2(SO_3)_3 + LiF$$

Check your responses against the balanced equations:

$$8Ag_2S \rightarrow 16Ag + S_8$$

$$C_3H_8 + 5O_2 \rightarrow 3CO_2 + 4H_2O$$

$$2BF_3 + 3Li_2SO_3 \rightarrow B_2(SO_3)_3 + 6LiF$$

The Mole and Avogadro's Number

When chemists combine substances to make compounds, they need to use specific amounts of each substance. Chemists often use a measurement called the mole (abbreviated mol). A **mole** is equal to 6.02×10^{23} atoms or molecules. This quantity is called **Avogadro's number**, for the Italian scientist who invented the mole, Amedeo Avogadro. Think of a mole as being similar to a dozen. Just as a dozen eggs or a dozen donuts consists of 12 objects, a mole of sodium consists of 6.02×10^{23} atoms.

The diagram below shows a water molecule. Water is made up of hydrogen and oxygen atoms in a 2:1 ratio. This can be stated as: 2 parts hydrogen join with 1 part oxygen to produce 1 part water. It can also be stated as: 2 moles of hydrogen join with 1 mole of oxygen to produce 1 mole of water molecules.

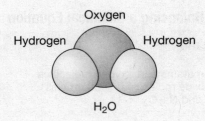

2 H atoms	+	1 O atom	→	1 H_2O molecule
2 parts H	+	1 part O	→	1 part H_2O
2 moles H	+	1 mole O	→	1 mole H_2O
$2(6.02 \times 10^{23})$ H atoms	+	6.02×10^{23} O atoms	→	6.02×10^{23} H_2O molecules

Mass and Moles

Why is the mole useful to chemists? When conducting experiments, chemists cannot count the number of atoms or molecules in a sample. However, by knowing the mass that is equal to one mole of a substance, they can measure out a mole of atoms or molecules using an electronic balance. How is mass related to moles?

Recall that protons and neutrons each have a mass of 1 atomic mass unit (amu). The combined mass of all the protons and neutrons in an atom's nucleus determines an element's *atomic mass*. The atomic mass of carbon-12 is exactly 12 amu. Avogadro determined that one mole should equal the number of atoms in 12 grams of carbon-12. This relationship between the number of carbon-12 atoms and the number of grams allows chemists to easily determine the number of grams equal to one mole of *any* substance.

A mole of any substance has a mass in grams equal to the atomic mass or molecular mass of that substance. For example, because the mix of isotopes in carbon gives it an average atomic mass of 12.01 amu, one mole of carbon atoms has a mass of 12.01 grams. Similarly, one mole of water molecules has a mass (in grams) equal to the molecular mass of water. The *molecular mass* is the sum of the average atomic mass of each atom in the molecule. Oxygen has an average atomic mass of 15.999 amu, and for hydrogen it is 1.008 amu. Adding 15.999 + 1.008 + 1.008 gives the molecular mass of water as 18.015 amu. Therefore, one mole of water can be measured as 18.015 grams of water.

1 mole = atomic or molecular mass = number of grams

Molarity describes the moles per liter in a solution and is a common way to express concentration in chemistry. Solutions and molarity are discussed further in Lesson 12.

An Example of Conservation of Matter

The law of conservation of matter makes it possible to determine the masses of the reactants and products of a chemical reaction. In the experimental setup below, a test tube that contains lead nitrate is placed upright inside a flask that contains potassium iodide (left). The reactants cannot mix because the test tube is upright. A stopper is placed in the mouth of the flask to form a *closed system*, or an environment which no matter can enter or leave. The system is then placed on an electronic balance.

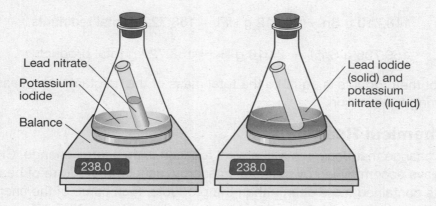

Once the mass is measured, the entire system is turned upside down so the lead nitrate from the test tube can mix with the potassium iodide in the flask. The chemicals react to form lead iodide and potassium nitrate. The right side of the illustration shows that, although the chemical properties of the matter changed as the reactants formed new products, the total mass of the system remains unchanged.

Calculating Mass in Chemical Reactions

Using the relationship between moles and grams, the law of conservation of mass, and the masses of the reactants, you can calculate the mass of products formed by a chemical reaction. Tin fluoride is often added to toothpaste to prevent cavities. The chemical equation below shows how tin fluoride forms:

$$Sn \text{ (tin)} + 2HFl \text{ (hydrogen fluoride)} \rightarrow SnFl_2 \text{ (tin fluoride)} + H_2 \text{ (hydrogen gas)}$$

Suppose that a 118.710-g sample of tin and 40.012-g sample of HFl, totaling 158.722 grams of reactants, are combined. How many moles of each reactant is this? The periodic table shows that the atomic mass of tin is 118.71 amu. Therefore, 1 mole of tin was used. Similarly, HFl has a molecular mass of 20.006 amu (H = 1.008 amu and Fl = 18.998 amu), so 2 moles of HFl are used in the reaction ($20.006 \times 2 = 40.012$).

The equation shows that 1 mole of tin combines with 2 moles of HFl to produce 1 mole of tin fluoride and 1 mole of hydrogen gas. The tin fluoride is measured and found to have a mass of exactly 156.706 grams. (This is equal to one mole of tin fluoride.) According to the law of conservation of mass, one mole of hydrogen gas is also produced. The mass of the hydrogen gas can be calculated as the number of grams in one mole of H_2. Adding the atomic mass of each atom of hydrogen in a molecule of H_2 yields $1.008 + 1.008 = 2.016$ grams.

Check this result by comparing the masses of the reactants and the products.

$$118.710 \text{ g Sn} + 40.012 \text{ g HFl} = 158.722 \text{ g total reactants}$$

$$156.706 \text{ g SnFl}_2 + 2.016 \text{ g H}_2 = 158.722 \text{ g total products}$$

The total mass of the products is equal to the total mass of the reactants. No mass was created or destroyed during the reaction.

Energy in Chemical Reactions

Another type of change that occurs in a chemical reaction is an energy change. Chemical changes are always accompanied by changes in energy, usually in the form of heat or light. If the original reactants contained more energy than the products, then some of the energy that was in the reactants must have been released to the surroundings. An **exothermic reaction** releases energy. Some of the energy may be released as light energy, such as when a substance burns.

Recall that the atoms that form molecules are held together by chemical bonds involving electrons. The energy released in a chemical reaction comes from the potential energy stored in the bonds of the reactants. Sometimes, the products formed in a reaction have more energy stored in their bonds than did the reactants. In this case, energy must have been added, or absorbed. An **endothermic reaction** absorbs energy. This energy may be in the form of added heat or light and is stored as potential energy in the bonds of the products that form. An endothermic reaction may occur at room temperature. As the reaction absorbs heat from its surroundings, the temperature of its surroundings decreases.

A chemical reaction is started by energy that speeds up the molecules in the reactants. This causes them to collide with greater force, breaking the bonds between the atoms. **Activation energy** is the energy needed to get a reaction going. When bonds between atoms break, the freed atoms form new electron bonds and rearrange themselves into different molecules. The diagrams below show the energy changes in both endothermic and exothermic reactions.

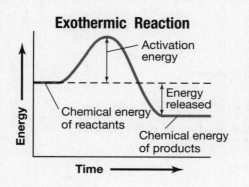

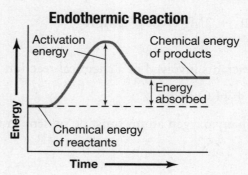

Discussion Question

Some cold packs used for injuries during sporting events do not need to be frozen. They are simply crushed slightly, starting a chemical reaction inside the pack. The pack then becomes cool. Is the reaction inside the pack an exothermic or an endothermic reaction? Explain.

Lesson Review

1. The average atomic mass of potassium (K) is 39.1 amu. The average atomic mass of bromine (Br) is 79.9 amu. What is the mass of 2 moles of potassium bromide (KBr)?

   A. 59.5 g

   B. 119 g

   C. 238 g

   D. 476 g

2. Photosynthesis is a chemical reaction. Plants use energy from the sun to change carbon dioxide and water into glucose and oxygen.

   $$6CO_2 + 6H_2O \rightarrow C_6H_{12}O_6 + 6O_2$$

   Which statement is true about this reaction?

   A. It is exothermic because the reactants have less energy than the products.

   B. It is endothermic because the reactants have less energy than the products.

   C. It is exothermic because the reactants have more energy than the products.

   D. It is endothermic because the reactants have more energy than the products.

3. Which chemical equation is properly balanced?

   A. $4Ba + S_8 \rightarrow 2BaS$

   B. $4HgO \rightarrow 4Hg + 3O_2$

   C. $2FeO + 4C \rightarrow Fe + 2CO_2$

   D. $SiI_4 + 2Mg \rightarrow Si + 2MgI_2$

4. The reactants involved in a chemical reaction are shown.

   $Na_2O + H_2O \rightarrow$?

   How many oxygen atoms must be present in the product of this reaction?

   A. 1

   B. 2

   C. 3

   D. 4

5. Which of the following is true in every balanced chemical equation?

   A. Matter is conserved.

   B. The energy change is exothermic.

   C. All coefficients have to be multiples of two.

   D. Atoms are created when products are formed.

Acids, Bases, and pH

Key Words • solution • solute • solvent • concentration • polyatomic ion • acid • base • neutral • neutralization reaction • pH scale • indicator

Getting the Idea

Some combinations of substances form acids or bases. Acids and bases have chemical and physical properties that make them important in many fields of science and in everyday uses. Whether a substance is acidic or basic is indicated by a measure called pH.

Solutions, Solutes, and Solvents

Recall that a mixture is matter made up of two or more substances that are combined physically. A **solution** is a mixture in which the particles of the substances making up the mixture are evenly distributed. The substance that dissolves in a solution is the **solute**. The substance in which the solute dissolves is the **solvent**. Most often, the solute is a solid or powder, and the solvent is a liquid, such as water.

The **concentration** of a solution is the amount of solute in a given quantity of solvent or solution. Concentration can be stated in several ways. The *percent composition* of a solution is the mass of the solute divided by the mass of the entire solution. For example, the solution called formalin is 37 percent formaldehyde by mass. Concentration can also be given in *parts per million* (ppm), which is a ratio of the parts of solute to a million parts of solution. One part per million is equal to 1 mg of solute per kilogram of solution. For example, trout from the Great Lakes contain PCB pollutants at a concentration of about 1.3 ppm.

Finally, a common way to express concentration in chemistry is *molarity*, or moles per liter.

$$\text{molarity } (M) = \frac{\text{moles of solute}}{\text{liters of solution}}$$

Recall from the previous lesson that a mole (mol) is 6.02×10^{23} atoms or molecules. A one-molar solution contains 1 mole of solute per liter of solution. For example, when we dissolve 0.75 mol of a solute in 2.50 L of a solution, the molarity is 0.300 *M*.

$$\frac{0.75 \text{ mol}}{2.50 \text{ L}} = 0.300 \ M$$

Water, Hydroxide, and Hydrogen Ions

A solution in which the solvent is water is called an *aqueous solution*. Acids and bases are compounds that have certain chemical properties when dissolved in an aqueous solution. It is helpful to first consider the water molecule and the ions that can form from it. The formula for water is H_2O. A water molecule can lose a *hydrogen ion* (H^+) and form a negative *hydroxide ion* (OH^-). The hydroxide ion is a **polyatomic ion**, meaning it is made up of more than one atom. Normally, very few water molecules form ions.

$$H_2O \rightarrow OH^- + H^+$$

Acids and Bases in Solution

An **acid** is any substance that releases or donates hydrogen ions (H^+) in solution. Acids are often recognized because their chemical formulas begin with the symbol for hydrogen, H. The equation below shows how the acid hydrogen chloride (HCl) forms hydrogen and chlorine ions when it dissolves in water:

$$HCl \rightarrow Cl^- + H^+$$

Acetic acid, the acid that gives vinegar its tartness, also produces hydrogen ions in solution:

$$HC_2H_3O_2 \rightarrow C_2H_3O_2^- + H^+$$

Notice that in both examples, the acid also produces a negative ion in addition to the hydrogen ion. Many common foods and drinks are slightly acidic. These include vinegar, lemon juice, coffee, and many fruits. Acidic substances taste tart or sour. Highly acidic solutions are corrosive, meaning they can dissolve substances, and should be handled carefully. Most acids, bases, and salt solutions also conduct electricity (see Chapter 3).

A **base**, or *alkali*, is a substance that accepts hydrogen ions in solution and releases hydroxide ions (OH^-). Many bases have chemical formulas that end in OH. For example, sodium hydroxide (NaOH) is a base used in drain cleaner.

$$NaOH \rightarrow Na^+ + OH^-$$

Calcium hydroxide, $Ca(OH)_2$, is a base used in fertilizer.

$$Ca(OH)_2 \rightarrow Ca^{2+} + 2OH^-$$

Note that many bases are compounds of metals and the hydroxide ion. Recall from Lesson 7 that the Group 1 elements are called alkali metals and the Group 2 elements are called alkaline earth metals. They are given those names because they form strong bases when combined with hydroxide. Common bases include antacids such as milk of magnesia. Bases tend to taste bitter and feel slippery. Very basic solutions, such as drain cleaner, should be handled with caution.

Neutral Solutions and Neutralization Reactions

A solution in which the concentrations of H^+ and OH^- ions are equal is considered **neutral**. Pure water is neutral. Neutral solutions are neither acids nor bases.

When an acid and a base combine in solution, a neutralization reaction occurs. A **neutralization reaction** is a chemical reaction in which an acid and a base combine to form water and a salt. It is helpful to think of the hydrogen ions from the acid and the hydroxide ions from the base combining to form water. The remaining components of the acid and base form the salt. The salt remains in the neutralized solution and may settle to the bottom as a solid or be removed from the water by other means. An example of a neutralization reaction is shown below.

$$H_2SO_4 \quad + \quad Ca(OH)_2 \quad \rightarrow \quad CaSO_4 \quad + \quad 2H_2O$$

$$\text{acid} \quad + \quad \text{base} \quad \rightarrow \quad \text{salt} \quad + \quad \text{water}$$

$$2H^+ + 2OH^- \rightarrow 2H_2O$$

$$(SO_4)^{2-} + Ca^+ \rightarrow CaSO_4$$

The pH Scale

A solution with a higher concentration of hydrogen ions (H^+) than hydroxide ions (OH^-) is acidic, while a solution with a higher concentration of hydroxide ions is basic. The **pH scale** quantitatively describes how acidic or basic a solution is. A pH level below 7 indicates a higher concentration of hydrogen ions and an acidic solution. Solutions with very low pH levels are extremely acidic. For example, the digestive juice produced by the human stomach has a pH between 1 and 3 and is able to dissolve iron nails. A solution with a slightly higher pH, such as 5 or 6, is slightly acidic.

At a pH of 7, the concentrations of H^+ ions and OH^- ions are equal, and the solution is neutral. Pure water is a neutral substance with a pH of 7. A pH level greater than 7 indicates a solution with more OH^- ions than H^+ ions. The concentrations of these two ions are inversely related. As the concentration of H^+ ions decreases, the concentration of OH^- ions increases. Solutions with pH levels above 7 are basic, or alkaline. Human blood is slightly basic, with a pH of 7.4. The strongest bases have a pH of 14. The illustration matches some common substances with their pH levels.

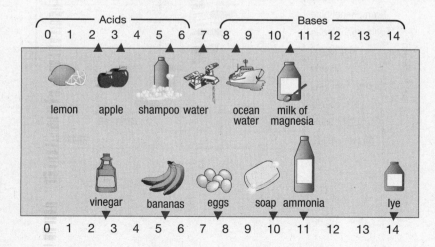

The pH scale ranges from 0 to 14 and is based on the concentration of hydrogen (H^+) ions. The molar concentration of a solute is represented with square brackets: $[H^+]$. The pH of a solution is the negative base-ten logarithm of this concentration, as shown by the equation below.

$$pH = -\log[H^+]$$

If the hydrogen ion concentration is 0.001 M (0.001 moles per liter), then the pH is the negative logarithm of this number: $-\log(0.001) = -\log(10^{-3}) = -(-3) = 3$. It is easier to see the relationship when the hydrogen ion concentration is converted to a base-ten exponent. The negative logarithm of 10^{-x} is equal to x. Therefore, if $[H^+] = 0.0001 = 10^{-4}$, then pH = 4. If $[H^+] = 0.00001 = 10^{-5}$, then pH = 5. Every time the hydrogen ion concentration decreases by a factor of 10, the pH increases by 1. Therefore, a solution with a pH of 7 has 10 times more hydrogen ions than a solution with a pH of 8, and 100 times more hydrogen ions than a solution with a pH of 9.

Determining pH with Indicators

One way to measure pH accurately is with a probe called a pH meter. Indicators can also measure pH with moderate accuracy. An **indicator** is a substance that changes color in response to a change in pH. Some common indicators are litmus papers, pH papers, and compounds such as phenolphthalein and bromthymol blue.

Litmus papers and pH papers contain chemicals that change color depending on pH. Blue litmus paper turns red when dipped in an acid. Red litmus paper turns blue when dipped in a base. More accurate, though, are pH papers, because they turn different shades at various H^+ concentrations. By comparing the paper color to a color chart, you can determine the pH of the solution.

Indicator compounds change color only at certain pH ranges. For example, bromthymol blue is pale blue at pH levels around 7. Lowering the pH at this point causes the indicator to turn yellow. Lowering the pH from 5 to 1 does not cause any further color change. Adding a base turns bromthymol blue a darker blue. Phenolphthalein is another indicator and turns dark pink when the pH rises above 8. The color change ranges of some indicators are shown below.

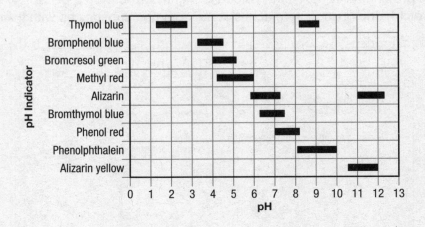

Discussion Question

Water spontaneously forms hydrogen ions at very low rates. The concentration of hydrogen ions in plain, neutral water is 10^{-7}. Why is water not usually thought of as an acid? By how much would the hydrogen ion concentration need to increase to lower the pH of water to 2?

Lesson Review

1. An unknown substance is dissolved in water. The solution is corrosive, conducts electricity, and has a higher concentration of hydroxide ions than hydrogen ions. What kind of solution does this unknown substance form?

   A. salt

   B. basic

   C. acidic

   D. neutral

2. An acid and a base are combined in a neutralization reaction. What substance or substances will be the products of the reaction?

   A. only water

   B. another acid

   C. another base

   D. water and a salt

3. Sodium chloride, a salt, is dissolved in water. Which of the following correctly describes this combination of substances?

   A. Sodium chloride is the solvent, water is the solute, and salt water is the solution.

   B. Sodium chloride is the solvent, water is the solution, and salt water is the solute.

   C. Sodium chloride is the solution, water is the solute, and salt water is the solvent.

   D. Sodium chloride is the solute, water is the solvent, and salt water is the solution.

States of Matter

• state of matter • solid • liquid • gas • plasma • state change • melting • vaporization • evaporation • boiling • sublimation • condensation • freezing • kinetic molecular theory

Getting the Idea

You probably know that ice, liquid water, and water vapor are different forms of water (H_2O). If they are all the same substance, why do they have different physical properties? The answer is energy. Substances can change form if enough heat energy is added or taken away. Matter changes form because of changes in the arrangement, motion, and attractive forces of its particles.

States of Matter

A **state of matter** is a physical form in which matter exists. States of matter are also called *phases* of matter. All matter is made up of particles—atoms and molecules—that are always moving. These particles are arranged differently depending on the state of matter. There are four main states of matter: solid, liquid, gas, and plasma. On Earth, matter generally exists in a solid, liquid, or gas state. The table below provides a summary of matter in each of these states.

States of Matter and Their Properties

Example/Property	Solid	Liquid	Gas
Shape	Definite shape	No definite shape	No definite shape
Volume	Definite volume	Definite volume	No definite volume
Particle arrangement	Densely packed	Close	Far apart
Forces between particles	Very strong	Strong	Weak

Particles and State

The state of a substance is determined by the arrangement and motion of its particles. A **solid** is a substance with a definite shape and volume. The particles in a solid are packed close together in a rigid structure. The attractive forces between the particles are very strong. The particles in a solid cannot move about freely and only vibrate in place. The lack of motion of its particles is what gives a solid a definite shape and volume.

A **liquid** is a substance that has a definite volume but no definite shape. The particles of a liquid are close together but are not as densely packed or as rigidly held in place as those of a solid. The attractive forces between the particles in a liquid are weaker than the forces between particles in a solid. The particles of a liquid can move around and slide past one another. Therefore, a liquid does not have a definite shape but takes the shape of any container into which it is placed. The volume of a liquid stays the same no matter what shape it takes.

A **gas** is a substance that has neither a definite shape nor a definite volume. The attractive forces between the particles of gases are weaker than in solids or liquids. The particles in a gas can spread out and move independently of one another. The weak attractions between the particles of a gas allow it to expand or contract, so the volume of a gas can change. Gases tend to expand to fill their containers. The diagram below illustrates the differences in the arrangement and movement of particles making up solids, liquids, and gases.

Particles in Solids, Liquids, and Gases

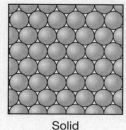
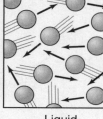
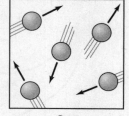

Solid
(low energy)

The particles are held tightly in place and move only by vibrating in place.

Liquid
(moderate energy)

The particles are able to slide past one another.

Gas
(high energy)

The particles move quickly and independently of one another.

Plasma is a state of matter that forms when temperatures are high enough to remove electrons from their atoms. Atoms are usually electrically neutral because they have the same number of electrons and protons. Plasma forms when a gas is heated to such a high temperature that its electrons gain enough energy to escape from their atoms. When an atom loses electrons, it becomes a positively charged ion. Plasma is a mixture of electrons, ions, and neutral atoms. Like a gas, plasma has no definite shape or volume. Unlike a gas, plasma is a good electrical conductor. Although plasma is not common on Earth, most of the matter in the visible universe exists as plasma. Stars, including the sun, are made up mainly of plasma.

Changes of State

A **state change** is a physical change of a substance from one state to another. All state changes require that matter either absorb or release energy. Most often, the energy involved is *thermal energy*, or heat. Recall from Lesson 11 that chemical reactions are described as *endothermic* or *exothermic*. State changes can also be described this way, according to whether they absorb energy (endothermic) or release energy (exothermic).

If a solid absorbs enough energy, **melting** occurs. The solid changes to a liquid once the solid reaches the *melting point* temperature. Similarly, when a liquid absorbs enough energy, it changes to a gas. The change from a liquid to a gas is called **vaporization**, and it can happen in two ways. If a liquid changes to a gas only at its surface, the process is called **evaporation**. This is how a puddle of water dries up on a sunny day. When bubbles of gas form throughout a liquid and rise to the surface, the process is called **boiling**. (Some chemical changes also cause the formation of bubbles.) A substance can evaporate at different temperatures, but each substance has a certain temperature at which it boils, called the *boiling point*. **Sublimation** occurs when a solid changes directly to a gas, without first becoming a liquid. These state changes are endothermic because they absorb energy.

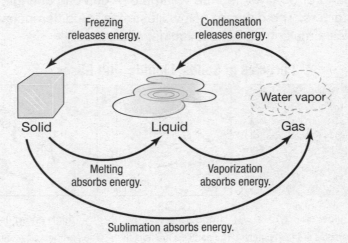

Other state changes are exothermic because they release energy. If enough energy is removed from a gas, the gas changes to a liquid through the process of **condensation**. Dewdrops on grass in the morning form from water vapor that condenses as the air temperature drops at night. The change from liquid to solid is called **freezing**, and the temperature at which a substance freezes is called its *freezing point*. The freezing point and melting point for most substances are the same. For example, when the temperature of water falls below 0° Celsius, water freezes to form ice. When the temperature rises above 0° Celsius, ice melts to form liquid water.

The change in state from a gas to a plasma is endothermic. Lightning bolts form a plasma as electricity passes through the atmosphere. Neon lights glow when electricity passes through neon gas and turns the gas into a plasma. The opposite change, from a plasma to a gas, is exothermic.

Kinetic Molecular Theory

The **kinetic molecular theory** of matter states that particles of matter are always moving in a random fashion. Even in a solid substance, the particles vibrate in place. (This theory is also called the *kinetic theory of matter*.) The average kinetic energy of the moving particles is related to the temperature of the substance. The faster the particles move, the higher the temperature. The slower they move, the lower the temperature. When thermal energy (heat) is added to a substance, its particles normally gain kinetic energy and move faster, causing the temperature to rise. When an endothermic state change occurs, the added energy causes the particles to be held together more loosely.

Similarly, when the temperature of the surroundings drops, thermal energy is removed from a substance. This causes the average kinetic energy of the particles to decrease. When an exothermic state change occurs, the loss of energy causes the particles to become more tightly bound to each other.

The graph below shows how the temperature of a substance changes over time when heat is added at a constant rate. This kind of graph is called a *heating curve*. At first, the temperature rises as heat is added, but during the change of state from solid to liquid, the temperature stays constant. The added energy is used to overcome the forces that hold the particles together. After the substance has melted, the temperature rises. It stays constant during the change from liquid to gas, and then rises again. The same pattern of temperature and state changes happens in reverse when heat is removed from a substance.

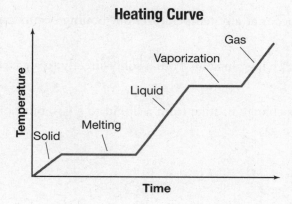

Discussion Question

One day when the outside temperature is low, you are boiling a pot of water indoors. As a result, a film of water forms on the insides of windows. What changes of state are taking place in this scenario? Are they endothermic or exothermic? Explain your answers.

Lesson Review

1. In which state of matter do particles spread and fill the volume of the container that holds them?

    A. gas

    B. solid

    C. liquid

2. What happens to the temperature of a solid as it melts?

    A. It increases.   **C.** It remains the same.

    B. It decreases.   **D.** It increases and then decreases.

3. Which of the following changes of state are endothermic?

   A. melting and vaporization

   B. freezing and vaporization

   C. melting and condensation

   D. freezing and condensation

4. Which of the following is a difference between evaporation and boiling?

   A. Evaporation occurs only at a specific temperature, but boiling can occur at any temperature.

   B. Evaporation can occur at any temperature, but boiling occurs only at a specific temperature.

   C. Evaporation is the change in state from a solid directly to a gas, but boiling is the change from a liquid to a gas.

   D. Evaporation is the change in state from a liquid to a gas, but boiling is the change from a solid directly to a gas.

The Behavior of Gases

Key Words • diffusion • ideal gas • pressure • Boyle's law • density • absolute zero • Charles's law

Getting the Idea

Because gases can change in volume and exert different amounts of pressure, scientists have studied their behavior under various conditions. The gas laws describe the behavior of gases. The gas laws treat all gases as ideal gases. The specific chemical identity of a gas or gas mixture does not matter. As long as the chemical identity resembles an ideal gas, it will obey the gas laws.

The Properties of Gases

Recall from Lesson 13 that kinetic molecular theory states that all matter is made up of tiny particles (atoms and molecules) that are in constant motion. In gases, the particles have enough energy to separate from one another and move about freely in all directions. It is this property of gases that allows gas particles to spread out and completely fill all space made available to them. A gas will completely fill any container into which it is placed.

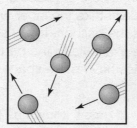

Gas
The particles move quickly and independently of one another.

Kinetic molecular theory helps explain the behavior of gas particles. When gas particles are released into a space, they will eventually spread until they are evenly distributed throughout the space. This is called **diffusion**. Diffusion occurs because gas particles move randomly in all directions.

Ideal Gases

When scientists study the behavior of a gas, they treat the gas as an ideal gas. An **ideal gas** is a gas with certain properties and behaviors:

- Its particles take up almost no volume compared to the volume of the space occupied by the gas.
- There are no (or almost zero) attractive forces between the particles.

An ideal gas is theoretical—it does not actually exist. However, most gases behave like ideal gases at low pressure and high temperature. Scientists also study gases at *standard temperature and pressure* (STP), a set of conditions that includes one atmosphere of pressure and a temperature of 0°C. (Though 0°C may seem like a low temperature, the next section explains why it is not.) At STP, an ideal gas has a volume of exactly 22.4 liters per mole of gas particles. The volume of an ideal gas depends only on the number of particles of gas present, and not on the mass of those particles. Therefore, adding more particles to an ideal gas will increase its volume. Changing the particles so that they are larger or heavier will not affect the volume of the gas.

Pressure and Volume: Boyle's Law

Ideal gases have predictable behaviors. Three factors affect the behavior of gases: pressure, volume, and temperature. **Pressure** is the amount of force exerted per unit area. The SI unit of pressure is the *pascal* (Pa), which is equal to a force of one newton per square meter. One atmosphere (atm) of pressure is equal to 1.01×10^5 Pa, which is the pressure at STP.

Imagine you are holding an inflated balloon. The gas particles inside the balloon are in constant motion. The collisions of the gas particles with the walls of the balloon exert pressure that keeps the balloon inflated. The gas particles inside the balloon spread out to take up all of the available space. However, they can be squeezed together to take up less space. If you squeeze the balloon together at its center, you create two smaller chambers. This causes the gas particles in each chamber of the balloon to squeeze together and occupy less space. The pressure the gas particles exert is determined by how frequently the particles strike the inner walls of the balloon. When you decrease the volume, the particles strike the inner walls more often, increasing the pressure the particles exert on the walls of the balloon. If you stop holding the balloon closed at its center, you increase the total volume available to the particles. The pressure inside the balloon decreases because the gas particles have more space to move around and strike the walls less often.

The balloon example illustrates a property of gases known as Boyle's law. **Boyle's law** states that, if temperature remains constant, decreasing the volume of a container of gas will cause the pressure of the gas to increase. The reverse is also true. If temperature remains constant, increasing the volume of a container holding a gas will cause a decrease in pressure. In the equation below, P_1 and V_1 are the starting pressure and volume, and P_2 and V_2 are the ending pressure and volume.

$$\text{Boyle's law equation: } P_1V_1 = P_2V_2$$

Suppose the initial pressure of an ideal gas in a 2.0-L container is 3.0 atm. The gas is transferred to a larger, 3.0-L container. All the gas particles from the original container end up in the second container, and no additional gas particles are added. What is the pressure of the gas in the second container? The Boyle's law equation allows us to solve for the final pressure, P_2, because we know the other three variables:

$$P_2 = \frac{P_1V_1}{V_2} \qquad P_2 = \frac{3.0 \text{ atm} \times 2.0 \text{ L}}{3.0 \text{ L}} \qquad P_2 = 2.0 \text{ atm}$$

Does this answer make sense? As the space available to a gas increases, holding temperature constant, the particles will strike the internal walls of the container less often. Therefore, the pressure will decrease, as it did in this example. Our answer makes sense.

Density is a measure of the mass of a substance per unit volume. The density of a gas is affected by changes in pressure. This occurs because increasing pressure on a gas forces gas particles closer together. Decreasing pressure on a gas allows the particles to move farther apart. This lowers its density.

Absolute Zero and the Kelvin Temperature Scale

Recall that *temperature* is a measure of the average kinetic energy of the particles in a substance. The temperature of a gas is the average kinetic energy of its particles. Notice that the temperature at STP is 0°C. Does this mean that gas particles at STP have zero kinetic energy? Actually, they are still moving at high speeds at this temperature and at temperatures far below 0°C. That is why scientists use a different temperature scale, the Kelvin scale. The values of the Kelvin scale are positive at any temperature above absolute zero. **Absolute zero**, or 0 kelvins, is the point at which particles have no motion at all. It corresponds to a temperature of −273°C. No temperature can be lower than 0 kelvins.

To convert a temperature from degrees Celsius to kelvins, add 273 to the Celsius temperature. A temperature of 0°C is equal to 273 kelvins (273 K), and a temperature of 25°C equals 25 + 273 = 298 K.

Volume and Temperature: Charles's Law

When the air inside a hot air balloon is heated, the gas particles move farther apart. As the temperature of the air in the balloon increases, the volume of the balloon also increases, and the density of the air in the balloon decreases. This allows the balloon to float. The graph below illustrates how changes in temperature affect the volume of a gas when pressure is held constant. Note that in this example, each 100°C increase in temperature causes a 0.3 L increase in volume.

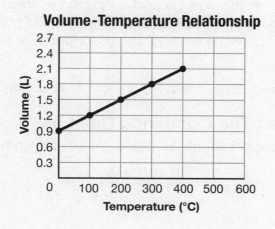

Volume-Temperature Relationship

The graph shows a behavior of gases known as Charles's law. **Charles's law** states that the volume of a gas increases as temperature increases when pressure is held constant. The mathematical equation shown below summarizes how the volume of a gas changes in response to a change in temperature. In the equation below, V_1 and T_1 are the starting volume and temperature, and V_2 and T_2 are the ending volume and temperature.

$$\text{Charles's law equation: } \frac{V_1}{T_1} = \frac{V_2}{T_2}$$

Suppose that an air-filled balloon at 25°C has a volume of 2.00 L. The balloon is then cooled to 0°C. What is the new volume of the gas? The Charles's law equation allows us to solve for the final volume, V_2, because we know the other three variables. However, we must first convert the temperatures from degrees Celsius to kelvins: 25°C = 298 K and 0°C = 273 K.

$$V_2 = T_2 \times \frac{V_1}{T_1} \qquad V_2 = 273 \text{ K} \times \frac{2.00 \text{ L}}{298 \text{ K}} \qquad V_2 = 1.83 \text{ L}$$

Does this answer make sense? As the temperature of an ideal gas decreases, the particles move more slowly and, holding pressure constant, take up less volume. The final volume is less than the starting volume, so our answer makes sense.

Pressure and Temperature: Gay-Lussac's Law

Some of the examples in this lesson discussed gas in an inflatable balloon. A balloon responds to the pressure the gas exerts by changing its volume and expanding. Its volume increases as pressure or temperature increases. Now, consider a gas in a container that cannot expand. It has a fixed volume. Its volume cannot change, but its pressure and temperature can. How are these variables related?

Heating a gas increases the average kinetic energy of the gas particles. They move at greater speeds and collide with the internal walls of the container with greater force. This corresponds to an increase in gas pressure. Cooling the gas has the opposite effect. The slower-moving particles exert less pressure on the container walls.

Gay-Lussac's law states that, when volume is held constant, the pressure of a gas is proportional to the temperature. Another form of this law shows that the ratio of pressure to temperature is equal to a constant. In the equations below, P stands for pressure and T for temperature (in kelvins).

$$\text{Gay-Lussac's law: } P \propto T \quad \text{or} \quad \frac{P}{T} = \text{constant}$$

Putting It All Together: The Combined Gas Law

The gas laws can be put together into the combined gas law shown below.

$$\frac{P_1 V_1}{T_1} = \frac{P_2 V_2}{T_2}$$

The combined gas law allows us to solve problems relating the three variables of pressure, temperature, and volume. For example, a gas sample fills a volume of 0.50 L at a temperature of 25°C. It exerts a pressure of 50 kilopascals (kPa) on the internal walls of the container. What will the pressure of the gas be if its temperature is increased to 100°C, and its volume is decreased to 0.25 L?

$$\frac{P_1 V_1}{T_1} \times \frac{T_2}{V_2} = P_2 \qquad P_2 = \frac{50 \text{ kPa} \times 0.50 \text{ L}}{298 \text{ K}} \times \frac{373 \text{ K}}{0.25 \text{L}} \qquad P_2 = 125 \text{ kPa}$$

Discussion Question

The Kelvin temperature scale includes an absolute zero point, at which a particle has no motion at all. Does the behavior of gas particles at a temperature of zero kelvins fit with the ideal gas law assumptions? What would be the volume and pressure of a gas at 0 K?

Lesson Review

1. The pressure of a gas doubles if its temperature doubles while its volume remains the same. Which of the following describes this behavior?

   A. Boyle's law

   B. Charles's law

   C. Gay-Lussac's law

   D. kinetic molecular theory

2. If the temperature and volume of a gas double, the pressure exerted by the gas remains the same. Which of the following explains this behavior?

   A. As the temperature of the gas increases, the particles require less space to move.

   B. As the volume of the container increases, the gas particles will move faster.

   C. The increased volume provides more space to the gas particles, even though the rise in temperature causes the particles to move faster.

   D. The increased volume provides more space to the gas particles, even though the increase in temperature causes the particles to move more slowly.

3. Which statement explains why increasing the temperature of a gas decreases its density?

   A. The motion and distance between gas particles remain the same.

   B. The motion of the gas particles and the distance between them increase.

   C. The motion of the gas particles and the distance between them decrease.

   D. The motion of the gas particles increases, but the distance between them decreases.

Chapter 2 Review

Combustion is the reaction between oxygen and a fuel to release water vapor and energy. For example, the equation for the combustion of methane (CH_4), which also releases carbon dioxide, is shown below:

$$CH_4 + 2O_2 \rightarrow CO_2 + 2H_2O$$

During the eighteenth century, the prevailing view of combustion was that combustible substances contain a substance called phlogiston. According to this theory, heating combustibles in the presence of air produces a powdery substance called calx. The weight of the resulting calx is generally less than the weight of the original substance. For example, when wood burns, the resulting ash weighs less than the wood. The explanation for the reduction in weight was that phlogiston was lost from the material and released into the air.

$$Combustible \rightarrow Calx + Phlogiston$$

However, the heating of some substances resulted in a quantity of calx heavier than the initial combustible substance. For example, when sulfur and phosphorus were heated in air, the resulting calx weighed more than the original sample. Some proponents of the phlogiston theory explained this phenomenon by saying that in some substances, phlogiston has a negative weight.

The French scientist Antoine Lavoisier doubted the phlogiston theory. He suspected that when substances burn, they either combine with a substance in the air or release a substance into the air, accounting for the gain or loss of weight in the resulting material.

In 1779, Lavoisier carried out a historic experiment, illustrated in Figure 1. Pure mercury was placed in an open container (right) and in a swan-necked flask (left). A glass bell jar was placed over the mercury in the open container so that no air could enter or leave the jar. The opening of the swan-necked flask entered the bell jar from underneath. The level of mercury in the bell jar would rise or fall, depending on the amount of gas in the jar. The mercury in the swan-necked flask was heated over a furnace.

After the first few days of heating, Lavoisier observed a reddish powder on the surface of the mercury in the swan-necked flask. The powder continued to form over 12 days, during which the level of mercury in the bell jar rose to one-fifth of the capacity of the bell jar. After that, the formation of reddish powder stopped, and there was no further increase in the level of mercury in the bell jar.

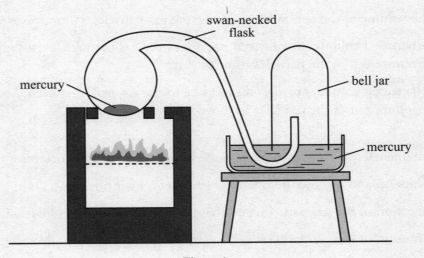

Figure 1

When tested, the gas left in the bell jar was unfit for breathing and could not support combustion. Lavoisier called this gas *azote*. Lavoisier then collected the reddish powder and heated it. He obtained a shiny, metallic substance (mercury) and a colorless, odorless gas. The volume of the gas he obtained from this second experiment was equal to the volume of gas lost in the first experiment. Furthermore, the gas given off by the reddish powder could support combustion.

Lavoisier concluded that when mercury was heated, it combined with a gas in the air to form the reddish powder. When the reddish powder was heated, it gave off the same gas and reverted back to the metal mercury.

1. What is the formula for the reddish substance Lavoisier formed by heating pure mercury?

   A. Hg_2
   B. HgO
   C. $HgCO_2$
   D. HgH_2O

2. What happened to the mass of the air that was lost as the mercury was heated in the swan-necked flask?

   F. An equal mass was lost as mercury in the bell jar, and later gained when the mercury was burned.
   G. An equal mass was gained as mercury in the bell jar, and later released when the mercury was burned.
   H. An equal mass was lost by the mercury as it formed a reddish powder, and later gained when the reddish powder was burned.
   J. An equal mass was gained by the mercury as it formed a reddish powder, and later released when the reddish powder was burned.

3. After Lavoisier heated mercury for 12 days, the formation of red powder stopped because:

   A. the mercury did not contain any more oxygen.
   B. the oxygen in the flask and bell jar had been depleted.
   C. the air in the vessel and bell jar was saturated with phlogiston.
   D. the surface of the mercury was completely covered with phlogiston.

4. Why did Lavoisier use closed containers, which did not allow the entry or exit of gases, in his experiment?

   F. He wanted to isolate azote gas for further experiments.
   G. He wanted to measure changes in the quantity of gas present.
   H. He wanted to measure changes in the quantity of mercury present.
   J. He wanted to ensure that the chemical reaction went to completion.

5. Which of the following combustion reactions is consistent with the law of conservation of matter?

   A. $C_2H_6 + 4O_2 \rightarrow 2CO_2 + 2H_2O$
   B. $C_3H_8 + 5O_2 \rightarrow 3CO_2 + 4H_2O$
   C. $C_5H_{12} + 8O_2 \rightarrow 4CO_2 + 6H_2O$
   D. $C_7H_{16} + 9O_2 \rightarrow 7CO_2 + 8H_2O$

6. Which conclusion is supported by the results of Lavoisier's experiments with mercury?

   F. Burning substances give off oxygen.
   G. Burning substances give off nitrogen.
   H. Air is four-fifths oxygen and one-fifth nitrogen.
   J. Air is about one-fifth oxygen and four-fifths nitrogen.

Chapter 3 Energy

Potential and Kinetic Energy

Key Words	• energy • mechanical energy • thermal energy • chemical energy • sound energy • electrical energy • electromagnetic energy • nuclear energy • kinetic energy • potential energy • law of conservation of energy

Getting the Idea

A simple definition of **energy** is the ability to change matter or do work (you will learn more about work in Lesson 23). Energy exists in different forms. It can move among different substances, and it can change from one form to another. All changes in the universe require some form of energy.

Energy Forms and Transformations

Energy takes many forms, including the following:

- **Mechanical energy** is the energy of position and motion. The water in a flowing river has mechanical energy. Your legs have mechanical energy when you walk.

- **Thermal energy** is the energy of the moving particles (atoms and molecules) that make up matter. The thermal energy of particles increases as the particles move faster. Thermal energy moving between two objects at different temperatures is known as *heat*. Thermal energy is discussed in Lesson 16.

- **Chemical energy** is energy stored in the bonds that hold atoms together in molecules. Substances such as food and fuel contain chemical energy. Batteries also store chemical energy.

- **Sound energy** is the energy of vibrating matter that creates waves of pressure. We perceive these waves through our sense of hearing. Sound is discussed in Lesson 18.

- **Electrical energy** is the energy of moving electrical charges. This form of energy powers most of the appliances we use.

- **Electromagnetic energy** is energy that can travel through empty space in the form of waves. Visible light is one type of electromagnetic energy. Radio waves, X-rays, microwaves, ultraviolet waves, and infrared waves are other forms. You will learn more about these in Lesson 18.

- **Nuclear energy** is energy stored in the nuclei of atoms. This energy has been used to make extremely powerful bombs. It also has peaceful uses, such as generating electricity in nuclear power plants and diagnosing and treating disease.

One property of energy is that it can be changed from one form to another. The conversion, or change, of energy from one form to another is known as *energy transformation*. For example, a hydroelectric power plant transforms the mechanical energy of falling water into electrical energy. A lightbulb converts electrical energy into electromagnetic (light) energy and thermal energy.

Kinetic and Potential Energy

Energy can also be classified into two broad categories: potential energy and kinetic energy. **Kinetic energy** is energy due to the motion of an object. Any object in motion has kinetic energy. **Potential energy** is the energy an object has because of its position or composition. Gravitational potential energy, due to the position of an object in relation to Earth's surface, is the most familiar type of potential energy. However, a stretched rubber band has elastic potential energy, and compounds have chemical potential energy stored in their bonds. Potential energy can become kinetic energy under the appropriate conditions.

The potential energy in an apple hanging from a tree changes to kinetic energy as the apple falls. Food contains potential energy stored in chemical bonds. When an organism's cells break down the nutrients in food, the chemical energy can be converted into kinetic energy that the organism can use for its life functions. A stick of dynamite has potential energy stored in the chemical bonds of its molecules. The potential energy changes to kinetic energy when the chemical bonds break, and the dynamite explodes.

You are involved in many energy transformations each day. For example, plants transform the electromagnetic energy of sunlight into chemical energy through photosynthesis. The plants store this chemical potential energy in their cells and tissues. When you eat plants, some of the chemical energy is transferred to your body. Then your cells release some of this stored energy, converting it to mechanical energy that your muscles use to move. Your nervous system transforms some of the chemical energy into electrical energy and uses it to send signals throughout your body. When you talk, you transform some chemical potential energy into kinetic energy to move your mouth and vocal cords, and those movements are transformed into another form of kinetic energy, the sound energy of speech. You also convert chemical energy into thermal energy that helps keep your body at a constant temperature. Recall that thermal energy is the kinetic energy of the particles making up a substance.

The Law of Conservation of Energy

The **law of conservation of energy** states that while energy can be transformed from one form to another, it can never be created or destroyed. The amount of energy before a transformation is equal to the amount of energy after the transformation. This is known as the *first law of thermodynamics*.

Physicists measure and understand energy in terms of open and closed systems. A *closed system* is an environment where mass and energy cannot enter or leave—they do not interact with their environment. For example, if we were to consider only the exchange of heat energy, the inside of a completely insulated box would be a closed system, since no heat could get in or out. In an *open system*, matter and energy can leave or enter—they interact with their environment. For example, a pot of water on a stove is an open system because the stove adds heat energy to the water in the pot and the pot transfers energy to the air around it.

Many objects have both potential and kinetic energy. For example, a roller coaster car has its greatest potential energy when it is at the top of the tallest hill. As the roller coaster car moves down the hill, some of its potential energy is converted to kinetic energy. The kinetic energy is greatest just as the roller coaster car races through the bottom of the hill. This is when the car is moving fastest. Its kinetic energy decreases as it moves up the next hill, changing to potential energy again.

Can the roller coaster be considered a closed system? As the roller coaster car moves along the entire track, its potential energy changes to kinetic energy and back again many times. It is important to recognize, however, that although energy is conserved, energy transformations are never completely efficient. Some energy is always changed to thermal energy and released as heat. This is what happens to the coaster's kinetic energy as it is changed to thermal energy due to friction. Because this energy is no longer available for use, it is sometimes described as "lost" energy. However, the law of conservation of energy states that this energy is not truly lost. It is simply converted to a form that is no longer useful.

Calculating Gravitational Potential Energy

Gravitational (or mechanical) potential energy is energy due to an object's height. The rocks shown below have potential energy because of their positions above the ground. (Note that any height above the ground can be considered zero height for calculating potential energy. However, the potential energies of two or more objects must be compared in terms of the same zero point for height.)

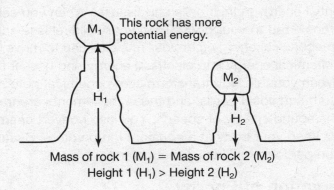

Mass of rock 1 (M_1) = Mass of rock 2 (M_2)
Height 1 (H_1) > Height 2 (H_2)

The potential energy of each rock can be calculated by multiplying the rock's mass in kilograms (kg) by the acceleration due to gravity (g = 9.8 m/s/s or m/s^2) by the rock's height in meters (m). The unit for energy is the joule (J). The formula for potential energy (PE) is:

potential energy = mass × acceleration due to gravity × height
$$PE = mgh$$

In this example, both rocks have the same mass, but the height of the first rock is greater than that of the second rock. Because of this, the first rock has more potential energy than the second rock. If M_1 is 100 kg and H_1 is 15 m, then the potential energy of the rock on the left is:

$$PE = 100 \text{ kg} \times 9.8 \text{ m/s}^2 \times 15 \text{ m} = 14,700 \text{ J}$$

Calculating Kinetic Energy

An object's kinetic energy can be calculated using its mass and motion. Kinetic energy is equal to one-half an object's mass in kilograms (kg) multiplied by the square of the object's velocity, or speed, in meters per second (m/s). The formula for kinetic energy is:

$$\text{kinetic energy} = \tfrac{1}{2}\,\text{mass} \times (\text{velocity})^2$$

$$KE = \tfrac{1}{2}\,mv^2$$

An object's kinetic energy changes if its mass or its velocity changes. A change in velocity results in a greater change in kinetic energy because velocity is squared. The example below illustrates this point. A car travels at different speeds. Each time, the car stops suddenly. The distance the car skids depends on its kinetic energy.

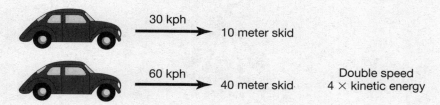

30 kph → 10 meter skid

60 kph → 40 meter skid — Double speed 4 × kinetic energy

If the mass of the car is 900 kilograms and its speed is 30 kilometers per hour (or 8.33 m/s), then its kinetic energy is:

$$KE = \tfrac{1}{2}\,(900 \text{ kg})(8.33 \text{ m/s})^2 = 31{,}225 \text{ J}$$

Energy Changes in Moving Objects

Objects have both potential energy and kinetic energy. For example, a chair on a backyard deck has potential energy because its position means it could fall to the ground. Some of this potential energy can change into kinetic energy if a force exerted on the chair causes it to fall off the deck. As the chair falls, its potential energy changes into kinetic energy. By the time the chair hits the ground, almost all of its potential energy (as measured from a zero height at ground level) has changed into kinetic energy. Since it cannot fall farther, the chair stops moving when it strikes the ground. At that time, it has no kinetic energy.

Potential energy is converted to kinetic energy and back again in a pendulum. A *pendulum* consists of a weight, called a bob. The bob is suspended so it can swing back and forth over its lowest point under the influence of gravity. The clock shown in the diagram uses a pendulum. Note that the potential energy of the pendulum is highest when the bob is at the highest point in its swing, as identified by the PE labels. At its lowest point, all the potential energy has been converted into kinetic energy, as identified by the KE label. Halfway between the highest and lowest points in the pendulum's swing (labeled PE + KE), the bob has both potential energy and kinetic energy in nearly equal amounts.

PE   PE   KE   PE   PE
  +   +
  KE   KE

Discussion Question

Study each pair of illustrations. Then identify and describe the various energy transformations that are taking place in each pair. Keep in mind that several transformations may be required to go from the first to the second illustration in each pair.

Energy Transformations

① ② ③ ④

Lesson Review

1. Which of the following is an example of the transformation of electromagnetic energy to chemical energy?

   A. car engine burning gasoline

   B. hydroelectric dam supplying power

   C. sunlight heating the water in a lake

   D. plant producing food by photosynthesis

2.   A ball falls from a diving board at a height of 10 meters above the water. The mass of the ball is 1.0 kg. What is the ball's kinetic energy at the instant before it hits the water? (Ignore the effects of air resistance and use $g = 9.8$ m/s^2.)

   A.   0.98 joules

   B.   96 joules

   C.   98 joules

   D.   196 joules

3.   The diagram shows the path of a pendulum. The bob starts at Position I and reverses direction at Position III.

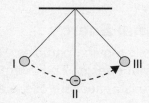

   Which of the following is true regarding the height of the bob at the positions shown?

   A.   The height of the bob at Position III is greater than the height at Position I because the pendulum gained kinetic energy at Position II.

   B.   The height of the bob at Position III is less than the height at Position I because some kinetic energy was converted to thermal energy.

   C.   The height of the bob at Position III is greater than the height at Position I because energy can be lost in an open system.

   D.   The height of the bob at Position III is less than the height at Position I because the pendulum gained gravitational potential energy.

4.   Which **best** summarizes the law of conservation of energy?

   A.   Energy cannot be created or destroyed.

   B.   Energy can be destroyed, but it cannot be created.

   C.   Energy can be created, but it cannot be destroyed.

   D.   A small amount of energy is lost in each energy transformation.

Thermodynamics

Key Words • thermodynamics • thermal energy • heat • law of conservation of energy • entropy

Getting the Idea

Every second, energy is transferred from the sun to Earth in the form of electromagnetic radiation. This energy heats Earth and allows life to continue to exist. Similarly, Earth continually loses heat to space. The study of how heat moves between and within systems is called **thermodynamics**.

Temperature and Thermal Energy

All matter is made up of randomly moving particles. Recall that the energy of those moving particles is called **thermal energy**. The thermal energy of an object depends on its temperature. *Temperature* is a measure of the average kinetic energy of the particles in a substance. The faster the particles move, the higher the temperature. You know that a cup of hot tea has a higher temperature than a glass of iced tea. This is because the particles in the hot tea are moving faster than the particles in the iced tea.

The thermal energy of an object also depends on its mass. Picture a small cup of water and a large pot of water on a stovetop. The pot contains a larger mass of water, so you would need to add a lot of thermal energy to raise its temperature and make it boil. The smaller mass of water in the cup requires much less thermal energy to heat up and boil. So, after heating, the big pot of water would have much more thermal energy than the small cup of water. To find the total thermal energy of an object, you would need to add up the thermal energy of all of its particles.

Heat Flow Has a Direction

Heat is the transfer of thermal energy between objects or substances at different temperatures. If a cool object is placed next to a warm object, the cool object will become warmer, and the warm object will become cooler. Heat always flows from an object with a higher temperature to an object with a lower temperature. Heat will continue to flow in this way until all materials are at the same temperature.

35°C   25°C

A   B
Heat Flow

An object's temperature changes when its particles gain or lose thermal energy. When heat moves into an object, its particles gain energy and move faster. This increases the temperature of the object. Similarly, when an object releases heat, its particles lose energy and its temperature decreases.

The Laws of Thermodynamics

Recall that the **law of conservation of energy** states that while energy can be converted from one form to another, it cannot be created or destroyed. The *first law of thermodynamics* states that energy added to an object must be conserved. For example, if you add heat (a form of energy) to an object, that heat is converted into the thermal energy of the particles in the object. This increased thermal energy means the temperature of the object increases. Other types of energy can also be converted into thermal energy. You use energy to rub your hands together on a cold day. The amount of thermal energy produced is equal to the amount of energy it takes to rub your hands together.

When heat flows from a warm object to a cold object, the total amount of thermal energy in the universe is conserved. This is consistent with the first law of thermodynamics. If, instead, heat spontaneously moved from the cold object to the warm object, this would also conserve the total amount of heat energy. The *second law of thermodynamics* states that heat naturally flows from warmer objects to cooler objects. In order to do the opposite, energy must be used to change the objects. For example, a refrigerator motor uses energy to pump heat out of a refrigerator. If the motor is turned off, the heat naturally flows back inside.

Heat Loss and Efficiency

Scientists discovered the second law of thermodynamics when steam engines began to power trains and machines. A steam engine converts thermal energy to mechanical energy. Scientists discovered that, for any type of engine, some energy is always lost to the surroundings as heat. Another way of stating the second law of thermodynamics is that no engine can convert 100 percent of the energy put into it to useful work. (You will learn more about work in Lesson 23.) The percentage of energy a machine can convert to a useful form is called its *efficiency*. The best steam engine has an efficiency of about 40%.

A steam engine works by heating water until it changes into steam. The steam expands and pushes on part of the engine (such as a piston or a turbine) and causes it to move. This movement can be used to do something useful, such as turn the wheels of the train and make it move. When the steam pushes on the piston, the piston gains energy of motion and the steam loses energy. Since the steam has lost energy, it cools somewhat.

However, after pushing the piston, the steam is still warmer than the water before it was heated. Some of the added thermal energy still remains in the steam. So not all the energy from heating the water was used to turn the train wheels. This leftover thermal energy in the steam is called waste heat.

Entropy

Waste heat is an example of energy that cannot be used to do useful work. This type of useless energy is called **entropy**. Yet another way to consider the second law of thermodynamics is to understand that the amount of entropy never decreases, and that energy will always spread more widely throughout the universe over time. For this reason, the second law of thermodynamics is known as the law of entropy. The total amount of entropy in the universe is always increasing.

Picture a block of gold sitting on a block of silver. If heat causes those bricks to melt, they will mix together. The gold and silver will no longer be completely separate. They will form a disordered mess. Entropy can also be thought of as the amount of disorder in a system. According to the law of entropy, natural processes will always cause the total amount of disorder in the universe to increase.

Imagine an object (such as a cup of hot tea) containing a certain amount of energy at a point in time. No energy is added to the object. At a later point in time, that object will contain less energy because some of the thermal energy will have moved to the surroundings. This spreading of energy is entropy, and entropy always increases.

Think of a machine that does useful physical work as a system. When energy is in the form of thermal energy and spreads outside of this system, it is no longer available to do useful work. The second law of thermodynamics states that the amount of useful energy in the universe is always decreasing, and the amount of disorder is always increasing.

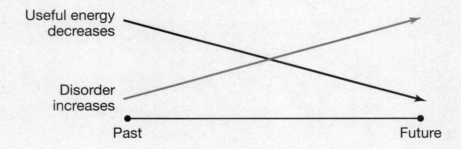

Entropy, Energy Loss, and Life on Earth

Matter does not (usually) enter or leave the Earth system, but energy does. Energy enters Earth constantly in the form of electromagnetic radiation from the sun. This energy heats Earth's atmosphere, powering the water cycle and causing weather changes. The sun's light allows plants to grow and animals to survive. Energy also leaves Earth constantly, moving into the surrounding space.

Life on Earth requires energy that is available to do work. If entropy always increases, and the amount of useful energy decreases, then how can life on Earth continue to exist? Will Earth run out of useful energy available to sustain life?

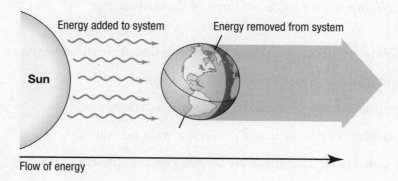

Although the total amount of entropy in the universe as a whole always increases, the entropy of a system can remain constant or even decrease if energy is added to it. Compare this to the examples of the refrigerator and air conditioner. Both appliances *decrease* the amount of disorder or entropy in a system by preventing thermal energy from spreading inside of the refrigerator or cooled room. However, in order to do this, additional energy must be supplied in the form of electrical power. Similarly, useful energy remains available on Earth because the sun continually supplies additional energy.

Also, in the case of the refrigerator, waste heat is released into the kitchen air, outside the refrigerator. For the air conditioner, waste heat is released into the outside environment, so while entropy within the home decreases, entropy outside the home increases. The same is true for Earth. Energy from the sun is useful on Earth, but Earth releases useless energy into space, increasing the entropy of the universe.

Discussion Question

At one time, engineers tried to invent machines that could run without any source of power or energy (such as fuel). These are called perpetual motion machines. According to the second law of thermodynamics, can a perpetual motion machine exist?

Lesson Review

1. Three containers each contain water at the same temperature. Which container has the most thermal energy?

    A. 5-mL metal container

    B. 10-mL Styrofoam container

    C. 15-mL glass container

    D. All three containers have equal amounts of thermal energy.

2. Which of the following **best** summarizes the second law of thermodynamics?

    A. The amount of thermal energy is always conserved.

    B. The amount of entropy in the universe always increases.

    C. The total amount of energy in the universe always decreases.

    D. An energy-converting machine must be 100 percent efficient.

3. An ice cream machine cools the ingredients inside it. It also releases thermal energy into its surroundings. How is this machine consistent with the second law of thermodynamics?

    A. The amount of thermal energy released is equal to the amount removed from the ingredients.

    B. The amount of thermal energy released is greater than the amount removed from the ingredients.

    C. The amount of thermal energy released is less than the amount removed from the ingredients.

    D. The thermal energy moves from the cooler ingredients in the system to the warmer surroundings.

Chapter 3 • Lesson 17

Electricity and Magnetism

Key Words • electric current • potential difference • voltage • conductor • insulator • semiconductor • superconductor • magnetic field • electromagnetic induction • electromagnet

Getting the Idea

Recall that electrons are subatomic particles that have a negative electrical charge. Electrical energy, or electricity, results from the movement of electrons.

Electric Current

Some materials are composed of atoms joined by metallic bonds. (Recall the description of metallic bonds in Lesson 8.) Electrons in the outermost energy level of these atoms can escape and move freely between charged atoms (ions). Sometimes, instead of moving randomly, electrons move in a specific direction. The continuous flow of electric charge through a material is an **electric current**. Electric current is measured in units called amperes (A), or amps.

If a material has a higher concentration of charge in one location and a lower concentration of charge in another, it has a difference in potential energy between those two locations. The difference in electrical potential energy between two locations is known as **potential difference**. Electrons flow from a region of higher potential energy to a region of lower potential energy. Therefore, a potential difference causes electrons to flow, producing an electric current.

Potential difference is also called **voltage**, which is measured in units called volts (V). A battery is a device that converts chemical energy into electricity by creating a potential difference, or difference in charge, between its positive and negative terminals.

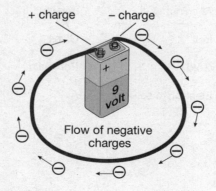

+ charge   − charge

Flow of negative charges

Because the sums of the positive and negative charges in the wire cancel each other out, the wire is electrically neutral. Every electron that moves from the battery to the wire at the negative (−) terminal is balanced by an electron moving from the wire to the battery at the positive (+) terminal.

An individual electron that starts out in the wire near the negative terminal of the battery does not move all the way to the positive terminal of the battery. An individual electron joins a nearby positive ion farther down the wire. An electron from that ion then moves to another ion farther down, and so on. Even though electrons themselves do not move all the way through the wire, the negative charge associated with electrons does.

Conductors and Insulators

An electric current does not flow equally well through all materials. A material or substance that electric current flows through easily is called a **conductor**. Most metals, including copper, aluminum, and iron, are good conductors of electricity. This property of metals, combined with being ductile, makes metals useful for electrical wires.

The atoms of most metals are held together in metallic bonds. A metallic bond is the result of positive metal ions being surrounded by moving electrons. (Recall that ions are charged particles that result from atoms gaining or losing electrons.) This free movement of electrons gives metals high conductivity.

Many substances are poor conductors of electricity. Materials through which electricity does not flow easily are called **insulators**. The electrons of insulators are more tightly attracted to their atoms than are those of conductors. The electrons are not free to move from one place to another. Electrical wires are often wrapped in insulators to prevent fires and injury. The table lists some examples of good conductors and good insulators.

Conductors	Insulators
Copper	Rubber
Silver	Wood
Aluminum	Plastic
Iron	Glass
Gold	Porcelain
Electrolyte solutions	Air

Semiconductors and Superconductors

The elements germanium (Ge) and silicon (Si) are examples of semiconductors. A **semiconductor** is a material with conductive properties between those of conductors and insulators. These elements are often metalloids. Semiconductors are very useful in modern technology. Germanium, for example, is often used to make electronic devices. Computer chips are made from silicon.

Semiconductors are very useful because:

1. Very small circuits can be etched onto the surfaces of semiconductors.
2. These circuits are good conductors of electricity.
3. Semiconductors are very energy-efficient.

Some metals and nonmetals, such as mercury (Hg), zinc (Zn), and some ceramics, are superconductors. A **superconductor** is a material that gains very high conductivity when its temperature drops below a certain point. At very low temperatures, superconducting materials allow electric current to flow through them without producing any heat. This property makes them much more efficient than ordinary conductors. Superconductors are used in MRI machines and maglev (magnetic levitation) trains and are being developed for power grids and electrical generators.

Magnets and Magnetic Forces

Every magnet has two poles—a north pole and a south pole. The diagram below shows that magnetic poles behave in the same way as electrical charges. Like poles repel each other, or push each other away. Unlike or opposite poles attract each other or pull each other closer. The push or pull between any two magnetized objects is called *magnetic force*.

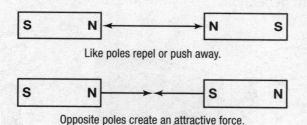

Like poles repel or push away.

Opposite poles create an attractive force.

The magnetic force between two magnets is similar to the electric force that exists between two charged objects. An electrical charge is surrounded by an electric field. In a similar way, a magnet is surrounded by a magnetic field. The **magnetic field** is the space in which magnetic force is exerted. The magnetic and electric forces are similar because magnetism and electricity are actually two aspects of the same force—the electromagnetic force.

Magnetic Fields and Electric Currents

In the 1800s, a Danish scientist named Hans Oersted performed some of the earliest investigations involving the electromagnetic force. He observed that a wire carrying current could cause the needle of a magnetic compass to move. This effect occurs because current flowing through a wire produces a magnetic field.

When a current flows through a straight wire, it produces a magnetic field that is directed around the wire. If you form a coil out of wire, a current flowing through the wire will produce a magnetic field that is directed along the axis of the coil, as shown below.

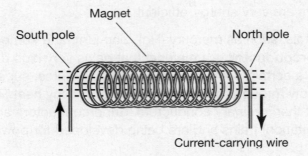

South pole   Magnet   North pole

Current-carrying wire

Just as an electric current produces a magnetic field, a magnetic field can produce an electric current. **Electromagnetic induction** is the process of generating an electric current in a wire by the relative motion of the wire and a magnetic field. Current can be induced by moving a magnetic field near a wire or by moving a wire through a magnetic field. Electric generators, like the one shown below, produce electricity by electromagnetic induction. Most of the electrical power you use comes from generators.

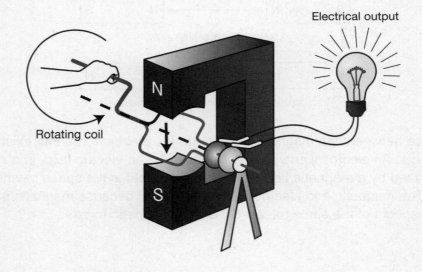

Electrical output

N

Rotating coil

S

Electromagnets

An **electromagnet** is a temporary magnet made by winding a coil of wire around an iron core. The iron core is included because it is easily magnetized and strengthens the magnetic field of the wire. When an electric current is passed through the coil, the device becomes a magnet. The strength of the magnet is directly proportional to the number of turns of wire in the coil and the strength of the current. Like other magnets, an electromagnet has a north and a south pole and a magnetic field.

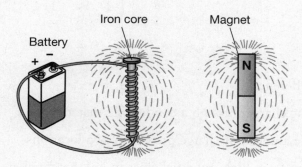

Electromagnets are useful because they can be turned on and off. For example, construction cranes often use electromagnets to lift steel beams. Because of its magnetic field, an electromagnet can be used to generate an electric current. For example, electromagnets are used to generate electricity in power plants.

Discussion Question

Some emergency radios for use during power outages do not have batteries. Instead, the user turns a crank to operate the radio. How does such a radio most likely work?

Lesson Review

1. Which substance is an insulator?

   A. iron

   B. wood

   C. copper

   D. aluminum

2. What is a potential difference?

   A. the flow of electric charge through a conducting material

   B. a difference in the amount of charge present in two locations

   C. the flow of charges from high-potential areas to low-potential areas

   D. a difference in the amount of current flowing through two materials

3. Which **best** describes electromagnetic induction?

   A. A magnetized wire generates an electric field within itself.

   B. A wire with a current flowing through it generates a magnetic field.

   C. A changing electric field produces a magnetic field in a nearby wire.

   D. A moving magnetic field produces an electric current in a nearby wire.

4. Which of the following is true of a superconducting material?

   A. A superconductor is extremely conductive at very high temperatures.

   B. A superconductor is extremely conductive at very low temperatures.

   C. A superconductor has conductive properties between those of conductors and insulators.

   D. A superconductor is very efficient because it produces large amounts of heat.

Sound and Light

Key Words • wave • electromagnetic wave • mechanical wave • medium • amplitude • crest • trough • wavelength • frequency • hertz • transverse wave • longitudinal wave • compression • rarefaction • intensity • decibel • sound quality

Getting the Idea

A **wave** is a disturbance that transfers energy through matter or space. You may have felt the energy of a large water wave lift you up when swimming or boating. Your ears detect the energy of moving air to allow you to hear sound. Your eyes interpret the energy of light waves to allow you to see.

Types of Waves: Electromagnetic vs. Mechanical

Recall from Lesson 15 that light and sound are forms of energy. Visible light is a form of electromagnetic energy. This type of energy consists of **electromagnetic waves**, which can travel through a vacuum. A vacuum is empty space containing no air or other matter. Electromagnetic rays from the sun travel through 1.5×10^{11} meters of empty space to reach Earth. These waves include visible light as well as X-rays, microwaves, and dangerous gamma rays.

In contrast, **mechanical waves** require a medium in order to transfer energy. A **medium** is a material (such as air or water) through which a wave travels. When traveling through a medium, a wave displaces the particles of the medium. In other words, the wave moves the particles from their resting, or *equilibrium*, positions, causing them to vibrate. However, the particles do not travel with the wave like passengers on a train. They move up and down or back and forth, transferring energy from one particle to the next, and then return to their equilibrium positions.

The Characteristics of Waves

Waves are described by their characteristics, including amplitude, wavelength, and frequency. **Amplitude** is the distance from the midpoint of a wave to either its highest or lowest point. The highest point of a wave is called the **crest**. The lowest point is called the **trough**. In a medium, wave amplitude is the maximum displacement of each particle from its equilibrium.

Wavelength is the distance over which a wave repeats. The most common way to measure wavelength is to find the distance from one crest to the next crest or from one trough to the next trough. Wavelength is represented by the symbol λ (lambda).

The diagram below illustrates wave amplitude and wavelength.

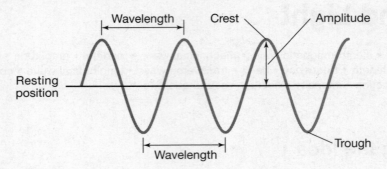

Frequency (*f*) is the number of repetitions of the wave at a given point in one second. The unit of measurement for frequency is the **hertz** (Hz), or cycles per second. For example, a wave that caused a particle to go from one crest to the next (one repetition) in one second would have a frequency of 1 Hz. Frequency and wavelength are inversely related. As wavelength increases, frequency decreases, and vice versa. This is shown by the following formulas, in which *v* represents the wave speed or velocity:

$$f = \frac{v}{\lambda} \qquad \lambda = \frac{v}{f}$$

Types of Waves: Transverse Waves versus Longitudinal Waves

If you flick a rope vertically, you will produce a wave. You will see the crest of the wave move horizontally through the rope, but each particle in the rope will be moving vertically, up and down. In this type of wave, a **transverse wave**, the particles of the medium are displaced *perpendicular* to the path of the wave. As shown in the diagram, the crests and troughs of a transverse wave are easy to see.

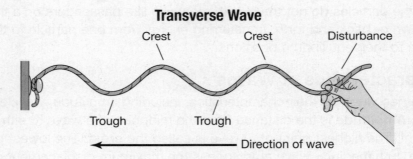

In a **longitudinal wave**, the particles of the medium are displaced in the same direction as, or *parallel* to, the path of the wave. You can produce a longitudinal wave in a coiled spring toy, such as a Slinky. Stretch out a Slinky, pull a few coils toward you, and then release them. A longitudinal wave will travel along the Slinky. Its coils will get closer together and then stretch apart as the wave passes. The part of a longitudinal wave where particles are pushed together is experiencing **compression**. The part of the wave where particles are spread apart is undergoing **rarefaction**, as shown on the next page.

Longitudinal Wave

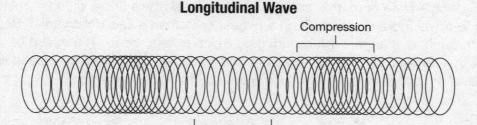

A longitudinal wave is often represented on a graph as a transverse wave. Each compression corresponds to a crest of the wave. Each rarefaction corresponds to a trough. Wavelength is measured from a point in a compression or rarefaction to the same point in the next compression or rarefaction.

Sound Waves

Sound waves are longitudinal, mechanical waves. Like all mechanical waves, they require a medium. Vibrating objects produce sound waves. If you pluck a guitar string, it vibrates. As the string moves back and forth, it pushes on particles in the air around it, vibrating them. As each air particle vibrates, it transfers energy to nearby particles and then returns to its equilibrium position. As the energy travels, the vibrations produce areas where the particles are pressed closer together (compressions) and other areas where they are spread farther apart (rarefactions).

Longitudinal Waves

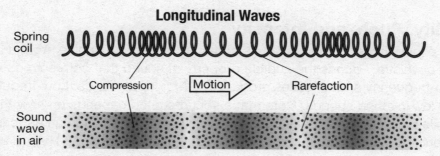

When a guitar string vibrates, particles of air vibrate in all directions away from the string. Each particle pushes its neighbor in the direction of the wave and then returns to its original position. Individual particles do not travel with the sound wave. Remember that waves transfer energy, not matter.

The Speed of Sound

Sound can travel through liquids and solids just like through air. The speed of sound depends on the state of matter and the density of the medium. In general, sound travels faster in solids than in liquids and faster in liquids than in gases. The particles in a solid are bound together tightly, and a change in the position of one particle will quickly affect the positions of nearby particles. Similarly, the particles making up a liquid are held more tightly together than those in a gas, and so sound travels more quickly through a liquid than through a gas.

However, for a single state of matter, such as solids or gases, we find a different relationship. Sound tends to travel more slowly through a denser solid than a less dense solid. Sound travels more slowly through air than through helium gas, which is less dense. The speed of sound in air depends on other factors, such as temperature and humidity, but a standard speed is 343 m/s. The table shows the speed of sound through media of different densities.

State	Medium	Density (g/cm^3)	Speed of Sound (m/s)
Gas	Helium	1.79×10^{-4}	1010
Gas	Air (20°C)	1.18×10^{-3}	343
Gas	Oxygen	1.33×10^{-3}	316
Gas	Carbon dioxide	1.98×10^{-3}	259
Liquid	Water (20°C)	1.00	1482
Solid	Glass	2.50	3960
Solid	Hardwood	7.00–9.00	3500
Solid	Steel	7.85	5960
Solid	Lead	11.34	1158

Sound Quality, Pitch, and Intensity

It is easy to tell a low-pitched sound, such as a deep rumble of an engine, from a high-pitched sound, such as a whistle. *Pitch* is the audible property of sound that corresponds to the frequency. High-frequency sound waves produce high-pitched sounds. Low-frequency sound waves produce low-pitched sounds. Note that a sound's pitch depends on how the human ear perceives it, while frequency is a measurable physical property. The human ear cannot perceive all sound frequencies. We can hear sounds with frequencies between 20 Hz and 20,000 Hz.

The volume or **intensity** of a sound is the amount of energy per unit area delivered by the sound wave, usually measured at a listener's location. The amplitude of a sound wave determines the intensity. The more energy a sound wave has, the more it will compress the medium and the larger its amplitude will be. Sound intensity is measured in units called **decibels** (dB). The decibel scale is based on how sound is perceived by the human ear, rather than its physical properties (such as amplitude). Like the pH scale (discussed in Lesson 12), the decibel scale is logarithmic. A sound with an intensity of 30 decibels is 1000, or 10^3, times louder than a sound of 0 decibels, which is the softest sound humans can hear.

Pitch and intensity are independent of each other. A low-pitched sound can have a large or small intensity, as can a high-pitched sound. The volume of the sound depends on the energy of the source. If you pluck the string of a guitar gently, the amplitude of the vibration will be small. If you pluck the string with more force, the amplitude of the vibration will be greater, and so will the intensity. The pitch, however, will stay the same.

In addition to pitch and volume, sounds may have different characteristics that make up **sound quality**. One characteristic is *timbre*, which includes additional frequencies associated with a sound. This allows us to tell, for example, that two notes with the same pitch and volume were produced by different musical instruments.

Light Waves

When talking about light, we usually mean visible light. However, sometimes when physicists talk about light, they are referring to all electromagnetic waves. Recall that an electromagnetic wave can travel through a vacuum or empty space. You can think of an electromagnetic wave as two transverse waves, an electric field and a magnetic field, linked together with amplitudes perpendicular to each other. They are both also perpendicular to the direction in which the wave travels, as shown in the diagram below.

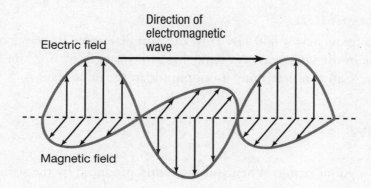

The sun emits a range of different electromagnetic waves including visible, infrared, and ultraviolet light. These waves do not require a medium, so they can travel through the vacuum of space. Electromagnetic waves deliver the energy that makes life on Earth possible. Each type of electromagnetic, or EM, wave has a different range of wavelengths.

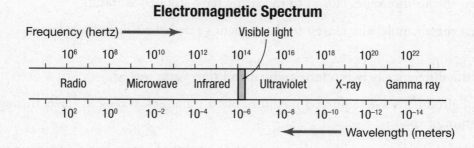

The range of all the different types of electromagnetic waves is known as the *electromagnetic spectrum*. The electromagnetic spectrum lists EM waves in order of their wavelength or frequency. Waves with long wavelengths have low frequencies, and waves with short wavelengths have high frequencies. The amount of energy transferred by an EM wave depends on its frequency. Higher-frequency waves generally have more energy than lower-frequency waves.

The Speed of Light

All EM waves travel at the same speed in a vacuum. The speed of light in a vacuum, known as c, is approximately 300,000 kilometers per second, or 3×10^8 meters per second. Recall that frequency and wavelength are inversely related. Because the speed of all EM waves is a constant, we can determine the frequency of any wave if the wavelength is known, and vice versa.

$$f = \frac{c}{\lambda} \qquad \lambda = \frac{c}{f}$$

The term c refers to the maximum speed of light—its speed in a vacuum. Light travels more slowly through different media, such as air or glass. In Lesson 19, you will learn about light speed in different media.

Discussion Question

A note of A sharp has a frequency of 440 Hz. How can you determine its wavelength? Can you determine its amplitude in the same way? An X-ray has a wavelength of 10^{-10} m. How can you determine its frequency? Can you determine its amplitude in the same way?

Lesson Review

1. A student plucks a guitar string. When will the sound produced by the string reach the student's ears?

    A. when the air molecules closest to the string reach the student's ears

    B. when the air molecules closest to the student's ears are compressed by the molecules next to them

    C. when the air molecules closest to the string have stopped vibrating

    D. when the air molecules closest to the student's ears have stopped vibrating

2. What is the difference between longitudinal and transverse waves?

    A. A longitudinal wave requires a medium, but a transverse wave can travel through the vacuum of space.

    B. A longitudinal wave can travel through the vacuum of space, but a transverse wave requires a medium.

    C. The particles in a longitudinal wave move perpendicular to the direction of the wave, but the particles in a transverse wave move parallel to the direction of the wave.

    D. The particles in a longitudinal wave move parallel to the direction of the wave, but the particles in a transverse wave move perpendicular to the direction of the wave.

3. Which musical note, traveling through air, will have the greatest intensity?

    A. a note with a wavelength of 1.50 meters and an amplitude of 0.010 newtons per square meter

    B. a note with a wavelength of 0.75 meters and an amplitude of 0.005 newtons per square meter

    C. a note with a wavelength of 0.50 meters and an amplitude of 0.050 newtons per square meter

    D. a note with a wavelength of 0.25 meters and an amplitude of 0.020 newtons per square meter

4. Which musical note, traveling through air, will have the highest perceived pitch?

    A. a note with a wavelength of 1.50 meters and an amplitude of 0.010 newtons per square meter

    B. a note with a wavelength of 0.75 meters and an amplitude of 0.005 newtons per square meter

    C. a note with a wavelength of 0.50 meters and an amplitude of 0.050 newtons per square meter

    D. a note with a wavelength of 0.25 meters and an amplitude of 0.020 newtons per square meter

The Behavior of Waves

Key Words • reflection • law of reflection • angle of incidence • angle of reflection • normal line • refraction • index of refraction • diffraction • interference • Doppler effect

Getting the Idea

A light shining on a small mirror produces a bright spot on an opposite wall. A shout in a large auditorium produces an echo heard seconds later. An ocean wave strikes a seawall and bounces back toward the sea. All of these examples are caused by the reflection of waves. Reflection is one possible result of a wave striking a barrier.

Reflection

When a wave strikes a barrier, such as a mirror, a shiny piece of metal, or a wall, the parts of the wave that are not absorbed by the barrier and do not pass through it are reflected. **Reflection** is the bouncing back of waves when they strike the surface of a new medium. The behavior of waves when they are reflected is shown in the diagram below. Water, sound, and light waves can all be reflected. When light rays strike a mirror, they are completely reflected from the surface.

Reflection

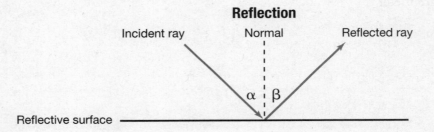

The law of reflection allows us to predict the direction of reflected waves. The **law of reflection** states that the angle at which any wave reflects from a surface is equal to the angle at which the wave struck the surface. The angle at which a wave strikes a surface is called the **angle of incidence** (α). The angle at which a wave reflects from a surface is called the **angle of reflection** (β). According to the law of reflection, the angle of incidence is equal to the angle of reflection. In other words, $\alpha = \beta$. The **normal line** is the imaginary line perpendicular to the surface.

Uses of Reflected Sound Waves

Bats use the reflection of sound waves for echolocation. Similarly, a ship's sonar device directs sound waves through the water toward the ocean floor and measures how long the waves take to reflect and return to the device. This measurement allows people to calculate how deep the water is. Sonar is used to produce detailed maps of the ocean floor and to locate objects, such as sunken ships. Sound waves have many other applications. For example, ultrasound technology uses reflected sound waves to create images of the inside of the human body.

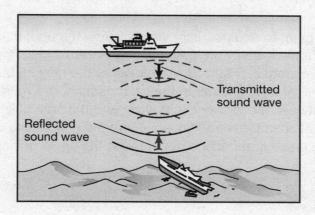

Transmitted sound wave

Reflected sound wave

Refraction

Light waves travel in straight lines as long as they are moving through the same medium. When a light wave enters a new medium, the direction of the light wave can change. **Refraction** is a change in the direction of waves as they pass from one medium to another. Light moves through different mediums at different speeds. The change in speed causes a change in the direction of the wave. Sound waves are also refracted but much less than light waves.

You can observe refraction by placing a pencil in a glass of water. The pencil appears bent or broken at the water's surface because the part of the pencil in the water looks as if it is in a slightly different place. The pencil appears bent because light travels at different speeds in air and in water. As light from the bottom half of the pencil travels out of the water, through the glass, and into the air, its path becomes bent. So, light waves from different parts of the pencil strike your eye from different angles.

In a vacuum, all electromagnetic waves travel at the same speed: 3×10^8 meters per second (m/s). When traveling through a medium, light slows down. A value called the **index of refraction** is used to calculate the speed at which light travels in a certain medium. The more similar the speed in the medium is to c (the speed of light in a vacuum), the closer the index of refraction is to one.

$$\text{Index of refraction } (n) = \frac{\text{Speed of light in a vacuum } (c)}{\text{Speed of light in a medium}}$$

When traveling from one point to another, light waves follow the path that takes the least amount of time. This is not necessarily the path with the shortest distance. When a wave enters a new medium, its speed changes. If light travels slower in the new medium, the wave bends toward the normal line. If light travels faster in the new medium, the wave bends away from the normal line. The angle between the incident light wave and the normal line is called the *angle of incidence*. The angle between the refracted wave and the normal line is called the *angle of refraction*. The size of the angle of refraction depends on the angle of incidence and the index of refraction.

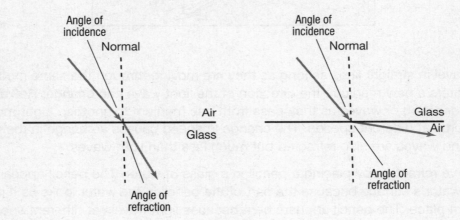

Refraction is also responsible for white light separating into different bands of color when it passes through a prism. Each color of light has a different wavelength and frequency. Higher frequency waves (such as violet light) are slowed down more than lower frequency waves (such as red light). Therefore, higher frequency waves bend more.

Diffraction

Diffraction is the spreading out of waves as they pass through an opening or move around an obstacle. The diffraction of sound allows you to hear people talking from a different room, even though you are not able to see them. Diffracted waves spread out in all directions. How much the waves are diffracted depends on the size of the opening relative to the length of the waves. Sound waves are much longer than visible light waves, so sound is diffracted much more than light. You can see the diffraction of light by shining a flashlight through a narrow slit in a piece of paper or cardboard.

Interference

Two or more waves that intersect will interact with each other in a process called **interference**. When two waves overlap so that the crests of one line up with the crests of the other, the waves are said to be in phase. The crests of troughs of these waves add together to act like a wave with a larger amplitude. This kind of interference is called *constructive interference*. In light waves, constructive interference makes the light brighter. Constructive interference of sound waves results in an increase in volume.

When two waves are out of phase, the crest of one wave may coincide with the trough of the other. In that case, the troughs of one wave can cancel out the crests of the other and vice versa. This kind of interference is called *destructive interference*. Destructive interference of sound waves results in a decrease in volume.

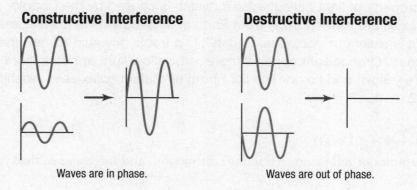

Constructive Interference	**Destructive Interference**
Waves are in phase.	Waves are out of phase.

The Doppler Effect

An emergency siren that is moving toward you sounds higher-pitched than one that is moving away from you. The pitch of a sound depends on its frequency. As an ambulance moves, it chases after the sound waves in front of it. This causes the crests and troughs of those waves to "bunch up" in front of the ambulance. These bunched-up sound waves seem to have smaller wavelengths and thus higher frequencies. At the same time, sound waves behind the ambulance seem stretched out, giving them longer wavelengths and lower frequencies. This frequency change is known as the **Doppler effect**.

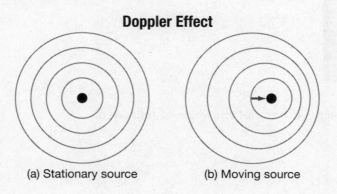

Doppler Effect

(a) Stationary source   (b) Moving source

The diagrams on the previous page illustrate the Doppler effect. The stationary source at left produces waves at a constant frequency. A stationary observer receives waves at that frequency. In the example on the right, as the wave source starts moving toward the right, it begins to catch up to the waves in front. With each new crest produced, the distance between the new crest and the previous crest is reduced. This shortens the wavelength between the two crests and increases the frequency. An observer in front of the source (to the right in the diagram) would hear a sound with a higher pitch, because the sound waves have a higher frequency. By contrast, an observer behind the source (to the left in the diagram) would hear a lower-pitched sound.

This shows that the motion of a wave source, as well as the motion of the observer, affects the frequency of the waves. If the wave source or the observer is moving toward or away from the other, the frequency of the waves changes.

Scientists use a property of light called *redshift,* which is caused by the Doppler effect, as evidence that galaxies are moving away from Earth in all directions. If a wave source is moving away from you, its wavelength increases. Redshift is a frequency shift toward the red end of the visible light spectrum. Orange light appears more red, yellow light appears more orange, green light appears more yellow, and so on. The light from all distant galaxies is redshifted, as you will learn in Lesson 52.

Discussion Question

What are some examples of reflection, refraction, diffraction, and interference that you notice from day to day?

Lesson Review

1. A ray of light strikes a mirror at the angle shown in the diagram.

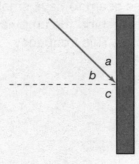

Which letter represents the size of the angle of reflection?

   A. angle *a*

   B. angle *b*

   C. angle *c*

2. A change in which of the following characteristics causes the refraction of light as it moves from one medium to another?

   A. speed   **C.** amplitude

   B. frequency   **D.** color

3. Two sound waves are out of phase with each other when they experience interference. Which of the following will result?

   A. The sound will be louder because the interference is destructive.

   B. The sound will be louder because the interference is constructive.

   C. The sound will be less loud because the interference is destructive.

   D. The sound will be less loud because the interference is constructive.

4. How will a sound wave be affected as it passes through a small, open window?

   A. It will change in speed and travel more slowly.

   B. It will not change because it remains in the same medium.

   C. It will change in frequency, and the pitch will be perceived differently.

   D. It will change in direction and be perceived as originating from the window.

5. The black arrow in the diagram represents a ray of light passing from one medium to another. The gray arrows represent possible paths that the light may take after it crosses the boundary between Medium 1 and Medium 2. The index of refraction for each medium is shown.

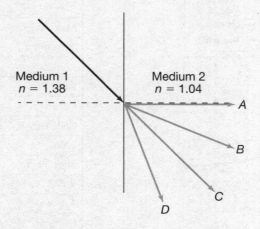

Which ray best represents the path the light will take when it passes into Medium 2?

   A. ray *A*   **C.** ray *C*

   B. ray *B*   **D.** ray *D*

Chapter 3 Review

Thermal energy can be transferred from one material to another by radiation, conduction, or convection. Conduction occurs between materials that are in contact with each other. A group of students in a physics class performed the following experiments on the rate of heat transfer by conduction.

The students filled an empty metal beverage can with water at 70°C and placed the can within a Styrofoam box filled with water at 5°C (Figure 1). They inserted two thermometers through the Styrofoam lid of the outer container: one for the cold water, and one for the hot water inside the can. The temperatures of the hot and cold water were recorded over time. The results are shown in Figure 2.

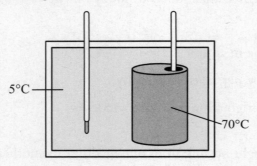

Figure 1

The students repeated the experiment. This time, however, they used a Styrofoam beverage cup in place of the metal container. The Styrofoam cup filled with hot water was placed inside the Styrofoam container holding cold water (Figure 3). The temperatures were recorded in the same way.

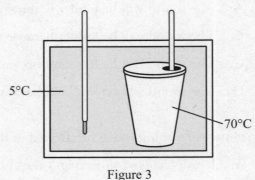

Figure 3

The effect of a material on heat transfer is often expressed in terms of the *heat transfer coefficient*. The higher the coefficient is for a particular material, the more rapidly the heat is transferred through that material. Table 1 shows the heat transfer coefficients for different materials.

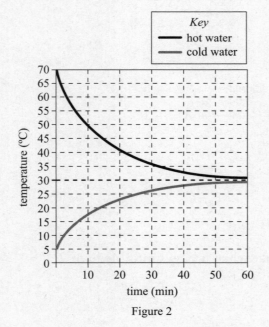

Figure 2

Table 1	
Material	Heat transfer coefficient
Aluminum	237
Iron	55
Ice	2.18
Concrete	1.5
Cellulose	0.039
Wool	0.029
Styrofoam	0.03
Wood	0.13
Argon	0.016
Oxygen	0.024

The rate of heat transfer is determined by the equation shown below. Four variables affect the rate of heat transfer between two locations: the difference in temperature between the warmer location (T_1) and the cooler location (T_2); the heat transfer coefficient of the material separating the locations (k); the surface area of the material (A); the thickness of the material (d).

$$\text{Rate} = \frac{kA(T_1 - T_2)}{d}$$

This equation can be used to calculate the rate of heat transfer through any surface.

1. According to Figure 2, how does the rate of heat transfer change over time?

   A. The rate of heat transfer remains constant over time.
   B. The rate of heat transfer decreases as the difference in temperature increases.
   C. The rate of heat transfer increases as the difference in temperature decreases.
   D. The rate of heat transfer decreases as the difference in temperature decreases.

2. Which physical law predicts the results shown in Figure 2?

   F. The first law of thermodynamics
   G. The second law of thermodynamics
   H. The law of conservation of energy
   J. The law of conservation of matter

3. What is the purpose of using an outer container made of Styrofoam for these experiments?

   A. To slow heat transfer from the system to the surroundings
   B. To slow the rate of heat transfer between the hot and cold regions
   C. To speed the rate of heat transfer between the hot and cold regions
   D. To prevent heat transfer from the inner container to the outer container

4. What is the most likely result of the second experiment, shown in Figure 3?

   F. The graph of the data looks similar to Figure 2, except the two lines take less time to meet.
   G. The graph of the data looks similar to Figure 2, except the two lines take more time to meet.
   H. The graph of the data looks similar to Figure 2, except the two lines meet at a lower temperature.
   J. The graph of the data looks similar to Figure 2, except the two lines meet at a higher temperature.

5. If the area through which heat is transferred is doubled, then the rate of heat transfer:

   A. doubles.
   B. quadruples.
   C. decreases to one-half.
   D. decreases to one-quarter.

6. Which of the following would be the most effective insulation based on heat transfer coefficients?

   F. Wood
   G. Argon
   H. Cellulose
   J. Concrete

Understanding Motion

Key Words	• motion • frame of reference • distance • displacement • speed • velocity • acceleration • slope

Getting the Idea

Even when you are asleep in your bed, you are racing eastward at 1440 km/h. This is because Earth turns on its axis at this speed. Compared to your bed and room, you are stationary, but compared to a point in space, you are rocketing along at a great speed. How you describe and measure motion depends on your frame of reference.

Motion and Frames of Reference

Motion is the change in the position of an object over time. To describe the motion of an object, you must first define a **frame of reference**, or reference point. The frame of reference is the place from which the motion is measured.

Any object or point in space can be a frame of reference. The frame of reference may be stationary, or it may be moving. Either way, you need to choose a frame of reference that is appropriate for the motion you are describing. Suppose you are on a train and want to describe the motion of a ball rolling down the aisle. You might describe the ball as moving at a speed of 20 km/h toward the back of the train car. In this case, the train car is your frame of reference. Since you are on the train, you treat it as if it is stationary and the ball moves in relation to it.

However, a person standing outside the train, watching it pass by, would see the situation differently. If the train were moving north at 20 km/h and the ball rolled south at 20km/h, the ball would stay in the same spot compared to the person outside the train. In this case, the frame of reference is the ground under the train. This frame of reference treats the ground as if it is stationary and the train and ball are free to move.

While on the train, if you look through the window, you might see a tree go past. If your frame of reference is the train car, the tree appears to be moving south at 20 km/h. This illustrates how the motion of an object depends on the frame of reference from which you measure.

Distance versus Displacement

All motion results in a change in position. This change can be described in terms of distance or displacement. **Distance** is a measure of how far an object moves, regardless of the direction. If a truck leaves a loading station and travels 30 kilometers to its first stop and then another 20 kilometers to its second stop, the total distance traveled is 50 kilometers. Distance can be described without describing a direction.

Displacement describes the change in an object's position as a result of motion. Total, net, or final displacement is the change in position relative to the starting point. If a truck travels 30 kilometers east, then 20 kilometers west, its total displacement is 10 kilometers east from its starting point. Notice that displacement requires a direction. If the truck travels 30 kilometers east and then another 20 kilometers east, its displacement is 50 kilometers east.

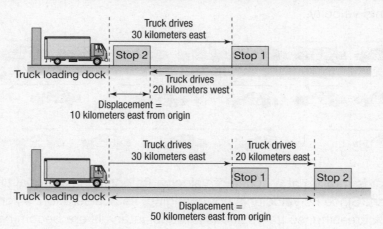

Speed versus Velocity

Speed is the distance an object moves in a certain time. You can calculate average speed using the equation:

$$\text{speed} = \frac{\text{distance}}{\text{time}} \quad \text{or} \quad s = \frac{d}{t}$$

If a car travels 120 kilometers in 2 hours, its average speed is its total distance divided by the elapsed time (120 km ÷ 2 h = 60 km/h). Speed is a rate and, like distance, does not require direction to describe it.

Velocity describes *both* the speed of an object and the direction of its motion. If the speed of an object is 50 km/h and it is moving north, its velocity may be described as 50 km/h north. Two motorcycles traveling at the same speed but in opposite directions will have different velocities. The velocity of an object changes if its speed *or* its direction changes.

Average velocity is the total displacement divided by the elapsed time. If it takes two hours to travel 100 kilometers west, your average velocity is 50 km/hour west. This does not tell you that you traveled at a constant speed or always in the same direction. You might have stopped for part of the time to buy gas or traveled north for a bit and then come back south.

The equation used to calculate average velocity is similar to the one for speed:

$$\text{velocity} = \frac{\text{displacement}}{\text{time}} \quad \text{or} \quad v = \frac{d}{t}$$

The equation can be rearranged to solve for displacement or time.

$$d = vt \qquad t = \frac{d}{v}$$

When speed is known, *d* equals total distance. When velocity is known, *d* equals total displacement. Remember, velocity requires both distance and direction. Speed requires only distance.

Acceleration

Most objects do not travel at a constant velocity. They start and stop, speed up and slow down. **Acceleration** is a change in an object's velocity over time. We usually think of acceleration as a speeding up, or *positive acceleration*. However, *negative acceleration* occurs when an object slows down. This is sometimes called *deceleration*. Look at Diagrams *A*, *B*, and *C*. The length of each arrow represents velocity.

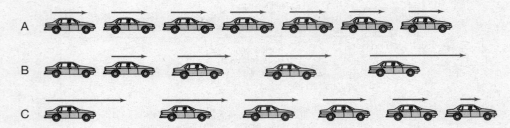

In Diagram A, the car is moving at a constant velocity. Its positions at equal time intervals are equal distances apart. Since its velocity is not changing, its acceleration is zero. In Diagram B, the car's velocity is increasing, so its positions at equal intervals are becoming farther apart. Because the displacement per unit time (velocity) is increasing, the car's acceleration is positive. In Diagram C, the car's velocity is decreasing, so its positions at equal intervals are becoming closer together. The acceleration is negative.

If the car turned left and kept moving at the same speed, it would have to accelerate because a change in direction is a change in velocity. Remember that velocity includes both speed and direction. An object accelerates whenever its speed or direction changes.

Determining Acceleration

Average acceleration is the overall change in an object's velocity during a certain time, divided by the amount of time. The equation used to calculate average acceleration is:

$$\text{acceleration} = \frac{\text{final velocity} - \text{initial velocity}}{\text{time}}$$

$$a = \frac{v_f - v_i}{t}$$

To solve for acceleration (*a*), subtract the initial velocity (v_i) from the final velocity (v_f). Divide this quantity by the total time (*t*). You can use dimensional analysis to find the final units for acceleration. In this example, the units for velocity are meters/second, while the units for time are seconds. The units for acceleration are (m/s − m/s)/s, or m/s/s, or m/s^2.

Example: A race car's velocity changes from 10 m/s to 60 m/s over 5 seconds along the northward straightaway. What is its average acceleration?

$$a = \frac{v_f - v_i}{t}$$

$$a = \frac{60 \text{ m/s} - 10 \text{ m/s}}{5 \text{ s}}$$

$$a = \frac{50 \text{ m/s}}{5 \text{ s}}$$

$$a = 10 \text{ m/s}^2$$

Determining Acceleration from a Graph

The graphs below are velocity-time graphs. A rising line means that velocity is increasing, so the object is accelerating. A falling line means that velocity is decreasing, so the object is decelerating. A horizontal line means that velocity is constant, so the object is not accelerating.

Velocity–Time Graphs

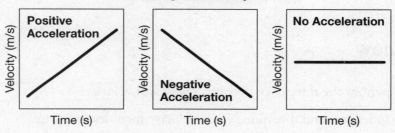

The shape of a velocity-time graph can be used to determine an object's acceleration. Because the graphs are all lines, we know the acceleration (positive, negative, or zero) is a constant number in each case. The value of the acceleration is equal to the **slope** of each line. Equations for calculating slope are shown below. Note that the symbol delta (Δ) stands for *change in*.

$$\text{slope} = \frac{\text{change in } y}{\text{change in } x} \quad \text{or} \quad s = \frac{\Delta y}{\Delta x}$$

The three graphs below are position-time graphs.

Position–Time Graphs

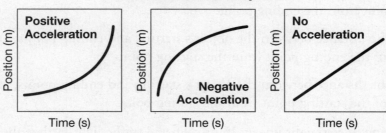

The slope of a position-time graph equals an object's velocity. In the first graph, the slope increases over time, so the object's velocity is increasing. It is accelerating. In the second graph, the slope decreases, so the object is decelerating. The third graph is a line, so the slope is a constant number. This means the object's velocity is constant, so it is not accelerating.

Types of Motion

There are different types of motion. The simplest type of motion is *linear motion*. When there is no acceleration, linear motion is *uniform linear motion*. An object traveling at a constant speed in a straight line travels in uniform linear motion. Motions other than uniform linear motion involve acceleration because any change in speed and/or direction involves acceleration.

Circular motion occurs when an object moves in a circle. Even if the object's speed is constant, it is constantly changing direction, so it is accelerating. A satellite in orbit moves in circular motion. When someone kicks a ball into the air, it travels in an arc and comes back down to the ground. This type of motion is called *parabolic* because the path resembles a parabola. *Periodic motion* is motion with a repeating pattern. A pendulum moves in periodic motion because it swings back and forth in a repeating pattern.

Discussion Question

If you make a left turn in a car while you keep the car at a constant speed, is the car accelerating? Explain your answer.

Lesson Review

1. Which **best** describes the difference between speed and velocity?

   A. Speed includes rate and direction, while velocity includes only rate.

   B. Speed includes rate and direction, while velocity includes only direction.

   C. Velocity includes rate and direction, while speed includes only direction.

   D. Velocity includes rate and direction, while speed includes only rate.

2. How can the total displacement of a moving object **best** be determined?

   A. Measure the length of the path traveled by the object, and determine the direction of the ending point from the starting point.

   B. Measure the length of the path traveled by the object, and determine the direction of the starting point from the ending point.

   C. Measure the distance between the object's starting and ending points, and determine the direction of the ending point from the starting point.

   D. Measure the distance between the object's starting and ending points, and determine the direction of the starting point from the ending point.

3. A truck is moving in a straight line at 25 m/s when a traffic light farther ahead turns yellow. The driver presses on the brake, and 10 seconds later the truck comes to a complete stop at the intersection. What is the truck's acceleration?

   A. -250 m/s^2 C. -15 m/s^2

   B. -25 m/s^2 D. -2.5 m/s^2

Newton's Laws of Motion and Gravitation

Key Words • force • net force • Newton's first law of motion • inertia • Newton's second law of motion • gravitation • inverse square law • Newton's third law of motion • action-reaction forces • inertial reference frame • accelerated reference frame

Getting the Idea

Forces act on you and everything around you. One of the most well-known forces is gravity, which is pulling you toward Earth right now. When the forces on an object are balanced, the object's motion does not change. You can use physical laws to understand forces and predict how they will affect an object's motion.

Force, Net Force, and Balanced Forces

A **force** is a push or pull on an object. Usually, several forces are acting on an object at any given time. We can calculate the sum of those forces, called the **net force**. When forces act on an object, they may or may not cause the object to move. The diagram shows two forces, A and B, acting on an object. The forces act in opposite directions. If forces A and B are equal in magnitude (size), then their effects will cancel each other. The net force on the object will be zero. When forces result in a net force of zero, they are *balanced* forces.

Individual Forces	Net Force
A → ▇ ← B	A + B = 0 ▇
A → ▇ ← B	A − B ▇

Suppose, instead, that force A is greater than force B. The net force would push the object toward the right. A net force that is not equal to zero results from *unbalanced* forces. Net force changes the motion of the object.

Newton's First Law of Motion: The Law of Inertia

An unbalanced force is required to start an object moving. **Newton's first law of motion** states that an object at rest will remain at rest, and an object traveling at a constant speed in a straight line will continue to do so, unless an unbalanced force acts on it. The tendency of all objects with mass to behave this way is called **inertia**.

You experience inertia when you ride in a car. Imagine you are seated in an unmoving car (a car at rest). Out the window to your right you see a tree. When the driver steps on the accelerator pedal, the force of the engine propels the car forward. You may feel like you are being pushed back in your seat. Your body has inertia that tends to keep it in that same spot, even with the tree. The seat of the car pushes you forward as the car accelerates. When this happens, the seat exerts a force on you that overcomes your inertia and pushes you forward. This is shown in the diagram at the left.

Seatbelt

Once the car is moving at a constant velocity, you no longer feel any push. If the car suddenly stops, you continue to move forward due to inertia. In response, the seatbelt you wear exerts an unbalanced force on your body. As a result of this force, your body again comes to rest in the seat. This is shown on the right side of the diagram.

Recall the definition of uniform linear motion from Lesson 20: motion in a straight line, at constant speed. Uniform linear motion is the *only* type of motion that does not involve any acceleration. Notice that Newton's first law says that an object will remain in uniform linear motion unless an unbalanced force acts on it. This is because any change in the uniform linear motion of an object (change in speed or direction) is an acceleration, which must be caused by an unbalanced force acting on it.

Newton's Second Law of Motion

Imagine pushing an empty grocery cart. If you give the cart a small push, it accelerates a small amount. If you give it a larger push, it accelerates to a greater speed. Acceleration is proportional to the force you exert.

As you add groceries to the cart, its mass increases. When you push the cart with the same amount of force as before, the cart will only accelerate a small amount. You must push it with a greater force to make it accelerate as much as it did when it was empty. Acceleration is also proportional to the mass of the object.

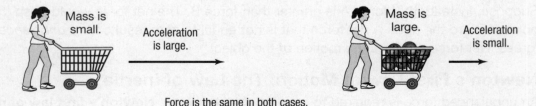

Mass is small.

Acceleration is large.

Mass is large.

Acceleration is small.

Force is the same in both cases.

Newton's second law of motion describes the relationship between force, mass, and acceleration. The force acting on an object is equal to its mass multiplied by its acceleration:

$$\text{force} = \text{mass} \times \text{acceleration} \quad \text{or} \quad F = ma$$

Usually, the unit of force is the newton (N), the unit of mass is the kilogram (kg), and the unit of acceleration is meters per second squared (m/s^2). Rearranging the equation shows that acceleration is inversely related to the mass of the object:

$$\text{acceleration} = \frac{\text{force}}{\text{mass}} \quad \text{or} \quad a = \frac{F}{m}$$

When mass increases, a given force results in a smaller acceleration. Increasing the force on a given mass results in a larger acceleration.

Newton's second law describes both nonmoving and moving objects. If an unbalanced force acts on an object at rest, the object begins to move in the direction of the force. If an unbalanced force acts on a moving object, the object's speed and/or direction will change.

Example: A bumper car with a mass of 100 kg is moving at 7 m/s. How much force is required to accelerate it by $2 \ m/s^2$?

$$\text{mass: 100 kg; acceleration: } 2 \ m/s^2 \qquad F = ma = 100 \text{ kg} \times 2 \ m/s^2 = 200 \text{ N}$$

Gravitational Attraction

When an object falls, its speed continually accelerates (until it reaches terminal velocity due to air resistance). The force of gravity, or gravitation, causes this acceleration toward Earth. **Gravitation** is a force that every mass exerts on every other mass. Newton developed the law of universal gravitation to describe why objects on Earth fall toward Earth and why planets orbit the sun.

The masses of the objects and the distance between them determine the amount of gravitational attraction between two objects. Very massive objects exert a stronger attraction on each other than do objects of smaller mass. Similarly, objects that are closer together attract each other more than objects that are farther apart. To calculate the force of gravity (F_g), you can use the equation

$$F_g = \frac{Gm_1m_2}{d^2}$$

In this equation, m_1 and m_2 are the masses of the two objects pulling on each other, and d is the distance between them. G is a constant called the gravitational constant.

The law of gravity is an **inverse square law**, meaning that the gravitational force between two objects is inversely related to the square of the distance between them. If the distance between two objects doubles, the gravitational force between them is divided by four. If the distance triples, the gravitational force is divided by nine ($9 = 3^2$).

Newton's Third Law of Motion: Action and Reaction

If you were to parachute out of a plane, you know that gravity would pull you down toward Earth. However, did you know that gravity is also pulling Earth up toward you? It's true. Because you have mass, gravity pulls objects, including Earth, toward you. Your mass is so small compared to Earth's mass, though, that the acceleration that Earth feels is very small, so small you do not even notice it.

Forces always act in pairs. **Newton's third law of motion** states that when one object exerts a force on a second object, the second object exerts an equal but opposite force on the first object. These equal but opposite forces are often called **action-reaction forces**.

To understand action-reaction forces, think about a pair of ice skaters, one boy and one girl. If the girl skater pushes the boy, both skaters will start moving away from each other. When she exerts a force by pushing him, his body exerts an equal but opposite force on her, causing her to move backward. If they have the same mass, they will move away from each other at the same speed. If the boy has more mass than the girl, he will receive less acceleration and move away at a slower speed than she will.

Action-reaction forces always act on different objects. If a bat exerts a force on a ball, the ball exerts a force on the bat. When a pencil exerts a force on a sheet of paper, the paper exerts a force on the pencil. Notice that the names of the objects are always switched when you state the action-reaction forces.

Inertial Mass and Gravitational Mass

Suppose you have an object of unknown mass. There are two different ways to calculate an object's mass. One way is to apply a force to the object and measure the acceleration it experiences. Then use the equation $F = ma$ to find the mass. This mass is called the object's *inertial mass*.

Another way to calculate an object's mass is to measure the force of gravity that it experiences. If you have another object whose mass you know, you can measure the force of gravity between the objects and then use the equation

$$F_g = \frac{Gm_1m_2}{d^2}$$

to find the unknown mass. This mass is called the object's *gravitational mass*. Whichever method you use, you will get the same answer because inertial mass is equivalent to gravitational mass.

Inertial and Accelerated Frames of Reference

Suppose you are sitting on a train that is standing still at the train station, and you look out the window to see a tree. The tree is stationary. According to Newton's first law, this means that no net force is acting on the tree.

Now suppose that the train is moving at a constant velocity. You see another tree out the window. The tree appears to move past the window at a constant velocity. The tree is not really moving, but its apparent motion is a kind of illusion produced by the train's motion. However, this apparent motion still fits Newton's first law: an object will continue moving at a constant speed if no force acts on it. The train moving at a constant velocity is an example of an **inertial reference frame**. From this frame of reference, you can still apply Newton's laws to examine the motion of the tree and other objects outside the train.

Now suppose the train is accelerating. A tree going past the window appears to be speeding up as it moves from the front of the train to the back of the train. But how can this be? You know that no net force is truly acting on the tree, so how can it be accelerating? An accelerating train is an example of an **accelerated reference frame**. In an accelerated reference frame, you cannot simply use the laws of motion to examine the motion of other objects.

Discussion Question

A pitcher throws a baseball toward home plate. The batter hits the ball with a bat, and the ball flies toward the outfield, where a player catches it. What are two action-reaction forces you can identify in this situation?

Lesson Review

1. A box is free to slide around in the back of a station wagon.

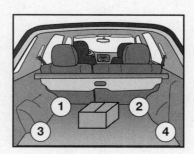

When the driver slows and makes a left turn, to which position will the box slide?

A. position 1

B. position 2

C. position 3

D. position 4

2. A ball rolls across a field in a straight line. According to Newton's first law of motion, why would the ball slow down as it rolled?

A. Inertia causes all objects in motion to come to rest.

B. A force acts on the ball and causes an acceleration.

C. All the forces acting on the moving ball were balanced.

D. A force is required to keep an object in uniform linear motion.

3. A student stands 10 m from a stop sign. He walks toward the stop sign until he is standing 5 m from it. Which of the following describes how the gravitational force between the student and the stop sign has changed?

A. It is about twice what it was.

B. It is about one half what it was.

C. It is about four times what it was.

D. It is about one fourth what it was.

4. The equation below shows the formula for weight, W.

$$W = mg$$

In the equation, g is the acceleration due to gravity. According to this formula and Newton's second law, how can weight **best** be described?

A. as a mass

B. as a force

C. as a velocity

D. as an acceleration

Momentum

Key Words • momentum • velocity • law of conservation of momentum

Getting the Idea

Mass is the amount of matter in an object. Mass is also a measure of an object's inertia—the more massive an object is, the greater its inertia (resistance to motion). The relationship between mass and inertia explains why it is more difficult to move a heavy object than a lighter object. It also explains why it is harder to stop the motion of a heavier object.

Momentum

A moving bowling ball has more mass and more inertia than a moving soccer ball. If these objects are moving at the same speed, the bowling ball will be harder to stop. However, if the soccer ball were moving much faster than the bowling ball, then the soccer ball would be more difficult to stop. What makes the motion of these objects hard to stop is their momentum. The **momentum** of an object is its mass multiplied by its velocity. Recall that **velocity** is an object's speed in a certain direction. Momentum is calculated as:

$$\text{momentum} = \text{mass} \times \text{velocity}$$
$$\text{or}$$
$$p = mv$$

In this formula, p represents momentum, m represents mass, and v represents velocity. Momentum is often measured in kg · m/s.

Example: A bowling ball with a mass of 5 kilograms rolls down the alley at 22.5 m/s. What is the momentum of the bowling ball?

$$p = mv$$
$$p = 5 \text{ kg} \times 22.5 \text{ m/s}$$
$$p = 112.5 \text{ kg} \cdot \text{m/s}$$

The momentum of an object depends on both mass and velocity. An object with a small mass can have more momentum than a more massive object, if the less massive object is moving faster. In karate, for example, a smaller person can deliver a blow with more momentum than a larger person can, by kicking faster. When a force is applied to an object, it changes the object's velocity and therefore its momentum.

Conservation of Momentum

Consider what happens when a bowling ball strikes bowling pins. The pins fall over, but the bowling ball continues to move. However, it moves at a slower velocity. What happened to the ball's momentum? Some of the ball's momentum was transferred to the pins in the collision. The pins gained momentum and the bowling ball lost momentum.

This is an example of conservation of momentum. The **law of conservation of momentum** states that the total amount of momentum in a system of objects does not change unless outside forces act on the objects. When two moving objects collide, some or all of the momentum of one object transfers to the other object. This causes the velocity of one or both objects to change.

You can see conservation of momentum in action when you play pool. Think about a fast-moving white ball rolling toward a stationary numbered ball. When the balls collide, the white ball loses some or all of its momentum, while the numbered ball gains momentum. Because the balls cannot exchange mass, their velocities change. The white ball slows or stops. The numbered ball begins to move. However, the total amount of momentum is unchanged. Momentum simply transfers from the white ball to the numbered ball.

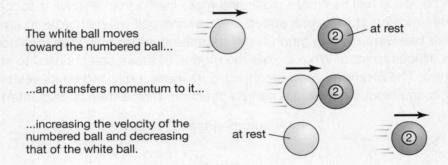

The white ball moves toward the numbered ball...

...and transfers momentum to it...

...increasing the velocity of the numbered ball and decreasing that of the white ball.

Conservation of momentum also explains why a cannon moves backward, or recoils, when it shoots a cannon ball. The explosion exerts equal and opposite forces on the cannon and cannon ball. The cannon ball is pushed forward, while the cannon is pushed backward. Both objects have equal momentum. Because the cannon is more massive than the cannon ball, its velocity is smaller. The cannon ball has less mass, so it moves faster.

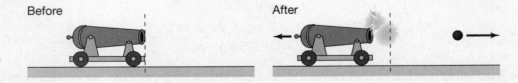

Before

After

Discussion Question

Notice that the velocity of the cannon and the velocity of the cannon ball on the previous page have opposite directions. What is the total momentum of this system? Did it change because of the explosion?

Lesson Review

1. Which of the following correctly summarizes the law of conservation of momentum?

    A. Momentum is lost in a collision between two objects in motion.

    B. When two objects collide, they will always bounce off each other.

    C. When two objects collide, momentum may transfer, but it is not lost.

    D. If two objects stick together after a collision, both objects gain momentum.

2. A ball with a mass of 1.5 kg moves through the air at 2 m/s. What is the momentum of the ball?

    A. 0.75 kg · m/s

    B. 1.33 kg · m/s

    C. 1.5 kg · m/s

    D. 3.0 kg · m/s

3. A shopping cart with a mass of 15 kg and a velocity of 4.0 m/s crashes into a second cart, at rest, with a mass of 10 kg. The velocity of the first cart decreases to 1.5 m/s. What is the velocity of the second cart after the collision? (Ignore the effects of friction.)

    A. 2.25 m/s

    B. 2.5 m/s

    C. 3.75 m/s

    D. 4.0 m/s

Work and Machines

Key Words • work • energy • joule • simple machine • inclined plane • wedge • screw • lever • pulley • wheel and axle • mechanical advantage

Getting the Idea

You may think of work as any activity that causes you to be tired or bored, but in physics work has a very specific definition. **Work** is done when a force moves an object over a distance in the direction of the force. The force transfers energy to the object. Fortunately, there are machines that make it easier for us to do work.

Energy and Work

In science, **energy** is defined as the ability to do work. Work is done only when something moves. The force transfers energy to the object, and the object moves. Work has been done. For example, a child does work when he picks up a ball off the ground. If the child drops the same ball, work is again done. This time, however, Earth's gravity does the work by pulling the ball down. No work is done while the child holds the ball.

Work can be expressed mathematically as:

$$\text{Work} = \text{Force} \times \text{Distance}$$
$$W = Fd$$

In this equation, W is the work done on the object, F is the force applied to the object, and d is the change in the object's distance as a result of that force. Force is measured in newtons (N) and distance in meters (m). The unit of work and energy is the joule (J). One **joule** is equal to one newton-meter.

Example 1: A man wants to lift a 300-N case onto a platform that is 0.5 m high. How much work must the man perform on the case?

$$F = 300 \text{ N}; d = 0.5 \text{ m}$$
$$W = Fd = 300 \text{ N} \times 0.5 \text{ m} = 150 \text{ J}$$

It will take 150 joules of work for the man to lift the case onto the platform.

Simple Machines

In Example 1, the man can do the same work on the case more easily using a simple machine.

A **simple machine** is a device that makes work easier by changing the size or the direction of the force being applied. Simple machines cannot change the amount of work done, but can only make the work easier to do. The *load* often refers to the object on which work is done.

One type of simple machine is a sloped or slanted surface, called an **inclined plane**. A ramp, a screw, and a wedge are examples of inclined planes. A ramp makes it possible to lift a heavy load by decreasing the force needed. However, a ramp increases the distance traveled. Recall the formula for work, $W = Fd$. A ramp decreases the amount of force that must be applied to an object (F), but increases the distance over which that force is applied (d). Moving an object over a ramp does the same amount of work as lifting it vertically the same height.

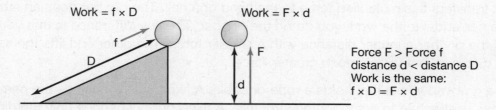

Work = f × D   Work = F × d

Force F > Force f
distance d < distance D
Work is the same:
f × D = F × d

A **wedge** consists of two inclined planes placed back to back. A wedge splits things apart by changing a force applied in one direction into a perpendicular force that is applied in two directions. Knives and axes are examples of wedges. The downward push on the knife's handle is converted to sideways forces that slice the food.

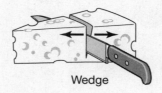

Wedge

A **screw** is an inclined plane wound around a pointed cylinder or shaft. A screw changes the direction of force from one that rotates the screw to one that points in the same direction as the screw. A small rotational force on the shaft exerts a large axial force on the load. As with a ramp, the screw increases the distance over which the force is applied.

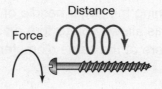

Distance

Force

A **lever** is a bar that pivots on a fixed point called a *fulcrum*. Bottle openers, scissors, seesaws, your arm, and pry bars are examples of levers. A pry bar makes work easier by multiplying the input force. When you press down on the long arm of the pry bar, the lever pivots at the fulcrum. This produces a large force pushing up on the head of the nail. The longer the pry bar, the easier it will be to remove the nail.

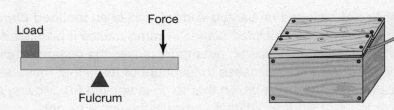

The pry bar transfers this multiplied force to the head of a nail. The pry bar does an amount of work on the nail equal to the work you do on the pry bar. The key difference is that you move your end of the pry bar a longer distance with a smaller force. The other end lifts the nail only a part of that distance, but with a much greater force.

A **pulley** is a grooved wheel that holds a rope or cable. A fixed pulley, such as the one shown at the left below, is attached to a supporting structure. A fixed pulley changes only the direction of applied force. A moveable pulley is not attached to a supporting structure. This kind of pulley can decrease the force required to do work. Fixed and movable pulleys are often used together, as shown in the center diagram below. Flagpoles and window blinds use pulleys to lift things.

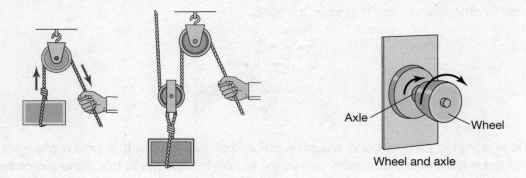

A **wheel and axle** also multiplies force over distance. When the large wheel is turned, force transfers to the smaller axle. Doorknobs, steering wheels, and screwdrivers are examples of this simple machine. For example, by turning the larger handle of a screwdriver, you multiply a force applied to the smaller metal shaft. This allows you to turn a screw more easily than you would if the handle (wheel) and shaft (axle) were of the same diameter.

Mechanical Advantage

An important characteristic of simple machines is **mechanical advantage**, or how much a machine multiplies force. Mechanical advantage (*MA*) is simply the ratio of the output force to the input force. The input force is the force applied by the user to the machine. The output force is the force applied by the machine to the object. The formula for mechanical advantage is:

$$\text{Mechanical advantage} = \frac{\text{output force}}{\text{input force}} \quad \text{or} \quad MA = \frac{F_{out}}{F_{in}}$$

Example 2: A woman uses a force of 30 N to push a 300-N box up a long ramp onto a platform. What is the mechanical advantage of the ramp?

Input force = 30 N; Output force = 300 N

$$MA = \frac{F_{out}}{F_{in}} = \frac{300 \text{ N}}{30 \text{ N}} = 10$$

The ramp multiplies the input force by 10. This is its mechanical advantage.

The mechanical advantage for a lever depends on the distance between the input force and the fulcrum. Think of a lever as being similar to a balance. In the lever at left, the weight of the load and the input force are balanced. They are the same distance (*d*) from the fulcrum. In the lever at right, a smaller input force is required to balance the load, because it is applied a greater distance away from the fulcrum. This results in a mechanical advantage of 60 N divided by 20 N, or 3.

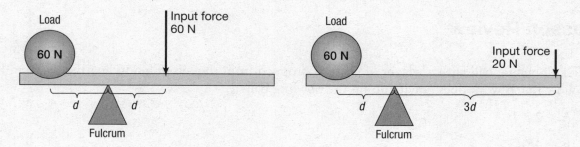

For a lever, mechanical advantage increases as the distance between the input force and the fulcrum increases. As with a balance, the forces must be in inverse ratio to their distances from the fulcrum. This means that the product of the load and its distance from the fulcrum must equal the product of the input force and its distance from the fulcrum. This is expressed as:

Force due to load × distance from fulcrum = Input force × distance from fulcrum

$$F_1 \times d_1 = F_2 \times d_2$$

Example 3: A woman uses a lever to move a load weighing 100 N. The load is a distance of 0.1 m from the fulcrum. If the woman wants to apply a force of 20 N, what distance from the fulcrum must she apply the input force? (Ignore friction.)

Output force (load) = 100 N; Distance 1 = 0.1 m; Input force = 20 N

$$F_1 \times d_1 = F_2 \times d_2$$

$$d_2 = \frac{F_1 \times d_1}{F_2}$$

$$d_2 = \frac{100 \text{ N} \times 0.1 \text{ m}}{20 \text{ N}} = 0.5 \text{ m}$$

Example 4: What is the mechanical advantage of the lever in Example 3? (Ignore friction.)

Input force = 20 N; Output force (load) = 100 N

$$MA = \frac{F_{out}}{F_{in}} = \frac{100 \text{ N}}{20 \text{ N}} = 5$$

The mechanical advantage of the lever is 5.

Discussion Question

Recall that work is a transfer of energy to an object. Do simple machines violate the law of conservation of energy (discussed in Lesson 15)? Does the concept of mechanical advantage suggest that energy is being multiplied or created? Explain.

Lesson Review

1. If a bowling ball with a weight of 45 N is dropped from the top of a building that is 16 m high, how much work does gravity do on the bowling ball?

   A. 2.8 J

   B. 45 J

   C. 355 J

   D. 720 J

2. What is the mechanical advantage of a lever that requires an input force of 3 N to lift a 9 N object?

   A. ⅓

   B. 3

   C. 6

   D. 27

3. Which of the levers below provides the greatest mechanical advantage?

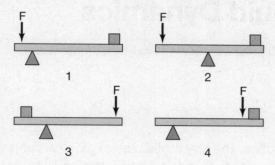

A. lever 1

B. lever 2

C. lever 3

D. lever 4

4. A lever is used to lift a load of 500 N, located 0.5 m from the fulcrum. A force is applied a distance of 1.25 m from the fulcrum on the other arm of the lever. How large must the force be to balance the lever?

A. 125 N

B. 200 N

C. 400 N

D. 1000 N

5. Below is a pulley.

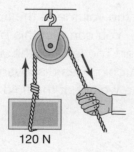

120 N

What is the mechanical advantage of this pulley?

A. 1

B. 2

C. 60

D. 120

Air Pressure and Fluid Dynamics

Key Words • fluid dynamics • buoyancy • air pressure • flow • aerodynamic • hydraulics

Getting the Idea

Even though you usually do not notice, the tiny molecules of air all around you have weight and exert force. The air around you exerts 1 kg of force on every square centimeter of skin. Air is a *fluid*, as are all gases and liquids. **Fluid dynamics** is the branch of science that studies the behavior of fluids.

Buoyancy and Archimedes' Principle

If you try to lift a 50-lb weight inside a swimming pool, you will find that less force is required to lift it than when you are outside of the pool. If you try to submerge an inflated balloon under water, you will notice a force pushing it up and out of the water. The force that a fluid, such as water, exerts on an object partially or totally submerged in it results in **buoyancy**.

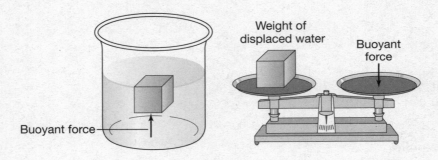

Weight of displaced water

Buoyant force

Buoyant force

When an object is submerged, it displaces some of the volume of the fluid. A simpler way of stating this is that the object takes up space. You can test this by placing an object inside a graduated cylinder filled with water. The level of the water in the cylinder increases. The ancient Greek philosopher Archimedes discovered that the size of the buoyant force on an object is equal to the weight of the fluid that the object displaces. This law is Archimedes' principle.

Pressure in Fluids

In addition to buoyancy, fluids also exert pressure on objects within them. This pressure is due to the combined forces of all the fluid particles. For example, **air pressure** is the combined force of all the molecules in the air on anything within the atmosphere (including us). Air pressure is not constant throughout the atmosphere. The air pressure in Chicago, located at sea level, has a value of 1 standard atmosphere (atm). However, air pressure decreases as altitude increases. The city of Denver, at an altitude of ~1500 m, has a somewhat lower air pressure: 0.97 atm.

This decrease in air pressure with altitude is caused by differences in air density. Gravity pulls most air molecules close to sea level. The air at higher elevations is "thinner," meaning less dense. Pressure is due to the combined weight of all the air molecules above an object. Where there are fewer air molecules, pressure is lower.

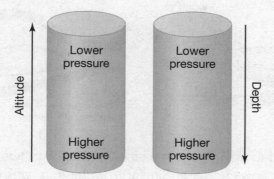

Similarly, the pressure in a liquid, such as water, increases as depth increases. Both the weight of the water and the weight of the air above it cause water pressure. At a depth of 10 m, water adds 1 atm of pressure. Combined with the weight of the air above it, the pressure at this depth is 2 atm. The additional water above the submerged object adds to the pressure, which increases by 1 atm for every 10 m of depth.

Bernoulli's Principle

In the 1700s, the scientist Daniel Bernoulli studied how fluids **flow**, or move through and around objects. Bernoulli compared the volume of water flowing through pipes of different diameters. The total amount of water flowing through the pipes below, per unit time, is the same. Since the pipe on the left is narrower, water must flow through it faster than through the wider pipe.

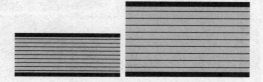

Recall from Lesson 15 that kinetic energy can be converted to potential energy, and that energy is conserved. Because the water in the narrower pipe flows faster, it has greater kinetic energy. This means that it must have less potential energy. Pressure is a type of potential energy. *Bernoulli's principle* states that whenever the speed of flow increases, the fluid's pressure must decrease.

We usually think of fast-flowing water as having higher pressure, but the opposite is actually true. If a spray of fast-flowing water strikes you, it transfers a large amount of momentum to you. (Remember, momentum = mass × velocity.) That is why we think of the water as having higher pressure. However, so much of that momentum is focused on moving forward that the water pushes less on the inside of the pipe. Fast-flowing water produces much less outward pressure on the inside of a pipe than slow-moving water does.

Bernoulli's work with fluids helped humans learn to fly. Airplanes depend on **aerodynamic** forces, or forces in moving fluids, to keep them up in the air. (Remember, fluid dynamics includes gases.)

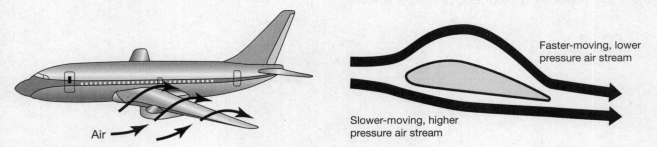

Faster-moving, lower pressure air stream

Slower-moving, higher pressure air stream

Air

An airplane wing is designed to split the air it passes through into two streams. One stream flows over the wing, and the other flows under it. Similar to water in a narrow tube, the air over the wing flows faster than the air under the wing. Therefore, the air over the wing has lower pressure. This pressure difference between the air above and below the wing produces the force known as *lift*, which helps keep the plane in the air.

Hydraulic Lifts

Car repair shops use hydraulic lifts to raise heavy vehicles several meters off the ground. **Hydraulics** studies the forces in fluids in closed containers. In a closed container, the pressure exerted by a fluid is the same throughout. Think of what happens when you apply pressure to an inflated balloon. Every part of the balloon increases in pressure. Car lifts rely on this property of fluids to create enough pressure to lift a vehicle. A diagram of a lift is shown.

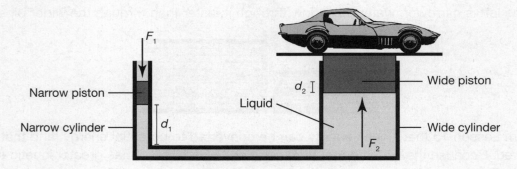

F_1

Narrow piston

Narrow cylinder

d_1

Liquid

d_2

F_2

Wide piston

Wide cylinder

The hydraulic lift consists of a narrow cylinder with a movable piston inside it and a larger cylinder with a second piston that supports the car. The cylinders are both connected to a tank filled with liquid. Pushing down on the narrow piston applies pressure to the liquid. Because this pressure is the same throughout the liquid, the force on the narrow piston raises the wider piston.

Similar to the simple machines discussed in Lesson 23, a hydraulic lift confers a mechanical advantage. A small force, applied on the smaller piston, produces a larger, upward force on the wider piston. However, the amount of work is conserved because the force on the small piston must be applied over a longer distance d_1. The mechanical advantage of a lift is the ratio of the input force pushing down on the small piston to the output force pushing up on the vehicle.

Example: The small piston of a hydraulic lift is pressed with a force of 100 N. This produces force on the large piston capable of supporting a car weighing 15,000 N. What is the mechanical advantage of the lift?

Input force: 100 N; Output force: 15,000 N

$$MA = \frac{F_{out}}{F_{in}} = \frac{15,000 \text{ N}}{100 \text{ N}} = 150$$

The mechanical advantage of the hydraulic lift is 150.

Discussion Question

Describe some examples of situations in which fluid pressure must to be controlled to protect health and safety.

Lesson Review

1. A rubber duck is partially submerged in a tub of water. Which **best** describes the buoyant force acting on the rubber duck?

   A. The buoyant force is equal to the weight of the water in the bathtub.

   B. The buoyant force is equal to the net force pressing down on the duck.

   C. The buoyant force is equal to the weight of the volume of water displaced by the duck.

   D. The buoyant force is equal to the weight of the duck.

2. The barrel below is filled with water.

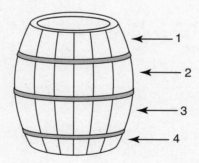

   In which location would a hole in the side of the barrel result in a stream of water with the highest velocity?

   A. location 1   **C.** location 3

   B. location 2   **D.** location 4

3. Water flows through a flexible hose. A length of the hose is squeezed, making its diameter narrower. How will the flow of water through this narrower section of the hose be affected?

   A. The water will flow more slowly and its pressure will increase.

   B. The water will flow more slowly and its pressure will decrease.

   C. The water will flow more quickly and its pressure will increase.

   D. The water will flow more quickly and its pressure will decrease.

4. A hydraulic lift has a mechanical advantage of 80. What input force is required to produce an output force of 3600 N?

   A. 2.22 N

   B. 45 N

   C. 600 N

   D. 480 N

Electrical Force

Key Words • electrical force • charge • positive • negative • neutral • inverse square law

Getting the Idea

The force of gravity pulls all matter on Earth down toward Earth's center. We feel the effects of gravity constantly. Gravity is very weak though, when compared to the electrical force. The **electrical force** exists between any two charged objects. Electric current is the result of electrical force pushing on electrons in a metal wire. We use the work done by electric forces to accomplish many tasks, from sharpening pencils to driving cars.

The Electrical Force

Though the gravitational force exists among all types of matter, the electrical force exists only among charged matter. It does not exist between objects with a neutral charge. Like gravity, the electrical force can pull objects together. Unlike gravity, the electrical force can also push objects apart.

Charged and Neutral Matter

Recall from Lesson 6 that protons and electrons are charged. A **charge** is a property of matter that describes how it reacts to electric force. Charges are classified as positive or negative. A **positive** charge is marked with a plus (+) sign, and a **negative** charge is marked with a minus (−) sign. These terms indicate that the charges are unlike, or opposite, but do not tell us anything about why. For example, it would be wrong to think that negatively charged objects lack some feature or property, or that positively charged particles have an extra amount of this feature. Two unlike charges are attracted to each other due to the electrical force between them. Two like charges repel each other.

Not all matter has charge. Matter can be **neutral**, or uncharged. Neutrons are uncharged. Matter is often uncharged because the numbers of positive and negative charges within it cancel each other. An atom has a net neutral charge if the numbers of protons and electrons inside it are equal. A charged atom is called an ion. A charged object contains different numbers of positively charged particles (such as protons or positive ions) and negatively charged particles (such as electrons or negative ions).

Inside atoms, electrical force keeps electrons in orbit around the nucleus, which contains protons. Electrical force also binds positive and negative ions together in ionic compounds, such as table salt, $NaCl$, which is composed of positive Na^+ ions and negative Cl^- ions.

Behavior of the Electrical Force

The equation for calculating electrical force (F_e) is:

$$F_e = \frac{k_e q_1 q_2}{d^2}$$

In this equation, q_1 and q_2 are the charges of the two objects, and d is the distance between them. The term k_e is a constant called Coulomb's constant. Electrical force obeys an **inverse square law**. As the distance (d) between two charges doubles ($d \times 2$), the force (F) between them drops to one-quarter ($F \div 4$). The strength of the electrical force is proportional to the product of the charges. The electrical force between an iron ion with a charge of $+2$ (Fe^{2+}) and a calcium ion with a charge of $+1$ (Ca^+) is twice as strong as the force between two calcium ions.

The diagram shows the electrical force between an electron and a proton, and between two electrons. (The diagram is not to scale; a proton actually has much more volume and mass than an electron.) Notice that the strength of the electrical force does not depend on the masses of the particles, only on their charges. The positive charge on a proton is the same magnitude or strength as the negative charge on an electron.

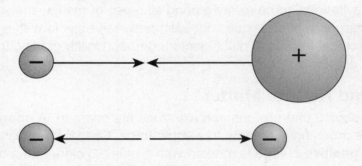

Comparing the Electrical Force and Gravity

Coulomb's constant, k_e, is much larger than the gravitational constant, G, because electrical force is actually much stronger than gravitational force. We notice the effect of gravity more because gravity is always an attractive force. In a sample of matter, the protons and electrons exert gravitational force together, pulling on other objects. If a free proton is far away from the sample, the electrons will attract it, but the protons will repel it. The push and pull cancel each other out, meaning that there is no net electrical force far from the sample.

The Electrical Force in Everyday Life

You can demonstrate the electrical force by rubbing two balloons on a wool sweater. This transfers electrons from the wool to the balloons, making the balloons negatively charged. The electrical force between the charged balloons causes them to repel each other.

The electrical force is actually much more important than this experiment shows. For example, friction is a force that resists the motion of objects that are in contact with each other. Friction results from the electrical forces between the atoms and molecules of the surfaces in contact. Devices such as tires depend on friction to work. The electrical force is also involved when a coiled spring compresses or expands. The spring responds by going back to its original shape due to the electrical force between the atoms making up the metal.

Discussion Question

How is the electrical force the basis of electric current and electrical power?

Lesson Review

1. Which of the following pairs of particles will experience an electrical attraction?

   A. two protons

   B. two electrons

   C. a proton and an electron

2. Which **best** describes the electrical force?

   A. It is responsible for holding protons together in the nucleus.

   B. Its strength is proportional to the masses of the charged objects.

   C. It is the result of electrical power produced by electric currents.

   D. Its strength decreases more rapidly than the distance between charges.

3. Which of the following statements correctly compares the electrical force and gravity?

   A. The electrical force is much weaker than gravity.

   B. The electrical force is much stronger than gravity.

   C. The electrical force has the same strength as gravity.

4. A potassium ion (K^+) and a bromine ion (Br^-), a certain distance apart, experience an electrical force equal to $F_{electrical}$. What is the electrical force between a magnesium ion (Mg^{2+}) and an oxide ion (O^{2-}), which are the same distance apart?

   A. $0.5 \times F_{electrical}$ C. $2 \times F_{electrical}$

   B. $1 \times F_{electrical}$ D. $4 \times F_{electrical}$

Chapter 4 Review

During Galileo's time, many people believed that heavy objects fell to the ground faster than lighter objects. People argued that gravity exerted a greater force on objects with more mass, causing them to fall to Earth faster than less massive objects. Galileo argued that if air friction were ignored, all masses would fall to Earth at the same speed. Perhaps the most famous of Galileo's experiments involved dropping two balls from a great height.

Some students wanted to replicate Galileo's experiment, but they wanted to measure acceleration due to gravity (g) on different masses, with more precision. They decided to test two different masses to determine if the mass affected acceleration due to gravity.

The students used a spark timer to measure the acceleration due to gravity (g).

A spark timer is a device that measures the distance an object moves at regular time intervals. It includes a marking device and a roll of non-sticking paper tape. Setting the time interval on the spark timer to 10 Hz, for example, causes the device to mark the tape every one-tenth of a second. If the tape moves as this happens, the distance traveled in each time interval can be measured.

The students attached a 50-gram mass to the end of the paper tape and set the spark timer to 60 Hz. Their setup is shown in Figure 1. They set the spark timer near the edge of a table and dropped the weight so that it fell to the floor. The weight pulled the paper tape through the timer. They then repeated the experiment with a 100-gram mass with the same volume as the first. The students used the data to find the average velocity over each interval. Then they constructed a graph (Figure 2).

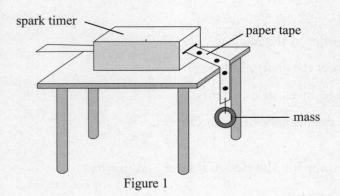

Figure 1

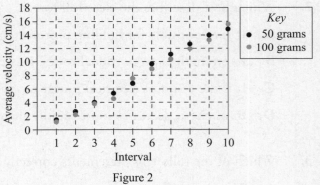

Figure 2

1. Which of the following is true of the average velocity over each time interval?

   A. The average velocity is equal to the distance between adjacent markings.

   B. The average velocity is equal to the distance between a marking and the weight.

   C. The average velocity is equal to the distance between adjacent markings, divided by the interval of time, $\frac{1}{60}$ second.

   D. The average velocity is equal to the distance between a marking and the weight, divided by the interval of time, $\frac{1}{60}$ second.

2. How can the graph in Figure 2 be used to calculate g?

   F. The average velocity is equal to g.

   G. The time required for the mass to travel a distance of one meter is equal to g.

   H. The slope of the line that connects the points is equal to g.

   J. The y-intercept of the line that connects the points is equal to g.

3. Why are the data for the two masses, shown in Figure 2, so similar?

   A. Objects with a greater mass fall faster because there is a greater force acting on a greater mass.

   B. Objects fall at the same rate because gravity exerts a greater force on more massive objects.

   C. Objects fall at the same rate because acceleration is always constant for moving objects.

   D. Objects with lesser mass fall faster because the force of gravity causes them to accelerate more than objects with a greater mass.

4. Which law of physics explains why objects of different masses fall at the same rate?

   F. The law of $F = ma$

   G. The law of inertia

   H. The law of conservation of energy

   J. The law of equal and opposite forces

5. Which of the following is most likely the largest source of error in the experiment?

   A. Controlling for the effect of mass on speed

   B. Measuring the masses of the two weights

   C. Measuring the distances between markings on the tape

   D. Measuring time intervals between markings on the tape

Chapter 5

Cell Biology

Cells

Getting the Idea

All organisms consist of one or more cells. A **cell** is the smallest unit that can carry out all the functions of life. The one cell that makes up a unicellular organism must carry out all the processes necessary for life. In a multicellular organism, each cell must carry out most of the basic processes necessary for sustaining itself. Each cell also interacts with other cells and contributes to keeping the entire organism alive.

The Basic Parts of Cells

The cell is the basic unit of structure and function in all living things. Cells maintain **homeostasis**, that is, stable conditions inside the cell despite changes outside the cell. All cells have a membrane that separates the inside of the cell from the outside environment. The **cell membrane** is a thin, flexible layer that surrounds the rest of the cell. This membrane supports and protects the cell. It also controls which materials enter and leave the cell, either from the external environment or from other cells of the same organism. (The cell membrane is also called the *plasma membrane*.) Inside the cell membrane is the **cytoplasm**, a thick, jelly-like material that holds the cell's internal structures. In addition, cells contain instructions for assembling the proteins that allow them to carry out their functions. These instructions are in the form of DNA. You will learn about this process in Lesson 31.

Prokaryotic Cells and Eukaryotic Cells

Cells are divided into two categories: prokaryotic cells and eukaryotic cells. Both kinds of cells are enclosed by a cell membrane, are filled with cytoplasm, and contain ribosomes and DNA. However, in most other ways, prokaryotic and eukaryotic cells differ.

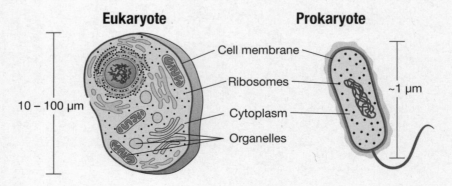

One obvious difference is that the eukaryotic cell is larger and more complex than the prokaryotic cell. Cells of **eukaryotes** have a distinct nucleus and other cell structures, called **organelles**, which are surrounded by their own membranes. These organelles are specialized for different functions. Many eukaryotic organisms consist of large numbers of cells that work together. Plants, animals, protists, and fungi are all eukaryotes. All plants and animals, and some protists and fungi, are multicellular. In eukaryotes, the organelles carry out most of the processes that sustain life.

Notice that the prokaryotic cell does not have membrane-bound organelles. In **prokaryotes**, most of the cell processes occur in the cytoplasm. Nearly all prokaryotes are unicellular. All bacteria are prokaryotes. Archae, discussed in Lesson 37, are also prokaryotes.

Structures and Organelles of the Eukaryotic Cell

The animal cell diagram shows the structures found in most eukaryotic cells.

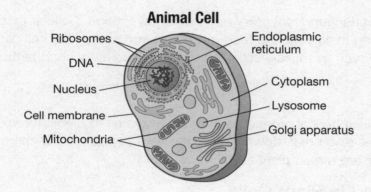

Animal Cell

Ribosomes
DNA
Nucleus
Cell membrane
Mitochondria
Endoplasmic reticulum
Cytoplasm
Lysosome
Golgi apparatus

Nucleus

The largest structure in most eukaryotic cells is the **nucleus**, the organelle that directs and controls most cellular activities. A double membrane called the nuclear membrane, or nuclear envelope, encloses the nucleus. This membrane controls the passage of materials between the nucleus and the cytoplasm. The nucleus contains the DNA that stores the instructions for assembling proteins. Prokaryotic cells lack nuclei, so their DNA floats in the cytoplasm.

Ribosomes

Small, dark structures called **ribosomes** are scattered throughout the cytoplasm of a cell. Proteins are assembled in ribosomes. Some ribosomes are attached to the **endoplasmic reticulum** (ER), a network of membranes and sacs that surrounds the nuclear membrane. Unlike most other organelles, free-floating ribosomes are not enclosed in membranes. Prokaryotes also have ribosomes.

Endoplasmic Reticulum (ER)

The endoplasmic reticulum transports molecules from one part of the cell to another. There are two types of ER. *Rough endoplasmic reticulum*, or rough ER, is dotted with ribosomes. It is most common in cells that make large amounts of protein. *Smooth endoplasmic reticulum*, or smooth ER, lacks ribosomes. Smooth ER helps regulate some cell processes. For example, it breaks down toxic substances in liver cells.

Golgi Apparatus

Proteins from the ER travel to the Golgi apparatus before they are sent to different parts of the cell or to other parts of the organism. The **Golgi apparatus** is a system of membranes that modifies proteins and lipids (fats) according to where they will be used. For example, proteins that belong in the cell membrane are treated differently than proteins that will be sent to the nucleus.

Mitochondria

Mitochondria (sing. *mitochondrion*) carry out cellular respiration. Cellular respiration is the process by which living things change food molecules into energy the cell can use. Cells that need a lot of energy, such as muscle cells, have many more mitochondria than cells with lower energy needs.

Lysosomes

Lysosomes are small, spherical organelles that use enzymes to digest (break down) complex molecules. Lysosomes also break down old organelles. Lysosomes are common in cells of animals and fungi but are rare in plant cells.

Structures Found in Plant Cells

The organelles discussed so far are found in most eukaryotic cells. The cells of some eukaryotes, particularly plants, have structures that are not found in other types of eukaryotic cells. Some of these structures are shown in the plant cell diagram below.

Plant Cell

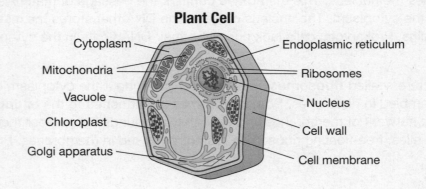

Cytoplasm
Mitochondria
Vacuole
Chloroplast
Golgi apparatus
Endoplasmic reticulum
Ribosomes
Nucleus
Cell wall
Cell membrane

Cell Wall

A **cell wall** is a rigid structure that surrounds the cell membrane and gives the cell additional protection and support. Cell walls are thicker than cell membranes but also control the passage of materials into and out of the cell. Plant cell walls are composed of *cellulose*, a substance made up of sugars. Fungi and some protists also have cell walls, as do all prokaryotic cells.

Chloroplasts

Plant cells contain **chloroplasts**, organelles that capture the energy of sunlight in a green pigment called *chlorophyll*. Chloroplasts carry out photosynthesis, a process in which the energy from sunlight is used to produce sugar (glucose) molecules from water and carbon dioxide. Some protists, including algae, also have chloroplasts. In bacteria that carry out photosynthesis, chlorophyll is scattered throughout the cytoplasm. (Photosynthesis is further explained in Lesson 29.)

Vacuoles

Plant cells have a large, central vacuole. A **vacuole** is an organelle that stores water and other important materials, including salts, proteins, and carbohydrates. The liquid-filled vacuole creates pressure that helps support heavy structures, such as leaves and flowers. Some animal cells have small vacuoles, which store substances and transport these substances within the cell. The cells of some protists also contain vacuoles that may store either useful materials or wastes.

Viruses

Viruses are not cells but depend on cells for their existence. A **virus** consists of genetic material enclosed in a protein shell, and is much smaller and simpler than any single-celled organisms (either eukaryotes or prokaryotes). Viruses are so small that they can be seen only with very powerful electron microscopes. Viruses share some characteristics with living things. For example, both have the ability to respond to the environment and to evolve. Like organisms, viruses can reproduce. Also, some viruses and some organisms can cause disease.

Despite these similarities, viruses are not considered to be living organisms because they are not composed of cells. In addition, all viruses need living cells in order to reproduce and to make proteins from DNA or RNA. Viruses can reproduce only when they infect a living host cell.

Discussion Question

Which features are common to prokaryotic cells, plant cells, and animal cells? Why do you think these features are found in all types of cells?

Lesson Review

1. How does a eukaryotic organism differ from a prokaryotic organism?

   A. A eukaryotic organism has nuclei, while a prokaryotic organism does not.

   B. A eukaryotic organism is made up of cells, while a prokaryotic organism is not.

   C. A eukaryotic organism contains genetic information, while a prokaryotic organism does not.

   D. A eukaryotic organism is always made up of one cell, while a prokaryotic organism has many cells.

2. Which two structures are **least likely** to be found in the same eukaryotic cell?

   A. small vacuoles and cell wall

   B. lysosomes and cell membrane

   C. mitochondria and chloroplasts

   D. ribosomes and endoplasmic reticulum

3. Which of the following structures separates the nucleus from its environment?

   A. cell membrane

   B. Golgi apparatus

   C. nuclear membrane

   D. endoplasmic reticulum

4. Which of the following is found in both viruses and eukaryotes?

   A. nucleus

   B. cell wall

   C. ribosomes

   D. genetic material

The Cell Membrane and Transport

Key Words • diffusion • concentration gradient • equilibrium • passive transport • selectively permeable • facilitated diffusion • osmosis • hypertonic • hypotonic • isotonic • active transport • endocytosis • exocytosis

Getting the Idea

The cell membrane is the boundary between the cell's interior and the outside world. In order to keep conditions inside the cell stable and keep the cell healthy, the cell membrane must regulate the flow of materials into or out of the cell.

Passive Transport: Diffusion and Facilitated Diffusion

Diffusion is the movement of particles from an area of higher concentration to an area of lower concentration. (Concentration and solutions were discussed in Lesson 12.) A difference in concentration between nearby areas is a **concentration gradient**. Particles will move down a concentration gradient. Eventually, the solution will have the same concentration across all areas, a state called **equilibrium**. When equilibrium is reached, the particles may still move around in the solution. However, the movement of particles will be random, and they will not move in a particular direction.

Particles move down a concentration gradient

At equilibrium, there is no net movement of particles

Cells have to take in nutrients to carry out their life functions. They must also remove wastes. One way materials enter and leave a cell is by diffusion across the cell membrane. When a substance is more concentrated outside of the cell, it will diffuse into the cell, and vice versa. Because diffusion involves a natural movement of particles— much like a ball rolling down a hill—it does not require the cell to use energy or do work. Diffusion is called **passive transport** because it occurs without work or the use of energy.

Diffusion

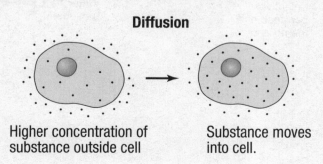

Higher concentration of substance outside cell

Substance moves into cell.

Not all particles can diffuse across a cell membrane. The cell membrane regulates the flow of substances into and out of the cell. Cell membranes are **selectively permeable**, or *semipermeable*. That is, they allow only some substances to pass through them. Glucose, for example, cannot pass directly through the cell membrane.

Another type of diffusion, known as **facilitated diffusion**, allows specific ions or molecules to cross the cell membrane. These substances pass through protein channels embedded in the cell membrane. Each protein channel allows a specific type of molecule to pass into or out of the cell. Protein channels in some cells, for example, allow only glucose to pass through. While the channel helps substances move across the cell membrane, the process is still diffusion, and it occurs only if there is a difference in concentration.

Facilitated Diffusion

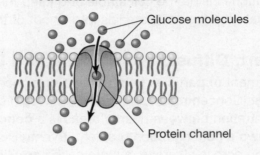

Glucose molecules

Protein channel

Osmosis

Living cells are made up mostly of water, and regulation of water is essential for the cell's survival. The diffusion of water molecules through selectively permeable membranes is known as **osmosis**. Water molecules move from a place of lower solute concentration to a place of higher solute concentration—either into or out of the cell. Osmosis is a form of passive transport. The diagram below illustrates the osmosis of water molecules across a membrane. The membrane is impermeable to sugar molecules, so only water can move across it.

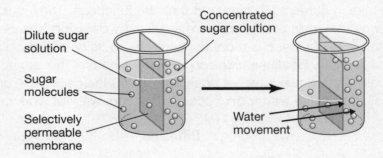

Dilute sugar solution

Concentrated sugar solution

Sugar molecules

Selectively permeable membrane

Water movement

Isotonic, Hypotonic, and Hypertonic Solutions

When a concentration gradient is present across the cell membrane, the solution outside the cell is either hypertonic or hypotonic. A **hypertonic** solution has a higher concentration of solute compared to that within a cell. When a cell is placed in a hypertonic solution, water diffuses out of the cell, and the cell shrinks. A **hypotonic** solution has a lower concentration of solute compared to that within a cell. When a cell is placed in a hypotonic solution, water diffuses into the cell. The cell swells and may burst. Molecules continue to diffuse across the cell membrane until the two solutions reach equilibrium. A solution with the same concentration as that within a cell is **isotonic**. The table below shows the different types of solutions and their effects on plant and animal cells.

Effects of Osmosis on Cells

Solution	Animal Cell	Plant Cell
Isotonic: The concentration of particles is the same inside and outside the cell.	Water in / Water out	Water in — Cell membrane / Cell wall / Water out
Hypertonic: Solution has a higher solute concentration than the cell.	Water out	Water out
Hypotonic: Solution has a lower solute concentration than the cell.	Water in	Water in

Active Transport through Protein Channel Pumps

Recall that the movement of materials across a cell membrane by diffusion and osmosis does not require energy. In some cases, a cell needs to move materials into or out of the cell against the concentration gradient. In other words, materials must be moved into an area of higher concentration from an area of lower concentration. This type of movement requires energy and is called **active transport**.

Like facilitated diffusion, active transport can use protein channels to move particles across the membrane. The transported substance binds to the channel proteins. One example of this is the sodium-potassium pump. Sodium ions (Na^+) are pumped out of the cell, and potassium ions (K^+) are pumped into the cell by specific channel proteins. The cell uses energy to move these ions. In mammals, the active transport of calcium into and out of cells is necessary for muscle contraction. Calcium ions (Ca^{2+}) are pumped into and out of the cell by active transport. Cells also use active transport to remove wastes.

Endocytosis and Exocytosis

Some large molecules are actively transported by movements of the cell membrane itself. Endocytosis and exocytosis are other forms of active transport. **Endocytosis** is a process in which a cell surrounds and takes in material from its environment. The cell membrane folds and then forms a pocket around the outside material. The pocket separates from the cell membrane and forms a vesicle inside the cytoplasm. This carries the material into the cell. The diagram shows an amoeba using endocytosis to feed.

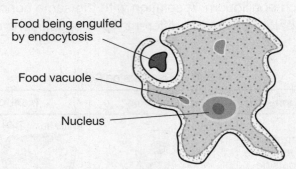

Food being engulfed by endocytosis

Food vacuole

Nucleus

Cells use the opposite process, **exocytosis**, to remove unwanted materials. The material moves toward the cell membrane inside a vacuole. During exocytosis, the membrane of the vacuole fuses with the cell membrane, and contents of the vacuole are expelled from the cell.

Discussion Question

Why is active transport important to a cell's life processes?

Lesson Review

1. Which of the following types of transport does **not** require the cell to expend energy or do work?

    A. exocytosis

    B. endocytosis

    C. active transport

    D. facilitated diffusion

2. In which type of cellular transport do molecules bind to channel proteins in order to move across a cell membrane against a concentration gradient?

    A. osmosis

    B. diffusion

    C. active transport

    D. facilitated diffusion

3. If an animal cell were placed in a solution of seawater, what would happen to the cell?

    A. The cell would swell because the water solution is hypotonic.

    B. The cell would swell because the water solution is hypertonic.

    C. The cell would shrink because the water solution is hypotonic.

    D. The cell would shrink because the water solution is hypertonic.

Enzymes and Reaction Rates

Key Words • reactant • product • catalyst • enzyme • protein • substrate • activation energy • buffer

Getting the Idea

To maintain homeostasis, cells must carry out thousands of chemical reactions every second. Cells use a special class of proteins to make many of these reactions possible.

Chemical Reactions

Recall that a chemical reaction is a change in the arrangement of atoms that yields different substances. All chemical reactions rearrange the atoms in the reactants to form products. **Reactants** are the atoms, molecules, or compounds that enter into a chemical reaction. The **products** are the atoms, molecules, or compounds that result from the reaction. All chemical reactions break chemical bonds in one or more reactants and form new chemical bonds in one or more products.

Consider these two simple chemical reactions:

Reactant	+	Reactant	→	Product
CO_2	+	H_2O	→	H_2CO_3
Carbon dioxide	+	Water	→	Carbonic acid

Reactant	→	Product	+	Product
H_2CO_3	→	CO_2	+	H_2O
Carbonic acid	→	Carbon dioxide	+	Water

The reaction on the left shows how carbon dioxide produced by your cells reacts with water to form carbonic acid. Your blood carries the carbonic acid to your lungs. The reaction on the right shows how the chemical reaction is reversed in the lungs. Carbonic acid from the bloodstream is converted to carbon dioxide and water. Both products exit your body when you exhale.

Enzymes Are Biochemical Catalysts

Everything that happens in a cell—growth, reproduction, interaction with the environment, and response to stimuli—is the result of a chemical reaction. The biochemical reactions in living things must occur at certain speeds, or rates, in order to be useful. A **catalyst** is a substance that increases the rate of a chemical reaction without itself being changed by the reaction. Most catalysts for biochemical reactions are enzymes, a kind of protein. An **enzyme** is a biochemical catalyst that increases the rate of a chemical reaction in the body. Without enzymes, many of the chemical reactions in living things could not happen. Others would occur much too slowly for the organism to survive.

Enzymes are proteins. A **protein** is a large organic molecule made up of smaller molecules called *amino acids*. Amino acids are protein building blocks that join together, end to end, to form chains. There are about 20 different amino acids, which can join together in a tremendous number of combinations to form very long chains. (Lesson 31 describes how proteins are made in the cell.) After an amino acid chain is made, it folds into a complex three-dimensional structure. This structure is important for the protein's function. The structure of an enzyme allows it to catalyze reactions.

Enzymes Act on Substrates

Enzymes give reactants a site, or place, where they can come together to react. The reactants that are affected by enzymes are known as **substrates**. The surface of an enzyme has a distinct shape that allows it to interact only with certain substrates. A single organism may have thousands of different enzymes. Each is specific to one chemical reaction. Substrates bind to a part of the enzyme called the *active site*. The shapes of certain substrates and the shape of an active site are complementary, or opposite. As a result, the enzyme and substrates fit together much like a lock and key.

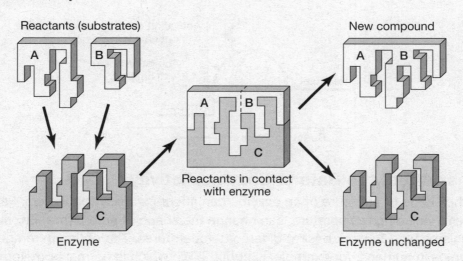

Reactants (substrates)

New compound

Reactants in contact
with enzyme

Enzyme

Enzyme unchanged

This lock-and-key model shows a reaction between an enzyme and two substrates, but it simplifies their actual shapes and how they make contact. The actual molecules and the way they fit together are much more complex. The model is helpful in showing that an enzyme and one type of reactant have complementary shapes, and that the active site of an enzyme molecule can fit, and catalyze, one set of reactants at a time.

When the enzyme and substrates are in contact, forces of attraction between the atoms and molecules hold them together. Together, they form an enzyme-substrate complex that stays bound together until the reaction is complete. When the reaction finishes, the products are released from the active site. The enzyme, which remains unchanged, can then repeat the process. Like all catalysts, it is not used up or changed in the reaction.

Enzymes Lower Activation Energy

Recall from Lesson 10 that for a chemical reaction to occur, reactants must come together with enough energy to break existing bonds between atoms and form new bonds. Enzymes speed up reactions by reducing the amount of energy that the substrates need in order to break these bonds. As described in Lesson 11, they reduce the activation energy of the reaction. The **activation energy** of a reaction is the minimum amount of energy needed for the reaction to proceed. This energy is usually in the form of heat.

A diagram can compare the energy levels of the reactants and products. Products may end up with more energy than reactants (endothermic reaction) or less energy (exothermic reaction). Both types of reactions require activation energy that is higher than the energy in either the products or the reactants. The peak in the middle of the graph represents the activation energy. When a catalyst lowers the activation energy, more reactants can chemically react than would otherwise be possible. Lowering the activation energy can also allow the reaction to take place at a lower temperature than would be possible without a catalyst.

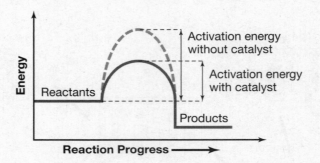

Factors that Affect the Rate of Enzyme Activity

A change in the shape or structure of an enzyme can affect its ability to function. Factors in the environment, including temperature, can change the shape of an enzyme. Enzymes from different organisms tend to work best at different temperatures. The optimum temperature for most enzymes in humans, for example, is about 37°C, which is normal body temperature. The optimum temperature in plants is about 25°C. Temperatures above 50°C generally destroy enzymes.

Another factor that affects enzyme activity is pH. Recall from Lesson 12 that the pH level describes how acidic or basic a solution is. Most enzymes function in very narrow pH ranges, which vary depending on the enzyme and its job. For most reactions, the optimum pH is close to 7, or neutral. Low (acidic) or high (basic) pH values tend to slow enzyme activity.

Cells must regulate their pH levels to function properly. Each enzyme works best in a solution that contains certain ions and other molecules and that has a specific pH. **Buffers** are substances that tend to neutralize acids and bases in solution. Cells use buffers to keep their pH levels in the right range for useful reactions to occur. Keeping pH in that range is an aspect of homeostasis.

Discussion Question

A change in pH can cause a change in the shape of a protein. How might a change in pH stop an enzyme from working?

Lesson Review

1. Why does the human body need enzymes to function properly?

   A. They enable the body to use energy to produce food.

   B. They keep the pH of the body within acceptable levels.

   C. They provide cells with energy they need to carry out life functions.

   D. They help biochemical reactions occur fast enough to maintain homeostasis.

2. The location where reactants bind to an enzyme is called the

   A. catalyst.   **C.** substrate.

   B. product.   **D.** active site.

3. How do enzymes help biochemical reactions take place?

   A. They provide energy to the reactants.

   B. They absorb energy from the products.

   C. They lower the activation energy of the reaction.

   D. They increase the number of available reactant particles.

4. An enzyme and its substrate are in a test tube where a catalyzed reaction can take place. Over time, which of the following will happen?

   A. The amount of enzyme and substrate will decrease, and the amount of product will increase.

   B. The amount of enzyme will decrease, and the amount of substrate and product will increase.

   C. The amount of enzyme will decrease, the amount of substrate will remain the same, and the amount of product will increase.

   D. The amount of enzyme will remain the same, the amount of substrate will decrease, and the amount of product will increase.

Energy in Cells

Key Words • photosynthesis • chloroplast • chlorophyll • ATP • cellular respiration • aerobic • anaerobic • glycolysis • Krebs cycle • electron transport

Getting the Idea

All organisms need a constant flow of energy to carry out their life processes. Plants (and some other organisms) use sunlight to make food, converting the energy of sunlight to chemical energy. Animals (and some other organisms) obtain their energy from the food made by plants. The cells of all organisms convert the chemical energy in food into forms that they can use.

Photosynthesis

Plants and some types of microorganisms carry out photosynthesis. **Photosynthesis** uses energy from sunlight to convert carbon dioxide (CO_2) and water (H_2O) into a sugar called *glucose* ($C_6H_{12}O_6$) and oxygen gas (O_2). This chemical process occurs in a series of steps, which are summarized in the following equation:

$$\text{energy} \;+\; \text{carbon dioxide} \;+\; \text{water} \;\rightarrow\; \text{glucose} \;+\; \text{oxygen}$$

$$\text{sunlight} \;+\; 6CO_2 \;+\; 6H_2O \;\rightarrow\; C_6H_{12}O_6 \;+\; 6O_2$$

Carbon dioxide and water are the reactants in photosynthesis. Glucose and oxygen are the products.

Photosynthesis actually involves two different series of chemical reactions. Both take place in cell organelles called **chloroplasts**. The first series of chemical reactions depends on light. A pigment called **chlorophyll**, which gives plants their green color, absorbs some of the energy from the light reaching it. The light excites some of the electrons in chlorophyll's atoms, causing them to rise or "jump" to higher energy levels. Enzymes then use the energized electrons to produce the compound ATP (adenosine triphosphate). **ATP** is the cell's primary energy carrier.

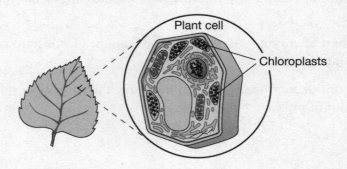

Plant cell

Chloroplasts

The second series of reactions in photosynthesis is called the light-independent reactions, dark reactions, or Calvin cycle. As these terms suggest, no light is needed for these reactions. During the Calvin cycle, the cell uses ATP to rearrange the atoms in water and carbon dioxide to form glucose and oxygen. Glucose molecules are then transported to the rest of the plant to be used for energy or stored for later use. For example, a potato is an underground plant organ that stores energy. A potato contains glucose molecules connected in chains called *starch*.

Cellular Respiration

Cellular respiration breaks the chemical bonds of glucose to release energy. This energy is captured as chemical energy in the form of ATP. The reaction for cellular respiration is summarized as:

$$\text{glucose} + \text{oxygen} \rightarrow \text{carbon dioxide} + \text{water} + \text{energy}$$

$$C_6H_{12}O_6 + 6O_2 \rightarrow 6CO_2 + 6H_2O + \text{ATP}$$

Cellular respiration is an **aerobic** process—that is, a process that requires oxygen. Most eukaryotes use cellular respiration to release energy when oxygen is available. Many prokaryotes rely on **anaerobic** respiration, which takes place without oxygen. Like cellular respiration, anaerobic respiration releases energy. However, it is much less efficient and produces fewer molecules of ATP per molecule of glucose.

Like photosynthesis, cellular respiration is a series of reactions. Instead of gathering the energy from sunlight and storing it in glucose molecules, respiration does the opposite: it breaks down glucose molecules to extract stored chemical potential energy. The three stages, or pathways, of cellular respiration are glycolysis, the Krebs cycle, and electron transport. At each stage, a bit more energy is "squeezed" out of the glucose molecule in the form of ATP.

Glycolysis

Glycolysis is the first stage of cellular respiration. It releases a small amount of energy from glucose. Glycolysis occurs in a cell's cytoplasm and does not require oxygen. In glycolysis, one molecule of glucose breaks apart to form two molecules of pyruvic acid. Glycolysis also produces four molecules of ATP. However, the cell uses two molecules of ATP to start glycolysis. The net energy gained from the reaction is two ATP molecules.

Krebs Cycle

At the end of glycolysis, most of the energy from the original glucose molecule is stored in the bonds of the pyruvic acid molecules. The second stage of cellular respiration, called the **Krebs cycle** or the citric acid cycle, occurs in a cell's mitochondria. There a series of energy-releasing reactions takes place. The pyruvic acid is broken down into carbon dioxide. The Krebs cycle is the source of the carbon dioxide that animals exhale. The Krebs cycle also produces high-energy electrons that are transferred, in the form of bonded hydrogen atoms, to two carrier molecules, FAD and NAD. The molecules $FADH_2$ and NADH form in this way. The $FADH_2$ and NADH molecules are the energy-carrying molecules that enter the next stage of respiration, electron transport. In addition, each molecule of pyruvic acid releases one molecule of ATP.

Electron Transport

Electron transport is a series of reactions that produces ATP from the NADH and $FADH_2$ molecules made in the Krebs cycle. In most cells, electron transport reactions depend on a series of proteins located on the inner membranes of the mitochondria. These proteins are called the *electron transport chain*.

During electron transport, the high-energy electrons of NADH and $FADH_2$ pass from one protein to another. They lose some of their energy at each step in the process. An enzyme at the end of the electron transport chain combines the electrons with hydrogen and oxygen to form water. The electron transport chain produces 32 molecules of ATP.

Aerobic cellular respiration produces a total of 36 ATP molecules from each glucose molecule: 2 from glycolysis, 2 from the Krebs cycle, and 32 from electron transport. The process of aerobic respiration is summarized in the diagram below. Compare this diagram to the equation for respiration on the previous page.

Glucose molecule → GLYCOLYSIS → 2 pyruvic acid molecules → 2 ATP → KREBS CYCLE → CO_2, NADH, $FADH_2$ → 2 ATP → O_2 → ELECTRON TRANSPORT → H_2O → 32 ATP

The ATP-ADP Cycle

A molecule of ATP includes three phosphate (PO_4) groups connected in a row. ATP is small enough to carry energy to chemical reactions throughout the cell. Energy is released when the high-energy bonds between the phosphate groups are broken. Usually, ATP transfers energy to a reaction when the bond joining the last phosphate group to the molecule is broken. This leaves a molecule with two phosphate groups, called ADP (adenosine *di*phosphate).

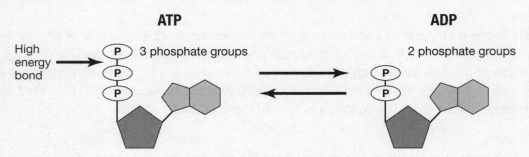

ADP can combine with a free phosphate group to form a new molecule of ATP. This is how ATP forms during respiration. The cell cannot store ATP, and so must constantly make more ATP to meet its energy needs. ADP is constantly converted to ATP, and ATP is constantly converted back to ADP to power the work of the cell. This continuous process is called the *ATP-ADP cycle*.

Discussion Question

Prokaryotic cells do not have mitochondria. Where do you think they carry out respiration?

Lesson Review

1. Which of the following is a product of cellular respiration?

   A. ADP

   B. water

   C. oxygen

   D. glucose

2. What are the reactants in photosynthesis?

   A. oxygen (O_2) and water (H_2O)

   B. water (H_2O) and glucose ($C_6H_{12}O_6$)

   C. carbon dioxide (CO_2) and water (H_2O)

   D. glucose ($C_6H_{12}O_6$) and carbon dioxide (CO_2)

3. Which is the correct sequence of events in cellular respiration?

   A. Krebs cycle → glycolysis → electron transport

   B. electron transport → Krebs cycle → glycolysis

   C. glycolysis → Krebs cycle → electron transport

4. Which of the following chemical reactions releases energy?

   A. production of ATP

   B. production of ADP

   C. production of glucose

   D. production of oxygen gas

Chapter 5 Review

Students in a molecular and cellular biology course isolate cell organelles from fresh green peas using a procedure called differential centrifugation.

Step 1

The students blend the peas in a blender and filter the mixture through a fine sieve to create a homogenate (H). They spin some of the filtered homogenate in a centrifuge, a machine that rapidly spins biological samples. The sample is centrifuged at low speed, subjecting it to forces 600 times the force of gravity, or *g*. This causes some components of the sample to settle at the bottom of the test tube in the form of a *pellet*. Other components remain in the *supernatant*, or the fluid above the pellet.

The students then transfer some of the supernatant to a new test tube for a second centrifugation. The fluid is centrifuged at a force of 3000 *g*. As a result, almost all organelles settle to the bottom to form the second pellet. Again, the supernatant and pellet are separated. Figure 1 summarizes this process.

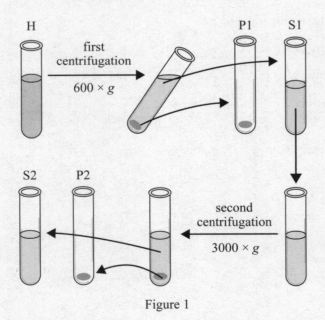

Figure 1

Step 2

Next, the students visually analyze each cell fraction for the presence of amyloplasts (starch-containing organelles) and chloroplasts. Both pellets are resuspended in isotonic buffer fluid. Iodine is added, which stains amyloplasts blue. The fractions are plated onto microscope slides and examined for the presence of these organelles. Table 1 shows the results.

Table 1			
Fraction	% Amyloplasts	% Chloroplasts	Total Number of Organelles
P1	100	0	3
S1	65	35	31
P2	64	36	39
S2	40	60	5

Step 3

The cell fractions are tested for the presence of mitochondria, which are difficult to visualize microscopically. Instead, students test the fractions for the activity of an enzyme, succinate dehydrogenase (SDH), found in the inner mitochondrial membrane. SDH catalyzes the biochemical reaction shown below. Succinate and fumarate are compounds derived from glucose.

$$\text{succinate} + \text{FAD} \rightarrow \text{fumarate} + \text{FADH}_2$$

To determine SDH enzyme activity, succinate, FAD, and the indicator DCPIP are added to a diluted sample of each cell fraction. When DCPIP reacts with $FADH_2$, it changes from its original dark blue color to colorless. The rate of color change is directly proportional to the amount of enzyme present. The treated samples are tested using a spectrometer, a device that measures the amount of a specific wavelength of absorbed light (Figure 2).

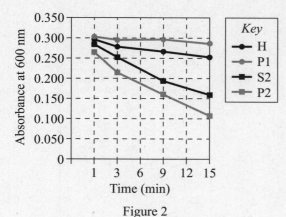

Figure 2

1. An alternative method of treating cells is to first destroy the cell walls, and then place cells in a hypotonic solution. If this method were used:

   A. the cell membranes would not rupture.
   B. the organelles would be likely to burst.
   C. a higher concentration of organelles would be isolated.
   D. a larger proportion of the organelles would be chloroplasts.

2. In Step 3, which of these is a substrate added to the cell fraction samples?

   F. FAD
   G. SDH
   H. DCPIP
   J. $FADH_2$

3. Based on Figures 1 and 2, which cell fractions contain mitochondria?

   A. S1 and P2
   B. P1 and P2
   C. S1, P1, and P2
   D. S1, P2, and S2

4. Cauliflower is a vegetable, similar to broccoli, with large white stems. The students repeat this experiment using cauliflower stems instead of peas. Which will be the most likely difference in the results?

   F. The amyloplasts will be more difficult to visualize.
   G. More mitochondria will be isolated in the cell fractions.
   H. Fewer chloroplasts will be observed in the microscope slides.
   J. The organelles will be more difficult to separate by centrifugation.

5. Differential centrifugation separates cell organelles based on mass. Stronger forces are required to cause smaller, less massive organelles to settle into a pellet. According to the information in Table 1 and Figure 1, amyloplasts and chloroplasts tend to settle into a pellet at forces:

   A. about 600 g.
   B. less than 600 g.
   C. greater than 3000 g.
   D. between 600 g and 3000 g.

Chapter 6

Heredity and Reproduction

The Structure and Role of DNA

Key Words	• trait • protein • DNA • nucleotide • nucleic acid • double helix • gene • chromosome • replication • genetics

Getting the Idea

Your eye color is an example of a trait that you inherited from your parents. A **trait** is a characteristic encoded in an organism's genetic information, which the organism inherited from its parents. In this lesson, you will learn how genetic information is stored and passed on.

Protein Structure and Function

Recall from Lesson 28 that enzymes are proteins. A **protein** is a large molecule made up of building blocks called *amino acids*, which are linked in a chain and folded into a three-dimensional structure. A large molecule made up of many similar subunits, such as a protein, is called a *macromolecule* or *polymer*.

Cells contain many types of proteins with many different roles. Proteins make up channels in the cell membrane, controlling the flow of substances into and out of the cell. Protein enzymes carry out important biochemical reactions. Proteins also make up cell structures.

The Structure of DNA

The genetic information in the nucleus determines the types and amounts of proteins the cell produces. This information is encoded in **DNA** (deoxyribonucleic acid), a macromolecule made up of smaller units called nucleotides. A **nucleotide** is made up of three parts: a five-carbon sugar, a phosphate group, and a nitrogen base. All the nucleotides in a DNA molecule are the same except for the nitrogen bases they contain. For simplicity, we refer to the bases by the first letters of their names: T = thymine, A = adenine, G = guanine, and C = cytosine.

DNA Nucleotides

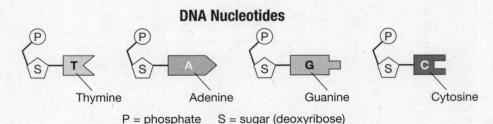

Thymine　　　Adenine　　　Guanine　　　Cytosine

P = phosphate　　S = sugar (deoxyribose)

A polymer made up of nucleotides is a **nucleic acid**. Cells contain two types of nucleic acids—DNA and RNA. You will learn more about RNA in Lesson 31.

A molecule of DNA is shaped like a **double helix**, or a twisted ladder. As shown in the diagram, the "sides" of the ladder are made up of phosphate and sugar molecules joined together. The "rungs" of the ladder are pairs of nitrogenous bases. The bases in DNA always pair in the same way: adenine with thymine, A-T or T-A, and cytosine with guanine, C-G or G-C. This rule is called *complementary base pairing*.

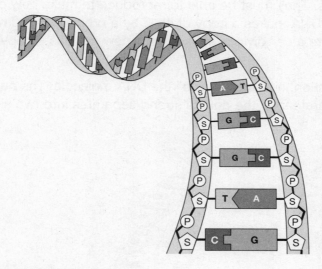

Genes and Chromosomes

The nucleotides that make up the "rungs" of a DNA molecule are like the letters of an alphabet. They spell out information that the cell reads and uses to build proteins. A section of DNA that codes for a protein or proteins is called a **gene**.

A single molecule of DNA can be quite long. For example, all of the DNA in the nucleus of a single human cell, stretched end to end, would be nearly two meters long. To fit inside the nucleus, each DNA molecule wraps around proteins and becomes tightly coiled, forming a single **chromosome**. Each species, or kind, of organism has a characteristic number of chromosomes in its cells. Humans have 46. Chromosomes contain the genetic information that is passed to new cells as they are formed and from one generation of organisms to the next. Each chromosome contains many genes. The diagram shows the relationship among genes, chromosomes, and DNA.

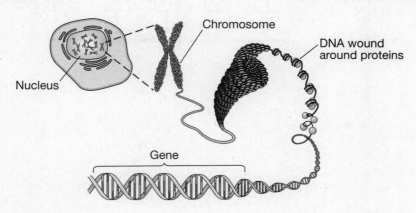

Recall that prokaryotic cells do not have nuclei. In prokaryotes, DNA molecules are attached to the cell membrane or float freely in the cytoplasm. They are also smaller and sometimes ring-shaped.

DNA Replication

Cells are living structures. They must be able to reproduce to make new cells like themselves. Before a cell divides, its DNA makes a copy of itself by a process called **replication**. DNA molecules replicate before a cell divides so that each new cell has a copy of the original cell's genetic material.

In the first step of replication, enzymes "unzip" the DNA molecule. The nucleotide pairs, which make up the rungs, separate, and the double strand separates into two single strands.

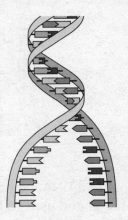

The sequence of bases on each single strand is used to construct a new double-stranded DNA molecule. Each single strand has a complementary sequence of bases. For example, if one strand "reads" ACTTG, then its complementary strand "reads" TGAAC, as shown below.

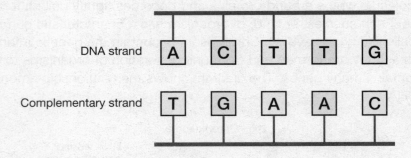

The new, complementary DNA strand is formed by enzymes in the cell's cytoplasm. The enzymes join nucleotides in the correct sequence. The diagram below shows this process. The DNA-synthesizing enzymes move nucleotides into the proper positions so that A pairs with T and G pairs with C. The result is two new DNA molecules, each made up of one strand from the original DNA molecule and a newly formed complementary strand. Each new molecule has a sequence of nucleotides identical to the original molecule of DNA.

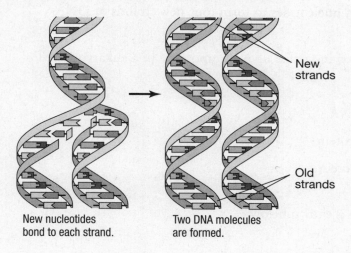

New nucleotides
bond to each strand.

Two DNA molecules
are formed.

New
strands

Old
strands

DNA replication allows newly formed cells to have the same genetic information as the parent cell. It also allows organisms to create gametes (sex cells) and pass their genetic information to offspring. The study of how genes are passed from parents to offspring is called **genetics**.

Discussion Question

How can so much information be transmitted by DNA if it is a sequence of only four letters?

Lesson Review

1.   In a DNA double helix, what makes up the sides of the "ladder"?

     A.   sugars and phosphates

     B.   nitrogen bases and sugars

     C.   nitrogen bases and phosphates

2.   In a DNA molecule, which nucleotide always pairs with thymine?

     A.   adenine   C.   cytosine

     B.   guanine   D.   thymine

3. What is the first step in replication of a DNA molecule?

   A. Enzymes break the bonds between sugars and phosphates.

   B. Enzymes break the bonds between pairs of nucleotides.

   C. Enzymes join nucleotides to form two complementary strands of DNA.

   D. Enzymes join nucleotides to form four new strands of DNA.

4. Which of the following make up a chromosome in a eukaryotic cell?

   A. DNA only

   B. DNA and RNA

   C. DNA and protein

   D. RNA and protein

5. A DNA sequence is shown below.

   CTGAGCT

   Which of the following is a complementary sequence?

   A. TCGAGTC

   B. TCAGATC

   C. AGTCTAG

   D. GACTCGA

The Structure and Role of RNA

Key Words • RNA • protein synthesis • transcription • messenger RNA (mRNA) • amino acid • codon • translation • ribosomal RNA (rRNA) • transfer RNA (tRNA) • anticodon

Getting the Idea

Recall from Lesson 26 that the ribosomes, small structures on the endoplasmic reticulum (ER) and in the cytoplasm, manufacture proteins. However, the instructions for each type of protein are coded as genes on chromosomes in the nucleus. Chromosomes cannot travel out of the nucleus, so how does the information they contain reach the ribosomes?

The Structure of RNA

The nucleic acid **RNA** (ribonucleic acid) plays an important role in the assembly of proteins. The nucleotides that make up RNA are each composed of a sugar, a nitrogen base, and a phosphate group, similar to those in DNA. The RNA nucleotides are shown below.

RNA Nucleotides

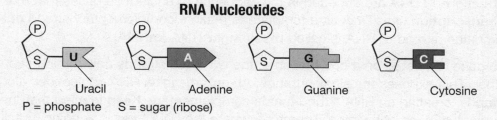

Uracil   Adenine   Guanine   Cytosine

P = phosphate   S = sugar (ribose)

RNA differs from DNA in three ways. First, the sugar in RNA is ribose instead of deoxyribose. The second difference is that RNA molecules contain the base uracil (U) instead of thymine (T). Uracil in RNA pairs with adenine in RNA or DNA. Third, the shapes of RNA and DNA are also different. Recall that a DNA molecule is a double-stranded helix. RNA usually exists as one strand twisted into a single helix, as shown below.

RNA
Ribonucleic Acid

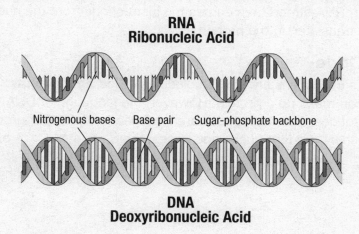

Nitrogenous bases   Base pair   Sugar-phosphate backbone

DNA
Deoxyribonucleic Acid

Making Proteins

Protein synthesis is the process by which cells make proteins. Proteins are assembled on ribosomes, which are located in the cytoplasm. However, the instructions for making proteins are in DNA in the nucleus. RNA carries the information needed to make proteins from the nucleus to the ribosomes. RNA molecules then direct and carry out the processes needed to make proteins. Protein synthesis occurs in two stages, transcription and translation, as shown below.

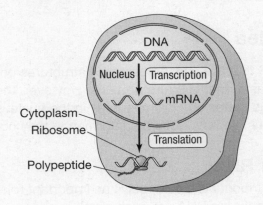

Transcription

The instructions in DNA are encoded in the sequence of nucleotide bases that make up a gene. **Transcription** uses DNA as a template to make a complementary strand of RNA. The complementary strand of RNA is called **messenger RNA (mRNA)**.

Where a gene is located on a chromosome, the two DNA strands unwind and separate from each other. This exposes the single strands. An enzyme joins RNA nucleotides along one of the DNA strands, creating an RNA strand that is complementary. Keep in mind that the RNA base uracil is used in place of thymine. Therefore, where the DNA base is adenine, uracil is joined to the RNA strand. The result is a single strand of mRNA containing nucleotides in the same sequence as one of the DNA strands.

Unlike DNA replication, in which the entire double helix separates, only a portion of the DNA separates during transcription. Once the mRNA strand is completed, the DNA strands reconnect. The genetic code for making a protein is passed from DNA to the mRNA molecule as a result of transcription. The mRNA strand then carries the instructions from the nucleus to the cytoplasm, where they will be translated into a protein.

The Genetic Code

The building blocks of proteins are small molecules called **amino acids**. There are 20 different amino acids that can make up a protein. However, the language of DNA and RNA contains only four types of nucleotides. The nucleotides are arranged in triplets, or groups of three, called **codons**. Because there are four nucleotide bases, there are $4 \times 4 \times 4$ or 64 possible codons.

The chart below shows the genetic code, which specifies the codons for each amino acid. For the codon AGU, first find the "A" block in the column titled First Base. That narrows your choices to the third row. Next, move to the "G" column in the section called Second Base. Finally, find the amino acid with the third base "U." The amino acid coded by AGU is serine.

The Genetic Code

First Base	Second Base				Third Base
	U	**C**	**A**	**G**	
U	phenylalanine	serine	tyrosine	cysteine	U
U	phenylalanine	serine	tyrosine	cysteine	C
U	leucine	serine	(stop)	(stop)	A
U	leucine	serine	(stop)	tryptophan	G
C	leucine	proline	histidine	arginine	U
C	leucine	proline	histidine	arginine	C
C	leucine	proline	glutamine	arginine	A
C	leucine	proline	glutamine	arginine	G
A	isoleucine	threonine	asparagine	serine	U
A	isoleucine	threonine	asparagine	serine	C
A	isoleucine	threonine	lysine	arginine	A
A	methionine	threonine	lysine	arginine	G
G	valine	alanine	aspartic acid	glycine	U
G	valine	alanine	aspartic acid	glycine	C
G	valine	alanine	glutamic acid	glycine	A
G	valine	alanine	glutamic acid	glycine	G

These amino acids combine in different sequences to form many different proteins. The order of the amino acids determines a protein's shape and function. The *stop codons*—UAA, UAG, and UGA—indicate that the end of the protein has been reached.

Translation

Translation converts the information in mRNA into a sequence of amino acids that makes up the specified protein. Translation begins after the mRNA moves from the nucleus into the cytoplasm, where it attaches to a ribosome. **Ribosomal RNA (rRNA)**, along with proteins, makes up the small organelles called ribosomes. Ribosomes carry out translation.

A strand of mRNA attaches to a ribosome in a way that exposes a single codon. In the surrounding cytoplasm are molecules of **transfer RNA (tRNA)**. Each tRNA molecule carries a single amino acid on one end. Each tRNA molecule also has a particular sequence of exposed bases on the other end, called an **anticodon**. An anticodon is a set of three nitrogenous bases on a tRNA molecule that are complementary to a codon on an mRNA molecule. The sequence of bases in an anticodon is specific to the amino acid it carries.

The anticodon of the tRNA aligns and pairs with the exposed codon of the mRNA. The same base pairing rules apply: A with U, and G with C. Only a tRNA with the complementary anticodon can pair with the mRNA. When the tRNA is in this position, the ribosome can attach the amino acid the tRNA molecule carries to the growing chain of amino acids.

Translation

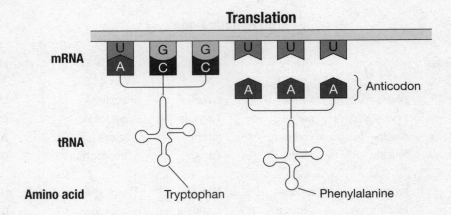

mRNA

Anticodon

tRNA

Amino acid   Tryptophan   Phenylalanine

After the amino acid is attached, the ribosome moves along the mRNA chain to expose the next codon. The process repeats, with the next amino acid being moved into place by a different tRNA molecule. The matching of codons on mRNA with anticodons on tRNA ensures that the amino acids join the chain in the correct order. Eventually a long sequence of amino acids joins in this way, forming a chain of amino acids called a *polypeptide*.

Once the amino acid carried by a tRNA molecule bonds to the growing polypeptide chain, it separates from the tRNA. The "used" tRNA molecule bonds with a free-floating amino acid in the cytoplasm and can be used again in translation.

The ribosome continues to attach amino acids to the chain until it reaches a stop codon in the mRNA strand. This tells the ribosome to release the polypeptide. When the polypeptide chain twists into a three-dimensional shape in the cytoplasm—sometimes in combination with other polypeptide chains—a complete protein is formed.

Discussion Question

A template strand of DNA has the following sequence of bases: TCT GAT AAG ATC. What sequence of bases will make up the strand of mRNA that carries the information from the DNA to the ribosome? What sequence of anticodons will attach to this mRNA strand? What sequence of amino acids will be produced?

Lesson Review

1. Which of the following statements about DNA and RNA is **true**?

    A. DNA contains uracil, while RNA does not.

    B. RNA is arranged in a double helix, while DNA is not.

    C. The kinds of sugar in the nucleotides of DNA and RNA differ.

    D. DNA contains phosphates and nitrogenous bases, while RNA does not.

2. Which DNA sequence produces an mRNA strand with the sequence AGUACA?

    A. TCATGT

    B. CAGTAC

    C. GUACAG

    D. UCAUGU

3. Transcription creates an mRNA molecule using DNA as a template. Where does this process occur?

    A. in the nucleus   **C.** in the ribosomes

    B. in the cytoplasm   **D.** outside the cell

4. The sequence of a strand of mRNA is GCAUUGUAA. How many amino acids does this strand code for, if the sequence includes a stop codon?

    A. 2   **C.** 6

    B. 3   **D.** 9

5. Which statement correctly describes transcription and translation?

    A. Transcription produces a polypeptide from DNA, and translation produces mRNA from DNA.

    B. Transcription produces mRNA from DNA, and translation produces mRNA from a polypeptide.

    C. Transcription produces a polypeptide from mRNA, and translation produces mRNA from DNA.

    D. Transcription produces mRNA from DNA, and translation produces a polypeptide from mRNA.

Mendelian Genetics

> **Key Words** • alleles • dominant • recessive • genotype • phenotype • homozygous • heterozygous • probability • Punnett square • law of segregation • law of independent assortment

Getting the Idea

In the mid-1800s, an Austrian monk named Gregor Mendel made discoveries that led to today's understanding of genetics. Using pea plants, Mendel studied how traits passed from one generation to the next. Although his work was ignored until 1900, Mendel's ideas eventually formed the foundation for the modern science of genetics. These ideas are now known as Mendelian genetics.

Mendel's Experiments with Pea Plants

Mendel developed true-breeding pea plants for his experiments. True-breeding plants can self-pollinate to produce offspring that are identical with their parent. Then Mendel began to cross, or interbreed, different true-breeding strains of peas. In one experiment, Mendel crossed purebred green-pod plants with purebred yellow-pod plants. All offspring resulting from the cross had green pods. This result was unexpected.

Mendel's Pea Plants

From his experiments, Mendel concluded that an organism has two factors for each trait and receives one factor from each parent. Today we know that these factors are genes. The genes from each parent may be the same, or they may code for different forms of a trait, such as green or yellow pods. The different forms of the gene for a specific trait are called **alleles**.

Mendel's true-breeding pea plants had identical alleles for each trait. The plants with green pods had two alleles for green pods, and the plants with yellow pods had two alleles for yellow pods. When they were crossed, each parent contributed one allele to each offspring. Therefore, all the offspring had two different alleles for pod color, one for green and one for yellow. If each offspring had both alleles, why were all the pods green (just like one parent plant) instead of greenish yellow (or some other combination, such as yellow with green patches)?

Having just one green pea pod allele was the same as having two green pea pod alleles. In contrast, having just one yellow pea pod allele had the same effect as having none at all. Mendel concluded that the allele for green pods masked or covered the allele for yellow pods. He described the allele for green pods as *dominant*. A **dominant** allele is always expressed in an organism. If a dominant allele is present, the organism shows that trait. The organism does not exhibit the trait coded for by the other allele.

If two matching alleles are required to express a trait, that allele is called **recessive**. To express yellow pea pods, the pea plants must have two matching recessive alleles for yellow pod color. A recessive allele is expressed only when paired with another recessive allele.

Genotype and Phenotype

The set of alleles an organism has for a particular gene is called its **genotype**. The trait that results from those alleles is the organism's **phenotype**. An organism's phenotype depends on its genotype. An organism with a genotype made up of two matching alleles, either dominant or recessive, is **homozygous** for that gene. An organism with two different alleles is **heterozygous**.

We often represent dominant alleles with uppercase letters and recessive alleles with lowercase letters. For example, green pea pod color is dominant over yellow. A pea plant's genotype could be described as *GG* (two dominant alleles), *Gg* (one dominant and one recessive allele), or *gg* (two recessive alleles).

In Mendel's experiment, the possible alleles for pod color were green or yellow. The parent plants were true-breeding, so they were homozygous. The homozygous green-pod pea plants had two alleles for green color (*GG*), and the homozygous yellow-pod plants had two alleles for yellow color (*gg*). When Mendel crossed the two types of plants, each parent contributed one allele to the offspring (first generation, or F_1). The results were heterozygous offspring, each of which had two different alleles for pod color (*Gg*).

Punnett Squares

We can predict the probability that different genotypes and phenotypes will result from a cross between two organisms. A **probability** is the mathematical chance that some event will occur. A *ratio* is the proportion of one quantity to another. Using a Punnett square can help determine the probability of a trait being passed to offspring and the probable ratios of different phenotypes and genotypes. A **Punnett square** is a diagram used to show possible combinations of dominant and recessive alleles in offspring based on the genotypes of the parents.

To create a Punnett square, divide a square into four sections. Write the genotype of one parent across the top of the square, placing one allele per column. Write the genotype of the other parent down the side, placing one allele per row. To complete the square, combine the alleles of one parent with those of the other parent in each box.

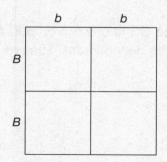 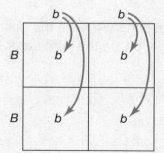 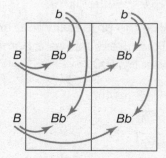

Recall that Mendel crossed pea plants that were homozygous for green pods (*GG*) and homozygous for yellow pods (*gg*). The Punnett square below shows the results of this cross.

Green-pod parent

	G	G
g	Gg green	Gg green
g	Gg green	Gg green

Yellow-pod parent (label at left, aligned with first row)

The F_1 plants can have only one genotype—*Gg*. The probability of inheriting this phenotype is 1, or 100 percent. Similarly, the only possible phenotype of the offspring is green, for a probability of 1 or 100 percent. How would these probabilities differ if we crossed two of the offspring from the F_1 generation? The Punnett square below shows this outcome for the second, or F_2, generation.

F_1 Cross

	G	g
G	GG Green	Gg Green
g	Gg Green	gg Yellow

In this cross, both parents are heterozygous for the pod color gene. Each parent has one of each allele. The result is a variety of offspring. The possible genotypes are *GG*, *Gg*, and *gg*, in a ratio of 1:2:1 (25 percent *GG*, 50 percent *Gg*, 25 percent *gg*). The possible phenotypes are green (*GG* or *Gg*) and yellow (*gg*). A plant will have green pea pods if it has at least one dominant allele. Because three of the four boxes contain a dominant allele (*G*), the offspring have a three-fourths or 75 percent probability of having green pea pods. The phenotypic ratio is 3:1 (75 percent green, 25 percent yellow).

Notice that the probability that any offspring will have the genotype *GG* is one out of four, or one-fourth. To express this as a percentage, divide the numerator by the denominator. Then multiply the answer by 100.

$$\frac{1}{4} = 0.25 \times 100 = 25 \text{ percent}$$

Keep in mind that a 25 percent probability does not mean that exactly 25 out of 100 offspring will have the *GG* genotype. It means you can predict that about one-fourth of the offspring will have this genotype. The more offspring, the closer the actual percentages will be to the predicted percentages.

Mendel's Laws of Segregation and Independent Assortment

Notice that each parent plant gives only one of its alleles to any offspring. Mendel's **law of segregation** states that alleles separate when gametes (sex cells) are formed, so each gamete contains only one allele of each gene. You will learn more about this in the next lesson.

Mendel also studied how multiple traits are inherited. For example, the allele for yellow peas (*Y*) is dominant to the allele for green peas (*y*). A plant that is heterozygous for both genes (*GgYy*) has green pods containing yellow peas. If two such parent plants are crossed, will the offspring "match" for both traits, having either two dominant phenotypes or two recessive phenotypes? Or will they produce new combinations, such as green pods and green peas (*Ggyy*)?

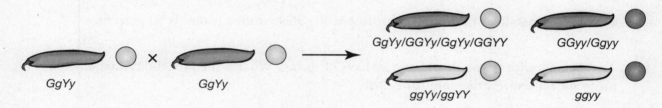

GgYy × *GgYy* → *GgYy/GGYy/GgYy/GGYY* *GGyy/Ggyy* *ggYy/ggYY* *ggyy*

Mendel's crosses produced offspring with all four possible combinations of phenotypes. This led Mendel to the **law of independent assortment**, which states that the alleles for different genes separate independently of each other when gametes form. You will learn more about how genes separate and about how gametes form in the next lesson.

Discussion Question

Which of Mendel's laws of genetics predicts that a parent with the genotype *Aa* can have a child with the genotype *aa*? Explain.

Lesson Review

1. Which of the following combinations of alleles represent the same phenotype but different genotypes?

   A. *Aa* and *AA*

   B. *Aa* and *aa*

   C. *AA* and *aa*

   D. *Aa* and *Aa*

2. A heterozygous parent and a homozygous dominant parent have offspring. What is the probability that any one offspring will be homozygous?

    A. 25 percent

    B. 50 percent

    C. 75 percent

    D. 100 percent

3. Which of the following **best** summarizes the law of independent assortment?

    A. A parent can pass on only one allele of each gene to any one offspring.

    B. A recessive trait will only be expressed if two recessive alleles are present.

    C. The chance of inheriting an allele is not affected by inheriting any other allele.

    D. The probability of offspring inheriting either allele from a parent is 50 percent.

4. Two parents with genotypes Aa and aa have offspring. What is the probability that any one offspring will express the dominant allele?

    A. 25 percent

    B. 50 percent

    C. 75 percent

    D. 100 percent

5. In fruit flies, the allele for normal wings (V) is dominant to the allele for small, vestigial wings (v). A fruit fly with normal wings is crossed with a fruit fly with vestigial wings.

Normal wing   Vestigial wing

What are the possible phenotypic ratios in the offspring?

    A. 4 normal : 0 vestigial *or* 2 normal : 2 vestigial

    B. 4 normal : 0 vestigial *or* 3 normal : 1 vestigial

    C. 3 normal : 1 vestigial *or* 1 normal : 3 vestigial

    D. 3 normal : 1 vestigial *or* 2 normal : 2 vestigial

Meiosis and Genetic Variation

Key Words • mitosis • meiosis • gamete • somatic cell • diploid number • homologous chromosomes • haploid number • crossing-over • genetic recombination • independent assortment • genetic variation • specialization • gene expression

Getting the Idea

More than seven billion people live on Earth. With the exception of twins, no two people are genetically identical. Earth's human population is diverse. For example, there are probably thousands of shades of skin color among the world's population. What allows for sexually reproducing organisms to have such genetic diversity?

Types of Cell Division

Cells divide to form two new cells called daughter cells. To ensure that each new cell receives all the necessary genetic information, the parent cell must copy its chromosomes before it divides. In prokaryotes (bacteria and archaea), this happens through a simple process called *binary fission*. First, the cell's DNA is replicated. Then, the cell divides in two. Each new cell receives a copy of the genetic information. Because prokaryotes have no nucleus and usually have only a single chromosome, this process is simple.

Cell division in a eukaryotic cell is more complicated because the nucleus contains multiple chromosomes. Each chromosome must replicate, and one copy must go to the nucleus in each new cell. The separation of replicated chromosomes into two new, identical nuclei in eukaryotes is called **mitosis**. Single-celled eukaryotes reproduce through cell division with mitosis. Multicellular eukaryotes use cell division with mitosis for growth and repair.

By contrast, **meiosis** is a process by which the number of chromosomes per cell is cut in half. Meiosis results in sex cells (sperm or eggs) called **gametes**. The gametes from two individuals join to form a fertilized egg. To understand why meiosis is necessary, it is important to understand chromosome number.

Chromosome Number

Recall that chromosomes are made up of the cell's genetic material, DNA. Each human **somatic cell** (body cell) has 46 chromosomes. The body cells of different species have a characteristic number of chromosomes. For example, the body cells of a cat contain 38 chromosomes, a rabbit 44, a crayfish 200, and a tomato 24. The normal number of chromosomes in a somatic cell is called the **diploid number** for that species.

In organisms that reproduce sexually, half the chromosomes come from the mother and half come from the father. The 46 chromosomes in a human body cell consist of 23 pairs of **homologous chromosomes**. Homologous chromosomes have matching pairs of genes but may have different alleles.

Each parent contributes one chromosome to each pair. During fertilization, two human gametes combine to form a cell with 46 chromosomes. Therefore, sexually reproducing organisms must make gametes with exactly half the number of chromosomes as somatic cells. Each gamete must contain exactly one chromosome from each homologous pair. The number of chromosomes in a gamete is the **haploid number**. Each gamete is different, so each organism inherits a different combination of genes. The varied combinations of genes give different offspring unique traits.

Mitosis: A Closer Look

The cells of eukaryotic organisms form new cells by mitosis, in which a cell nucleus divides in two. Mitosis is a continous process. However, biologists divide mitosis into four phases, as shown in the diagram below. Before mitosis begins, a cell's chromosomes are copied by the process of DNA replication described in Lesson 30.

Mitosis

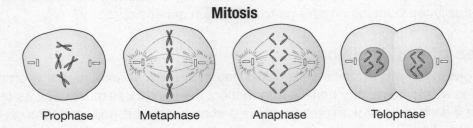

Prophase   Metaphase   Anaphase   Telophase

Prophase

During *prophase*, the first phase of mitosis, the chromosomes condense from a loose, spaghetti-like form to a more compact form. Pairs of replicated chromosomes (*sister chromatids*) are joined together at the *centromere*. The nuclear membrane breaks down. The centrioles, which are found in the cytoplasm, separate and travel to opposite poles of the cell. Spindle fibers form around each centriole and attach themselves to each centromere.

Metaphase

By the second phase of mitosis, *metaphase*, the nuclear membrane has completely broken down, and the chromosomes have lined up along the middle of the cell. Each chromosome is attached to spindle fibers at its centromere.

Anaphase

During *anaphase*, the third phase of mitosis, the sister chromatids are pulled apart by the spindle fibers and begin to move to opposite sides of the cell.

Telophase

In the final phase of mitosis, *telophase*, the chromosomes reach opposite sides of the cell. Spindle fibers break down, and two new nuclear membranes form. The cell now has two nuclei, each with a complete set of genetically identical chromosomes.

After mitosis is complete, the cell can divide. This process, called cytokinesis, actually begins during telophase and results in two separate cells.

Meiosis: A Closer Look

The steps of meiosis are similar to those of mitosis, but there are important differences. Meiosis produces four genetically different cells. The cell divides twice, in stages called meiosis I and meiosis II. Each stage goes through the four phases: prophase, metaphase, anaphase, and telophase. The diagram below illustrates how meiosis begins with a single diploid cell and produces four genetically different haploid cells.

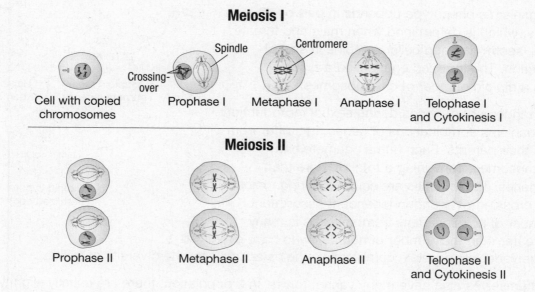

Early in meiosis, the homologous chromosomes of the parent cell pair up, and crossing-over can occur. **Crossing-over** is a process in which homologous chromosomes exchange segments of DNA. Crossing-over is an example of **genetic recombination**—the breaking and rejoining of DNA strands to form new molecules with different information. Crossing-over produces new combinations of alleles. After crossing-over, each of the sister chromatids in a homologous pair is genetically unique.

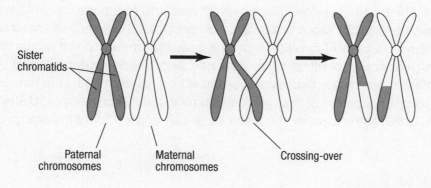

In metaphase I, pairs of homologous chromosomes line up along the center of the cell in a random fashion. As a result, homologous chromosomes separate randomly into the two daughter cells. This process, called **independent assortment**, is the basis of Mendel's law of independent assortment. Recall that this law states that the alleles for different genes separate independently of each other when gametes form.

Meiosis I results in two haploid daughter cells. Each has half the number of chromosomes as the original cell. However, each still has two copies of each chromosome.

The stages of meiosis II are nearly identical to those of mitosis except that meiosis II begins with haploid cells instead of a diploid cell. The two haploid daughter cells formed by meiosis I divide in meiosis II to form four haploid sex cells, or gametes. Each gamete has a unique set of chromosomes.

Each organism's phenotype depends in part on its genotype, which is determined when male and female gametes (sperm and egg cells) combine in sexual reproduction. The fertilized egg, called a *zygote*, receives a diploid number of chromosomes.

Haploid male gamete (sperm)

Haploid female gamete (egg)

Diploid zygote (fertilized egg)

The rearrangement of genes during sexual reproduction gives organisms combinations of genes that differ from those of their parents. Each human gamete has 23 chromosomes, containing a total of more than 20,000 genes. These genes are shuffled during meiosis I through crossing-over and independent assortment. The number of possible gene combinations is many times greater than the number of humans who have ever lived. This huge variety of possible combinations helps account for the diversity of traits.

Genes themselves also have many variant forms. In a population, there are usually slightly different versions of each gene. For example, two versions may differ by a single nucleotide. These differences may have large, small, or no effects on the organisms that carry them. **Genetic variation** is the range of different phenotypes in a population due to differences in genes.

Gene Expression

The zygote, or fertilized egg, goes through many rounds of mitosis. Eventually, it develops into a multicellular organism with many specialized somatic cells, tissues, and organs. **Specialization** is the process by which cells take on specific structures and functions, making them different from other somatic cells in the same organism. For example, the cells that make up the human brain have a different shape and function from the cells that make up the human heart. However, mitosis produces genetically identical cells. How can cells become specialized if they have the same genes? Different genes are expressed, or turned on, in each cell. Differences in gene expression lead to specialization of somatic cells in multicellular organisms. **Gene expression** is the process by which the information carried by genes is used to synthesize proteins (or noncoding RNA).

Discussion Question

How are meiosis I and meiosis II different? How are they similar?

Lesson Review

1. A normal cell from the lung of an organism contains 52 chromosomes. What is the haploid chromosome number for this species?

   A. 13

   B. 26

   C. 52

   D. 104

2. Which stage of meiosis is shown in the diagram?

   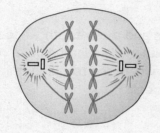

   A. prophase I

   B. anaphase I

   C. telophase II

   D. metaphase II

3. Which of the following describes one difference between meiosis and mitosis?

   A. Mitosis produces gametes, while meiosis produces somatic cells.

   B. Mitosis produces haploid cells, while meiosis produces diploid cells.

   C. Mitosis produces genetically identical cells, while meiosis produces genetically different cells.

   D. In mitosis, homologous pairs of chromosomes line up and separate, while in meiosis only sister chromatids separate.

4. Which process causes changes within chromosomes?

   A. independent assortment

   B. DNA replication

   C. crossing-over

   D. gene expression

Patterns of Inheritance

> **Key Words** • incomplete dominance • codominance • multiple alleles • sex chromosome • autosome
> • sex-linked • carrier • polygenic trait • linked genes

Getting the Idea

Mendel's laws of inheritance describe how simple traits, each determined by one pair of alleles, are inherited. However, not all traits follow Mendel's laws and observations. In this lesson, you will learn about some non-Mendelian patterns of inheritance.

Intermediate Traits

A cross between a snapdragon plant with red flowers and a plant with white flowers produces offspring with pink flowers. In this case, neither allele is dominant over the other. This is known as **incomplete dominance**, where the resulting trait in the offspring is a blend of the phenotypes seen in the parents.

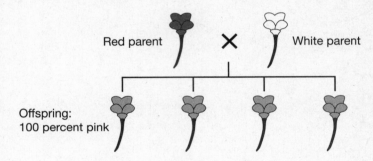

Red parent ✕ White parent

Offspring: 100 percent pink

Other organisms exhibit **codominance**, a condition in which both alleles are expressed in the same organism. Some chickens exhibit codominance regarding feather color. Mendel would have expected the heterozygous offspring of a black-feathered rooster and a white-feathered hen to be either black or white. Actually, the offspring have both black feathers and white feathers. In codominance, both alleles are expressed equally. This is different from incomplete dominance, which results in a new phenotype that is a blend of the two (such as gray feathers).

Some traits are determined by more than just two alleles—they are determined by **multiple alleles**. Although each organism has only two alleles for the trait, three or more alleles exist in the population. Human ABO blood types are an example of a trait with multiple alleles. A person's blood type can be A, B, AB, or O. Each individual can inherit two of three possible alleles: *A*, *B*, and *O*. Two of these alleles, *A* and *B*, are codominant. *A* and *B* are both dominant to *O*.

A cross between parents with blood types A and AB is shown below.

		AB parent: *A*	AB parent: *B*
A parent	*A*	*AA* **A type**	*AB* **AB type**
	O	*OA* **A type**	*OB* **B type**

Sex-Linked Traits

In humans and other mammals, **sex chromosomes** determine the sex of an organism. The sex chromosomes are the X and Y chromosomes. Females usually have two X chromosomes (XX), and males usually have one X and one Y chromosome (XY). Humans have two sex chromosomes and 22 pairs of non-sex-determining chromosomes, called **autosomes**.

	X	*Y*
X	*XX*	*XY*
X	*XX*	*XY*

A mammal receives an X chromosome from its mother and either an X or a Y chromosome from its father. The Punnett square of the cross of a male and a female shows the probability of male or female offspring to be 1:1, or 50 percent for each. The X chromosome carries genes for other traits in addition to sex. A trait determined by a gene on the X chromosome is called **sex-linked**. The Y chromosome has very few genes.

Red-green color blindness is an example of a recessive trait carried on the X chromosome. An affected person cannot distinguish between the colors red and green. A female will be color blind only if she has two copies of the recessive gene for color blindness. A male, who has only one X chromosome, will be color blind if he inherits one allele for the trait. The cross between a heterozygous female and a color-blind male is shown below. In this Punnett square, the X chromosomes have a *C* to indicate the dominant gene for regular color vision and a *c* to indicate the recessive gene for color blindness.

	X^c	Y
X^C	X^CX^c	X^CY
X^c	X^cX^c	X^cY

Recessive sex-linked traits appear most often in males. This is because a male receives only one X chromosome, from his mother. The Y chromosome inherited from his father does not have a matching allele for traits on the X chromosome. Therefore, a single recessive gene will produce the sex-linked trait in a male. A female will show the sex-linked recessive trait only if she inherits the recessive gene from both of her parents. A heterozygous individual with a single recessive gene is called a **carrier**.

Polygenic Traits and Environmental Influences

Most traits are **polygenic traits**, meaning they are controlled by two or more genes. Polygenic traits are usually continuous, meaning they can have any value in a range. Examples of polygenic traits in humans are eye color and skin color. At least three genes interact to produce a wide range of eye colors in humans. More than four genes control skin color in humans, leading to a wide range of variation in this trait.

Many inherited traits are affected by an organism's environment. For example, human height is the result not only of interacting genes but also of childhood diet. Weight is affected by diet and exercise as well as by genes.

Gene Linkage

Mendel discovered the law of independent assortment because the genes he studied are on different chromosomes in pea plants. When gametes form, these genes separate independently of each other. Genes that are far apart on the same chromosome can also be inherited independently because of crossing-over. However, crossing-over occurs less often between genes located closer together.

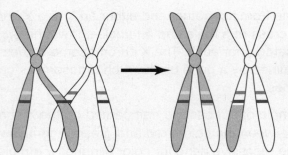

Crossing-over did not separate or "shuffle" the alleles of these genes.

Genes that are located close together on the same chromosome tend to be inherited together. Such genes are called **linked genes**. Linked genes do not usually follow the law of independent assortment. Crossing-over occurs less often between linked genes than unlinked genes, but it does sometimes occur between them.

Discussion Question

How do the inheritance patterns Mendel observed in pea plants differ from each form of inheritance discussed in this lesson?

Lesson Review

1. Which of the following statements about sex-linked traits is true?

    A. The Y chromosome carries many genes.

    B. The X chromosome has very few genes for traits other than sex.

    C. Sex-linked traits are caused by genes located on the Y chromosome.

    D. Recessive sex-linked traits appear more often in males than in females.

2. The colors of human hair and eyes are controlled by two or more genes. Which term describes this type of inheritance?

    A. codominance   **C.** polygenic traits

    B. multiple alleles   **D.** incomplete dominance

3. Cats that have completely white fur are more likely to be deaf than cats with other fur colors. Which of the following **best** explains this?

    A. linked genes   **C.** polygenic traits

    B. multiple alleles   **D.** sex-linked traits

4. Which of the following describes how incomplete dominance differs from codominance?

    A. In incomplete dominance, more than two genes influence a trait.

    B. In incomplete dominance, the traits of both parents are expressed.

    C. In incomplete dominance, more than one trait is affected by a single gene.

    D. In incomplete dominance, the offspring has a different trait from either parent.

5. Red-green color blindness is a sex-linked recessive trait. A man who has red-green color blindness has children with a woman who has normal color vision and is not a carrier. What is true about their children?

    A. All the sons have red-green color blindness.

    B. All the daughters are carriers for the color-blindness allele.

    C. Sons have a 50-percent chance of inheriting red-green color blindness.

    D. Daughters have a 50-percent chance of inheriting red-green color blindness.

Chapter 6 Review

Geneticists use gene linkage to determine the distances between genes located on the same chromosome. A *haplotype* refers to the combination of alleles of genes located on a single chromosome. Haplotypes can be either *parental*, meaning that they consist of the same allele combination as in the parent, or *recombinant*, meaning that they resulted from a recombination event between the parent's chromosomes. The frequency of recombinant haplotypes in the offspring is a measure of the recombination events that occurred between the genes.

In *Drosophila melanogaster*, the fruit fly, the genes for body color (black vs. gray) and wing shape (normal vs. vestigial) are located on the same chromosome. Let the letters C and c represent the alleles for body color, and W and w represent the alleles for wing shape. Geneticists performed a cross between a parent with normal wings and a gray body and a parent with vestigial wings and a black body. All of the resulting F_1 generation expressed normal wing shape and gray body color.

The geneticists then performed a cross between F_1 flies and test cross flies with the black body and vestigial wing phenotype (Figure 1). The resulting phenotypes for 1000 offspring resulting from this cross are given in Table 1. The distance between two genes is equal to the percentage of crossover events between the genes, which are indicated by recombinant phenotypes. This distance is expressed in units of centimorgans (cM), named after a scientist who made important contributions to the field of genetics.

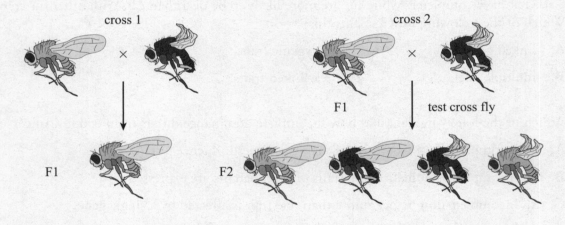

Figure 1

Table 1				
Number	415	405	92	88
Body color	gray	black	black	gray
Wing shape	normal	vestigial	normal	vestigial

1. According to Figure 1, which phenotypes require two recessive alleles?

   A. Gray body color and normal wings
   B. Gray body color and vestigial wings
   C. Black body color and normal wings
   D. Black body color and vestigial wings

2. Which of the following represents the haplotypes of the F_1 flies?

   F.
   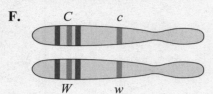

   G.
   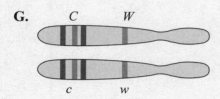

   H.
   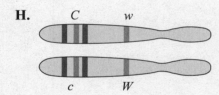

   J.
   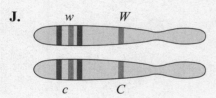

3. When did the crossover event that led to the recombinant haplotypes in the F_2 generation occur?

   A. During the formation of the gametes of the F_1 flies
   B. During the formation of the gametes of the F_2 flies
   C. During fertilization between the F_1 fly and the test cross fly
   D. During the formation of the gametes of the original parent flies

4. How do the results in Table 1 violate Mendel's law of independent assortment?

   F. There are many more dominant phenotypes than recessive phenotypes.
   G. There are many more recessive phenotypes than dominant phenotypes.
   H. There are many more parental phenotypes than recombinant phenotypes.
   J. There are many more recombinant phenotypes than parental phenotypes.

5. According to the information in the passage and Table 1, what is the distance between the body color and wing shape genes?

   A. 8.8 cM
   B. 9.2 cM
   C. 18.0 cM
   D. 49.3 cM

Chapter 7

Evolution and Classification

Natural Selection

Key Words • species • evolution • natural selection • adaptation • phenotype • fitness • gene pool

Getting the Idea

A **species** is a group of similar organisms that can breed and produce fertile offspring. The species that exist on Earth today are not the same species that existed 100 million, 10 million, or even 1 million years ago. In 1859, Charles Darwin, a British naturalist, published *On the Origin of Species by Means of Natural Selection*. In his book, Darwin proposed an explanation of how species change.

Natural Selection

The change in species over time, from the earliest forms of life to the wide range of organisms that exist today, is called **evolution**. Scientists today think that evolution has occurred at least partly through natural selection. **Natural selection** is the process by which organisms with favorable variations for their environment survive and reproduce, passing those variations on to the next generation.

Any organism must obtain resources from its environment to survive. Traits that increase an organism's chance of survival tend to become more common in a population. Such a feature is called an **adaptation**. Adaptations can be structural (related to an organism's form), functional (related to the way its body works), or behavioral. Darwin discovered the finches shown below during his voyage to the Galápagos Islands. The birds developed from a species that came to the islands from South America. The differences in their beak shapes show how they became adapted to the food sources available on each island.

| Leaves | Seeds | Fruit | Insects | Grubs |

Beak shapes in Galápagos Islands finches vary according to the type of food the finches eat.

How Natural Selection Works

Four key principles of natural selection include overproduction of offspring, competition for limited resources, variation, and differences in fitness.

Overproduction of Offspring

An oak tree produces thousands of acorns in its lifetime, and a spider may lay hundreds of eggs at a time. However, not all of these offspring survive to adulthood. Most are consumed by predators or do not manage to find a suitable place to grow. Relatively few survive to reproduce. Almost all organisms produce more offspring than can grow to adulthood.

Limited Resources in the Environment

The amount of space, food, water, shelter, and other resources in nature is limited. Organisms that share an environment must compete for these resources.

Variation within a Population

A *population* consists of the members of a single species that share an environment. Organisms in a population differ from each other in how well they can obtain resources from the environment and avoid *predation*, or the preying of one animal on others. Some of the variation is genetic variation, which is inherited, while some is due to affects of the environment.

Differences in Fitness

Recall that a **phenotype** is the form of a trait that an organism displays. Some phenotypes are better than others at helping an organism get resources and survive in its environment. If a phenotype that makes an organism successful results from its genes, the variation can be passed on to offspring. Organisms with traits better suited to their environment tend to produce more offspring than do other organisms in the same population. The ability of an organism to survive and reproduce in its environment is called its **fitness**. Traits that increase an organism's fitness are more likely to be passed on to the next generation. In this way, the traits of a population may change as the environment changes.

Natural Selection and Genes

Natural selection depends on variation in phenotypes. It acts on phenotype, not genotype. However, phenotype is the result of genotype, as you learned in Lesson 32. Traits are determined, at least partly, by genes. Therefore, natural selection can change the gene pool of a population.

A population's **gene pool** includes all the alleles carried by members of the population, whether or not the alleles are expressed. Suppose that an allele, t, results in a helpful trait that allows the organism to better survive in its environment. This organism will be more likely to have offspring, and those offspring are more likely to inherit the helpful allele. Over time, the allele becomes more common, while other alleles (such as T) become less common. In this way, natural selection changes the population's gene pool.

In order for natural selection to work, there must be genetic variation in a population. Suppose there is only one allele T for a gene, so that each individual has the genotype TT. Natural selection cannot act on this gene because there is no variation to select. Recall from Lesson 33 that meiosis and sexual reproduction increase genetic variation. When gametes form, variation arises from independent assortment and crossing-over. Some variations also arise from mutations, or changes in DNA. A variety of genotypes and phenotypes in a population makes it more likely that some members of the population will survive and reproduce in a variety of different environmental conditions.

Examples of Natural Selection

Pesticide resistance is an example of natural selection. People have developed chemicals called pesticides to kill insects. *Resistance* is an organism's ability to withstand a harmful agent. Occasionally, some insects in a population have an allele that enables them to survive a pesticide. Because these organisms have greater fitness, they pass the allele that makes them pesticide-resistant to the next generation of insects. Over several generations, this trait can spread to many or all members of the insect population.

Many adaptations relate to finding food, escaping predators, and reproducing in specific environments. For example, the light-colored beetles below are spotted by predators more easily against the dark background. Because the dark phenotype helps beetles survive and reproduce in this environment, the allele for dark color passes to the next generation more often.

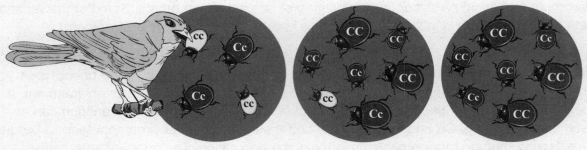

First generation   Second generation   Third generation

Natural selection does not eliminate every harmful allele from a population. Consider the allele that causes sickle-cell anemia, a disorder in which red blood cells are misshapen. People with two alleles for the sickle-cell gene (SS) experience pain, fatigue, and a shorter life span. Heterozygous people (AS) experience few symptoms, but they are less likely to be infected with malaria, a deadly disease. The sickle-cell allele is commonly found in populations that live where malaria is a problem. Although an allele may be harmful or lethal, it can persist in a population because heterozygous individuals are either more fit or not harmed by it.

Discussion Question

Fitness depends on an organism's environment. Give an example of a trait that would be favorable in one environment and unfavorable in another. How would natural selection affect the frequency of this trait if the environment changed?

Lesson Review

1. Which of these is **not** a principle of natural selection?

   A. More offspring are produced than will survive to reproduce.

   B. A phenotype that increases an organism's fitness tends to occur more frequently in subsequent generations.

   C. Organisms must compete for resources in their environment.

   D. Species with less variety are more likely to survive environmental change.

2. Which is the **best** definition of fitness?

   A. the ability to inherit dominant alleles

   B. the ability to pass on traits to offspring

   C. the ability to survive in an environment

3. A farmer plants a field of true-breeding corn plants. The plants are genetically very similar. What is a disadvantage of this similarity?

   A. The plants cannot pass on their traits to the next generation.

   B. The plants' phenotypes will be influenced by the environment.

   C. The plants are less likely to survive a change in the environment.

   D. The plants are more likely to develop a gene pool with recessive traits.

4. A disorder causes members of a mammal species to die soon after birth. The disorder is caused by inheriting two matching alleles for the disorder. What is **likely** to happen to this allele over time?

   A. It will disappear from the population because it decreases fitness.

   B. It will persist at the same frequency because natural selection cannot act on it.

   C. It will increase in the population because it allows parents to have more offspring.

   D. It will remain in the population because heterozygous individuals are not affected.

Fossils and Speciation

Key Words • fossil • radioisotope dating • relative dating • extinction • mass extinction • biodiversity • speciation • gene flow • geographic isolation • reproductive isolation • adaptive radiation • gradualism • punctuated equilibrium

Getting the Idea

Natural selection explains how populations and species can change over time. What has happened to species that once existed? How do new species come about? This lesson explains how species die out and new species form.

Fossil Evidence of Evolution

Much of the evidence for changes in life on Earth comes from **fossils**, the preserved remains or traces of organisms that lived in the past. Fossils also provide clues about when different species lived. Scientists can estimate the age of a fossil through radioisotope dating or through relative dating. **Radioisotope dating** measures the age of a fossil (or the surrounding material) by measuring the amount of a radioactive isotope present in the material. That amount is compared with the amount of the isotope's decay product or with the amount of a stable isotope of the same element. (Radioactive decay is discussed in Lesson 7.) The decay process happens at predictable rates, so radioisotope dating allows scientists to determine age within a certain number of years. Uranium-235 and carbon-14 are two commonly used isotopes.

Relative dating is another, less exact method for determining when a fossil organism formed. This method identifies the age of a fossil by comparing it to other fossils. Earth's surface consists of layers of different types of rock. In undisturbed layers, the newest layer is the one closet to the surface, while older rock layers are deeper. Scientists can compare the rock layers with the fossils they contain to determine the approximate age of a fossil. For example, the diagram below shows fossils in undisturbed layers of sedimentary rock. The fossil shown in Layer B of the illustration is older than the rocks and fossils in the shallower rock layers (C and D), and younger than the rocks and fossils below it (Layer A). Other fossils found elsewhere in Layer B are about the same age.

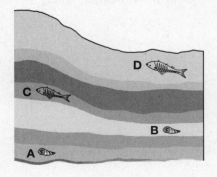

Loss of Species through Extinction

Species that cannot adapt to a changing environment may die out, or become extinct. **Extinction** is the permanent loss of a species. Some scientists estimate that as many as 99.9 percent of all species that have ever lived on Earth are now extinct. Although extinction is the end of the existence of a species, it is an important part of evolution.

A **mass extinction** is the extinction of very large numbers of species in a fairly short period. The fossil record shows that Earth's history has undergone several mass extinctions. At the end of the Permian period, about 250 million years ago, about 96 percent of all ocean invertebrates became extinct. Fossils of these animals do not appear in rock younger than this. Another mass extinction marked the end of the Cretaceous period, about 56 million years ago, when between 60 and 75 percent of ocean species became extinct. Dinosaurs, the dominant land animals, also became extinct during this period.

Biodiversity and Speciation

Although mass extinctions can be extremely destructive, in the long term they help increase Earth's biodiversity. **Biodiversity** is the variety of organisms living on Earth or in a specific area, as indicated by the number of species. The extinction of many species at the same time makes it possible for new species to develop and thrive. For example, the extinction of the dinosaurs allowed mammal species to flourish and diversify. The formation of one or more new species from an existing species is called **speciation**. According to the fossil record, there are periods in which a lot of speciation occurs, and others in which it is relatively rare.

Recall that a species is a group of organisms that can breed and produce fertile offspring. A new species can form when one population is isolated in some way from the rest of the species. Each population has its own gene pool, or set of alleles. **Gene flow**, the exchange of alleles between gene pools, occurs when members of different populations breed and produce offspring. A population becomes isolated when gene flow between it and other populations is blocked. The population's gene pool can change independently of the rest of the species, making the population different. Eventually, the differences can prevent organisms from being able to breed with members outside the population.

One type of isolation is **geographic isolation**, meaning that a physical barrier prevents members of a population from breeding with individuals outside the population. Physical barriers can result from natural changes to the land, such as earthquakes or flooding, or from changes caused by humans, such as building a highway through an area.

A second type of isolation is **reproductive isolation**. This happens when some members of a population do not breed with other members. For example, frogs breed at a certain time each year. If some members of a frog population breed earlier than usual each year, they prevent gene flow outside this early-breeding group. Eventually, the early breeders may form a new species. Or consider an insect species that breeds and lays eggs on a particular tree species. If some of the insects begin to breed on a different species of tree, they will form a distinct breeding population. Reproductive isolation happens as a result of geographic isolation, but it can also occur in organisms inhabiting the same area.

Speciation events can result from the extinction of competing species or from the sudden availability of new food sources and habitats. For example, recall that the extinction of dinosaurs allowed mammal species to diversify. Different mammal populations adapted in different ways to this change, and the number of mammal species increased rapidly. The evolution of many new species from a single ancestor is called an **adaptive radiation**. In the Galápagos Islands visited by Darwin, many species of finches formed after a few members of one species arrived on the islands from the mainland. The new environments, along with the geographic isolation of each island, allowed the adaptive radiation of the original finch species into the multiple species found there today.

Changes in Species

Organizing similar fossils by age helps scientists understand how species have changed through time. Although only some species form fossils, scientists have found some *transition fossils* that show the changes in traits as species evolve. One group of organisms for which transition fossils are known is whales. Modern whales live in the ocean, but their history goes back to hoofed mammals that lived on land. Fossils show that the ancestors of whales walked on land and could also swim. Later fossils suggest that over time, the hind limbs of the whales' ancestors shrank. Their forelimbs became flippers, and they evolved a powerful tail-like fluke.

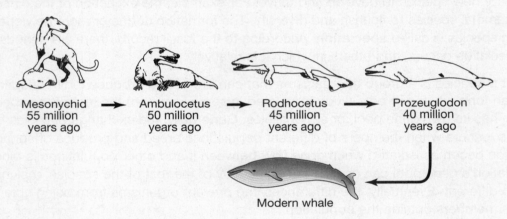

Mesonychid
55 million
years ago

Ambulocetus
50 million
years ago

Rodhocetus
45 million
years ago

Prozeuglodon
40 million
years ago

Modern whale

The illustration shows one possible sequence of stages in the evolution of modern whales. However, it is important to understand that species do not just form, one from another, in a straight line. The pattern of speciation is more like a branching tree. Millions of species that exist today are descended from one ancestral species. In the next lesson, you will learn more about how organisms are related to each other.

Rates of Evolution

There are two main views about the rate of evolution: gradualism and punctuated equilibrium. **Gradualism** is the idea that evolutionary change occurs slowly and steadily over a long period of time. This is how Darwin thought natural selection worked. In contrast, **punctuated equilibrium** states that evolution occurs in spurts. A period of rapid speciation will be followed by a long period of little or no change. The periods of rapid change may occur because of drastic, sudden changes in the environment.

Discussion Question

Why is it difficult to tell whether a fossil is the direct ancestor of a living organism?

Lesson Review

1. Which of these can scientists learn from relative dating of fossils?

    A. the exact age of a fossil

    B. the age of an organism when it died

    C. the age of a fossil compared to that of another fossil

    D. the exact age of a rock layer

2. How does isolation lead to a population becoming a new species?

    A. It increases gene flow in and out of the population.

    B. It decreases gene flow in and out of the population.

    C. It increases the genetic variation within the population.

    D. It decreases the genetic variation within the population.

3. How can mass extinction lead to an increase in biodiversity?

    A. It can prevent the flow of alleles between different species.

    B. It can allow surviving species to undergo adaptive radiations.

    C. It can increase gene flow between populations of surviving species.

    D. It can reduce the ways that species can adapt and survive in the environment.

4. Which of the following involves periods of rapid speciation and periods of relatively little change in species?

    A. gradualism

    B. mass extinction

    C. reproductive isolation

    D. punctuated equilibrium

Classifying Organisms

Key Words • taxonomy • kingdom • model • phylum • class • order • family • genus • species • binomial nomenclature • cladogram • dichotomous key

Getting the Idea

Earth is home to millions of different kinds of organisms. To aid in understanding and organizing information about all these life forms, scientists have devised systems for classifying them. **Taxonomy** is the field of biology that deals with classifying organisms. Modern taxonomists classify organisms by the ways in which they are related to each other through evolution.

The Five-kingdom and Six-kingdom Systems

The largest taxonomic groups are called *domains*. They include Bacteria and Archaea (prokaryotes) and Eukarya (eukaryotes). The next level down is the **kingdom**. The *five-kingdom system* recognizes the kingdoms Animalia, Plantae, Fungi, and Protista, all of which are eukaryotic. The fifth kingdom is Monera, which includes prokaryotes (bacteria and archaea). Recall from Lesson 26 that prokaryotic cells are smaller and simpler than eukaryotic cells, which contain a nucleus and membrane-bound organelles.

Five-kingdom System					
Animalia	Plantae	Fungi	Protista	Monera	
Eukaryotic, multicellular consumers; specialized cells and tissues	Eukaryotic, multicellular, photosynthetic; cells have walls made of cellulose	Eukaryotic, uni- and multicellular; cells have walls made of chitin	Eukaryotic, uni- and multicellular; includes algae (photosynthetic) and consumers	Unicellular prokaryotes, no nucleus, aerobic and anaerobic; have cell walls	
				Bacteria	Archaea; some are extremophiles
Animalia	Plantae	Fungi	Protista	Eubacteria	Archaebacteria
Six-kingdom System					

The *six-kingdom system* keeps the four eukaryotic kingdoms, but divides Monera into the kingdoms Eubacteria and Archaebacteria. This system highlights the differences between bacteria and archaea. The cell walls and cell membranes of archaea are different from those of bacteria. Also, archaea share some similarities with eukaryotes, such as chromosomal DNA wrapped around proteins. The kingdom Eubacteria includes the *Escherichia coli* species, which lives in the large intestine and helps in digestion, as well as the disease-causing *Mycobacterium tuberculosis*. The kingdom Archaebacteria includes *extremophiles*, or organisms that live in extreme environments. The organisms that give hot springs their bright colors are archaea.

These classification systems are competing **models**, or simplified representations of the natural world. Models change over time as new evidence is discovered and scientists debate how it should be treated. Scientific ideas are always changing based on new evidence and discoveries. Most scientists today prefer the six-kingdom model because it reflects recent discoveries about archaea.

Categories of Classification

Within each kingdom are six major levels of classification: phylum, class, order, family, genus, and species. As you move from the top to the bottom of this hierarchy, groups at each level become smaller and include organisms that are more closely related. As shown in the diagram, each type of organism within a kingdom is placed in a smaller and more specific group called a **phylum** (plural: *phyla*). Members of each phylum are then divided into different classes, such as birds or mammals. A **class** is made up of different orders. An **order** consists of similar families. Each **family** contains at least one genus (plural: *genera*). Each **genus** is then divided into species. A **species** is a group of similar organisms that can breed to produce fertile offspring. It is the smallest and most specific category.

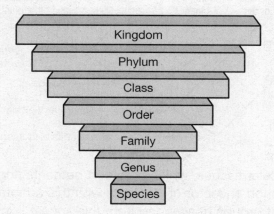

Species are named according to a system called **binomial nomenclature** because it gives each species a two-part name, such as *Felis domesticus* for house cats. The first part of the name identifies the genus to which the species belongs (*Felis*) and is always capitalized. The second part of the name identifies the species within that genus and begins with a lowercase letter. Species are identified by both names because the second part of the name may be used for more than one species. For example, the domestic pig is *Sus domesticus*. An organism's scientific name is the same in both the five- and six-kingdom systems.

Cladograms and Evolutionary Relationships

Taxonomists do not base classifications on physical similarities alone. Instead, they look for evolutionary relationships. Evolution is also called *descent with modification* because species descend from ancestors that were different. All organisms on Earth are related to each other in some way. To determine how closely, taxonomists look at similarities in physical structure, development, DNA sequences, and proteins. Taxonomists use this information to place organisms in groups that reflect their evolutionary history.

A **cladogram** is a diagram that shows evolutionary relationships. Each line or branch shows where a group of organisms, called a *clade*, descended from a common ancestor. All the descendents of that ancestor share one or more important adaptations. Organisms that are more distantly related branched from a common ancestor farther back in time, toward the bottom of a cladogram. More closely related organisms share a common ancestor more recently. Their lines branch off closer to the top of the cladogram.

The diagram below is a cladogram of the plant kingdom. All plants have specialized cells and tissues, meaning that they descended from an ancestor with this trait. This trait is shown where mosses and liverworts branch off from the line leading to all other plants.

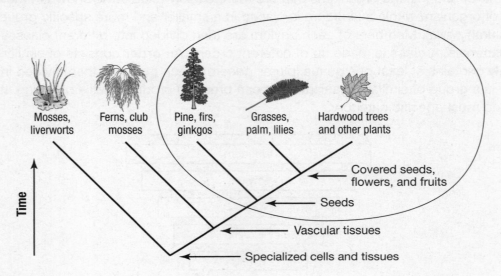

Only some plants have vascular tissues, which transport nutrients and allow plants to grow tall. An arrow points to the common ancestor of all plants with this adaptation. Later, seeds evolved in a vascular plant. The plant groups descended from this ancestor (circled) all produce seeds.

Using a Dichotomous Key

When scientists encounter an organism in nature, they try to identify the species it belongs to. A **dichotomous key** is a tool that helps them do this. It consists of pairs of statements. Based on observations, a scientist chooses one of the statements in the first pair. Each statement leads either to the species name or to another pair of statements.

A simple dichotomous key that can be used to classify wild cats is shown below.

Dichotomous Key: Types of Wild Cats

1. a. solid coat b. coat not solid	Go to 2. Go to 3.
2. a. smooth coat, long tail, no mane b. smooth coat with mane	*Puma concolor* *Panthera leo*
3. a. striped b. spotted	*Panthera tigris* *Acinoryx jubatus*

Discussion Question

According to the cladogram in the lesson, which plants are nonvascular (lack vascular tissue)? Seedless? Produce seeds but do not produce fruits or flowers? According to the dichotomous key, what type of cat is shown in the illustration?

Lesson Review

1. Which of the following groups includes organisms that are the most genetically similar?

    A. class

    B. order

    C. genus

    D. phylum

2. According to the dichotomous key, which type of insect is shown?

1. a. has one pair of wings b. has two pairs of wings	Go to 2. Go to 3.
2. a. wings vertical at rest b. wings horizontal at rest	*Mayfly* *Mosquito*
3. a. front wings shaped like the back wings b. front wings not shaped like the back wings	Go to 4. Go to 5.
4. a. wings covered with scales b. wings not covered with scales	*Moth* *Cicada*
5. a. abdomen with two tail-like projections b. abdomen without two tail-like projections	*Stonefly* *Termite*

    A. mayfly   **C.** stonefly

    B. termite   **D.** mosquito

3. According to the cladogram below, which letter represents the most recent ancestor shared by Species 1 and Species 3?

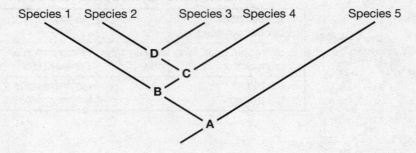

A. A

B. B

C. C

D. D

4. A unicellular organism lives in an environment that lacks oxygen. It does not have a nucleus or membrane-bound organelles, but it does have a cell wall. To which kingdom might the organism belong?

A. Fungi

B. Protista

C. Plantae

D. Archaebacteria

Chapter 7 • Lesson 38

Animal Phyla

Key Words • vertebrate • invertebrate • sponge • cnidarian • flatworm • roundworm • annelid • mollusk • arthropod • echinoderm • chordate

Getting the Idea

Dogs, fish, birds, and frogs are all familiar members of the kingdom Animalia. However, Animalia is made up of a great variety of organisms, including species that do not move at all.

Taxonomy of Kingdom Animalia

The organisms shown on the right side of the cladogram below make up only a small part of the animal kingdom. Fish, birds, amphibians, reptiles, and mammals (including humans) are all **vertebrates**, animals with a nerve cord surrounded by bony vertebrae. In contrast, most animal phyla are made up of organisms that lack these structures. They are called **invertebrates**. The cladogram below shows evolutionary relationships among some major groups in the animal kingdom. Refer to the cladogram as each animal group is described in more detail.

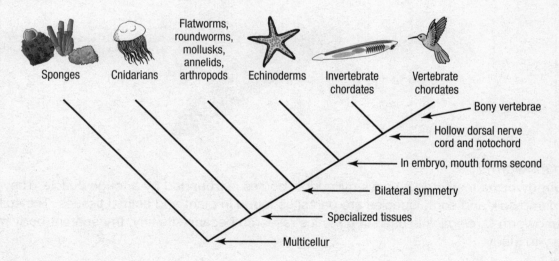

Sponges

Sponges, which make up the phylum Porifera, are the simplest animals. Sponges do not move but live attached to a surface. They filter food from the water in which they live. Sponges have specialized cells but not specialized tissues. All the tissues that make up a sponge are the same. The bodies of sponges have many shapes and are asymmetrical.

Cnidarians

Cnidarians are among the animals with specialized tissues and include jellyfish, sea anemones, corals, and hydras, some of which are shown below. Cnidarians have radial symmetry, like the spokes of a wheel. The basic body plan of a cnidarian includes a gut cavity surrounded by a ring of tentacles. In some organisms, such as jellyfish and anemones, the tentacles are capable of stinging. Cnidarians have specialized tissues but not organs.

Flatworms, Roundworms, Annelids, Mollusks, and Arthropods

Many groups of invertebrates have bilateral symmetry—that is, one side of their bodies mirrors the other side. These groups include flatworms, roundworms, annelids, mollusks, and arthropods.

Flatworms

Flatworms (platyhelminths) have flat bodies, which allow them to exchange oxygen and carbon dioxide with the environment without specialized organs. Flatworms include species that live in water or damp habitats, as well as parasites such as tapeworms.

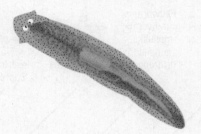

Roundworms

Roundworms (nematodes) have cylindrical bodies surrounded by a tough cuticle. They live in damp soil, and some species are parasites found in plant and animal tissues. The soil roundworm *C. elegans* is used in genetics research because its tiny, transparent body makes it easy to study.

Segmented Worms

Annelids (segmented worms) have cylindrical bodies divided into numerous similar regions, or segments. Annelid worms have organs organized into organ systems. Earthworms and leeches are examples of annelid worms.

Mollusks

The **mollusk** phylum includes oysters, clams, snails, slugs, octopuses, and squid. All mollusks, except land-dwelling snails and slugs, live in watery habitats. Mollusks have soft bodies, and many are protected by a hard shell made of calcium. The body plan of mollusks includes a *head-foot*, which contains sense organs and muscles for movement; a *visceral mass*, which contains most of the internal organs; and a *mantle* that (in some species) secretes the hard shell. Some mollusks have eyes.

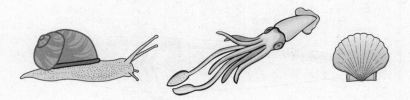

Arthropods

Arthropods include crustaceans, insects, and spiders. Arthropod bodies are segmented, or divided into sections. They have jointed appendages (such as legs and mouthparts) and a hard covering called an exoskeleton. The phylum Arthropoda includes more species than any other animal phylum. In fact, some scientists estimate that arthropods make up more than 80 percent of all living animal species.

Echinoderms, Chordates, and Vertebrates

It might seem unusual that vertebrates, such as humans, are more closely related to echinoderms (sea stars) than to insects or octopuses. **Echinoderms** include sea stars, sea urchins, sand dollars, and sea cucumbers. These organisms have body plans consisting of five symmetrical parts that radiate out from the center. Echinoderms move using tiny, fluid-filled "tube feet." As larvae (an early stage in development), echinoderms are bilaterally symmetrical, with a right side that is a mirror image of the left.

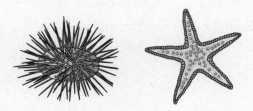

Echinoderm and chordate species all share an ancestor with a specific pattern of development in the embryo stage.

Chordates are animals with a hollow nerve cord along the dorsal, or upper, side and a long, flexible rod, called a *notochord*, just below the nerve cord. Chordates consist of both the vertebrates and *invertebrate chordates*, including tunicates and lancelets. Adult tunicates are cylindrical, nonmoving filter feeders with simple digestive systems. As larvae, tunicates can swim. Tunicate larvae resemble lancelets, which are rod-shaped filter feeders that are able to swim. Adult lancelets keep their body plan but bury themselves in the sand to feed. A lancelet is shown below.

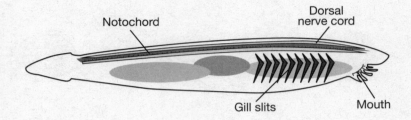

Vertebrates are chordates that have evolved a nerve cord (spinal cord) surrounded and protected by bony vertebrae. At some point in development, all chordates have a hollow nerve cord and a notochord. In vertebrates, the flexible notochord forms the disks between the vertebrae, providing cushioning for the spine. Vertebrates include fish, amphibians, reptiles, birds, and mammals.

Discussion Question

How many times did a body plan with a head and eyes evolve in the animal kingdom? Use the information in the cladogram and in the text to answer this question.

Lesson Review

1. Which phylum includes both lobsters and tarantulas?

A. mollusks

B. chordates

C. cnidarians

D. arthropods

2. Which of these are asymmetrical animals that live attached to surfaces and filter food from water?

   A. sponges

   B. cnidarians

   C. annelids

   D. echinoderms

3. Which animal phylum includes organisms with bodies protected by a cuticle?

   A. chordates

   B. arthropods

   C. echinoderms

   D. roundworms

4. To which animal grouping do snakes belong?

   A. mollusks

   B. arthropods

   C. vertebrates

   D. invertebrate chordates

Chapter 7 Review

The recent sequencing of the genome of the duck-billed platypus has provided evolutionary biologists with insights into the relationship of this lineage to marsupial and eutherian (placental) mammals. The platypus and the echidna, also known as a spiny anteater, are monotremes, a small group of mammals with unusual characteristics, such as egg-laying. Marsupials, such as the kangaroo and wallaby, are best known for nursing their young for prolonged periods in a pouch at the front of the body. Eutherians, such as mice, dogs, and humans, form a placenta during pregnancy. The embryo is nourished through the placenta. Comparisons of morphology (structure) and DNA sequences reveal how these three clades, along with avians (birds), are related (Figure 1). Characteristics of an organism that were present in the most recent common ancestor are considered *ancestral*. Characteristics that were not present in the most recent common ancestor are called *derived*.

The platypus embryo undergoes a type of cell division called meroblastic cleavage, which produces an embryo consisting of a sheet of cells. The cytoplasm of each cell is continuous with the yolk beneath it. In contrast, cleavage in marsupial and eutherian embryos is holoblastic, meaning that the cells divide completely.

Similar to eutherians, the platypus secretes a milky fluid to feed its offspring. Milk consists of a protein called casein. The gene for producing casein is present in marsupials and eutherians, as well as in the platypus. The gene for vitellogenin protein, present in yolk, is found in the monotreme and avian genomes but not in the other groups. Table 1 compares some of the traits and genes found in these groups.

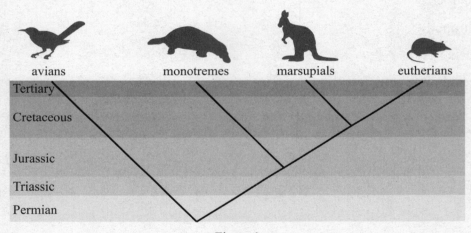

Figure 1

Table 1				
Trait	Avian	Monotreme	Marsupial	Eutherian
Casein gene	N	Y	Y	Y
Amniotic egg	Y	Y	Y	Y
Meroblastic cleavage	Y	Y	N	N
Vitellogenin gene	Y	Y	N	N
Electroreceptors	N	Y	N	N

1. Based on the information provided, in which era did the production of milk containing casein protein evolve?

   A. Jurassic
   B. Tertiary
   C. Permian
   D. Cretaceous

2. According to Figure 1, which groups of organisms most recently shared a common ancestor?

   F. Monotremes and avians
   G. Marsupials and eutherians
   H. Marsupials and monotremes
   J. Eutherians and monotremes

3. The common ancestor of monotremes, marsupials, and eutherians had which of the characteristics listed below?

   I   Casein gene
   II   Meroblastic cleavage
   III Electroreceptors
   IV   Vitellogenin gene

   A. I only
   B. II and IV only
   C. I, II, and III
   D. I, II, and IV

4. According to Table 1, which is an ancestral characteristic of the four groups?

   F. Casein gene
   G. Amniotic egg
   H. Electroreceptors
   J. Holoblastic cleavage

5. Which characteristic of eutherian mammals is derived?

   A. Amniotic egg
   B. Nursing of young
   C. Holoblastic cleavage
   D. Formation of a placenta

Chapter 8

Ecology

Ecosystems

Key Words • ecosystem • producer • consumer • decomposer • food web • ecological succession

Getting the Idea

Life on Earth has many different forms. Each species is adapted to thrive in a particular role in its environment, including in its relationships with other organisms. For example, some species must find organisms to eat and avoid being eaten. Ecology is the study of these interactions.

Food Webs and Ecosystems

An **ecosystem** is made up of all the populations of organisms in an area and their nonliving environment. Some organisms produce useable forms of matter and energy for the ecosystem, other organisms consume it, and still others help to recycle matter so it can be used by other species.

Recall from Lesson 29 that glucose is a basic nutrient used in cellular respiration. **Producers**, also known as *autotrophs*, are organisms that capture energy and store it in the chemical bonds of glucose and other simple molecules, usually through photosynthesis. Producers use these molecules for energy, to build larger bodies (growth), or to store them for later use. The energy in these molecules originated from sunlight, and the matter came from carbon dioxide and water, as well as nutrients in the soil. Plants, some kinds of bacteria, and algae are producers.

Consumers, also known as *heterotrophs*, are organisms that obtain their energy by eating other organisms. When a consumer eats a producer, energy and matter transfer from the producer to the consumer. Consumers are classified into levels. *Primary consumers* eat producers. *Secondary consumers* eat primary consumers, and *tertiary consumers* eat secondary consumers. All animals and many protists are consumers.

Ecosystems also contain **decomposers**, which get energy from organic wastes, such as fallen leaves or dead organisms. To get the energy they need, decomposers break down complex molecules. Fungi, such as mushrooms, and many soil bacteria are decomposers. Decomposers secrete chemicals that break down the food outside their bodies, and then they absorb the nutrients they need. Decomposition returns unused compounds to soil or water, where producers can take in the compounds again.

The path of matter and energy from producer to consumer to decomposer is called a *food chain.* All the interconnected food chains in an ecosystem make up a **food web**, which can be shown in a diagram like the one below. The arrows in the diagram point *from* an organism being consumed or decomposed *toward* the organism that consumes or decomposes it.

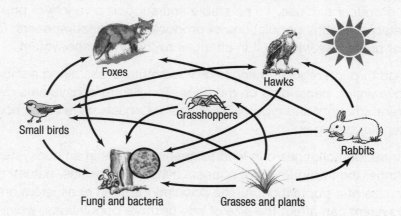

Energy in Ecosystems

The arrows in the food web diagram show the flow of energy through the ecosystem, from one organism to the next. Energy travels in one direction only. Unlike matter, energy does not return to producers once decomposers have used it.

All the energy in the organisms making up an ecosystem comes from the sun. Producers convert this energy to the chemical energy in matter. They use some of it to carry out life processes and store some of it in their bodies. Some energy is lost as heat. Primary consumers then eat the bodies of producers. They, too, use some of the stored energy for life processes, losing some of it as heat. Secondary consumers ingest the bodies of primary consumers, repeating the process. In this way, energy flows to higher levels of an ecosystem, with some getting "lost" when it is converted to heat at each step because of the second law of thermodynamics. Recall the laws of thermodynamics from Lesson 16.

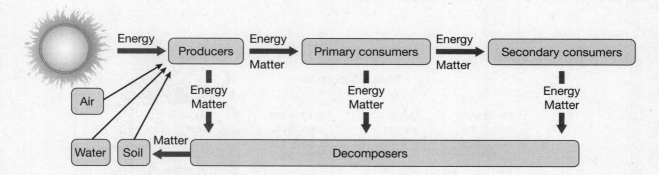

The producers contain most of the matter and energy in an ecosystem. Populations of producers are generally much larger than populations of consumers. Similarly, populations of primary consumers tend to be larger than populations of secondary or higher-order consumers.

Ecosystem Changes

Although an ecosystem can exist without consumers, no ecosystem can survive without producers and decomposers. The simplest food chain is producer → decomposer. The producer captures the energy that drives the system, and the decomposer breaks down wastes into molecules that the producer can use. To be stable and support a variety of populations, an ecosystem needs stable, healthy populations of producers and decomposers. Changes to the numbers or types of producers will result in changes to the entire ecosystem.

Many ecosystems go through regular changes. For example, areas along a shoreline may be under water or above water, depending on the tides. Temperate ecosystems cycle through seasons with different amounts and types of producers. Organisms in these ecosystems are adapted to these regular changes.

In contrast, large or sudden changes can lead to major changes in an ecosystem. These changes include climate change, the introduction of nonnative invasive species, natural disasters, or a large change in the size of a population. All the populations in an ecosystem are interconnected. Changes in an ecosystem can affect the size of one or more populations, which can in turn affect other populations. Many ecosystem changes are the result of human activity, as you will learn in Lesson 41.

Some ecosystem disturbances are dramatic enough that only soil or bare rock is left behind. Some species may be well adapted to the new conditions and will thrive. Other species may be poorly adapted to the new conditions and will decline. Species from nearby communities may move into the area. **Ecological succession** is a natural process in which one community of organisms gradually replaces another after a disturbance. Primary succession happens after an ecosystem is destroyed, leaving only bare rock. A volcanic eruption might cause such a change. Secondary succession happens when the existing soil is not destroyed, such as after a fire, hurricane, or tornado. The first organisms to colonize a bare environment include lichens, fungi, and mosses, which can live on bare rock. These organisms build new soil as they carry out their life processes. When enough soil has been created, small plants such as grasses start to grow. These may allow animals to begin moving into the ecosystem. In time, shrubs and then trees replace the small plants. Eventually, a stable community is created, and succession slows.

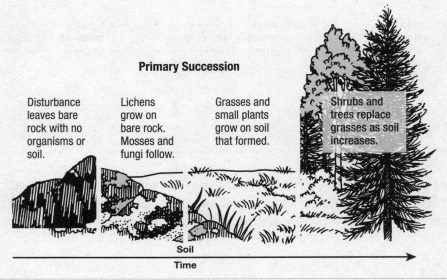

Primary Succession

Disturbance leaves bare rock with no organisms or soil.

Lichens grow on bare rock. Mosses and fungi follow.

Grasses and small plants grow on soil that formed.

Shrubs and trees replace grasses as soil increases.

Soil

Time

Discussion Question

Describe the different forms energy takes as it travels from the sun to producers and consumers. How does the transfer of energy through an ecosystem relate to the first and second laws of thermodynamics?

Lesson Review

1. Which of the following are essential components of any ecosystem?

    A. producers and consumers

    B. producers and decomposers

    C. decomposers and consumers

Use the food web shown below to answer questions 2 and 3.

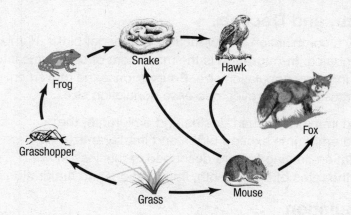

2. Which of these organisms in the food web is a primary consumer?

    A. frog   C. hawk

    B. grass   D. mouse

3. Which population in the food web is **most likely** the smallest?

    A. fox   C. hawk

    B. grass   D. snake

4. What is the role of decomposers in an ecosystem?

    A. Decomposers transfer energy and matter from producers to consumers.

    B. Decomposers recycle energy and matter so that producers can use it.

    C. Decomposers use the energy in dead organisms and return matter to the soil.

    D. Decomposers move unused matter and energy out of the ecosystem.

Population Dynamics

Key Words • population • immigration • emigration • limiting factor • abiotic factor • biotic factor • density-dependent limiting factor • population density • density-independent limiting factor • carrying capacity

Getting the Idea

Ecosystems are made up of nonliving factors in an environment as well as the populations that live in them. A **population** consists of all the organisms of the same species that live in an ecosystem at the same time. Many factors influence the size of populations.

Population Size, Growth, and Decline

Population size is determined by a combination of four factors: number of births, number of deaths, immigration, and emigration. **Immigration** is the movement of organisms into an area. Births and immigration increase population size. **Emigration** is the movement of organisms out of an area. Deaths and emigration decrease population size.

When there are more births and immigrants than deaths and emigrants, the population grows. If deaths and emigrants exceed births and immigrants, the population declines. The population-limiting factors described in this lesson are important because they affect the rates of birth, death, immigration, and emigration.

Factors That Limit Population

Population size often changes over time. However, most populations stabilize rather than continue to grow endlessly. Continual growth does not happen because, as a population grows, it puts more demands on its ecosystem. For example, a larger population of lions in a savanna needs more food than a smaller population does. If the ecosystem does not have the resources to feed the larger population, some lions will die, and fewer cubs will be born. As a result, the population will decrease.

The lion population is limited by the food supply. Anything in the environment that can limit the size of a population is called a **limiting factor**. In addition to food, other limiting factors include the amount of water, oxygen, and sunlight, as well as relationships with other organisms. Limiting factors can be either biotic or abiotic, and either density-dependent or density-independent.

Abiotic and Biotic Factors

Abiotic factors of an organism's environment are all the nonliving components of the ecosystem. Abiotic factors include the amount of sunlight an area receives, the temperature range in the area, the humidity and amount of precipitation, soil type and acidity, salinity of water, and the available amounts of oxygen and nutrients.

Biotic factors are all the living things in an organism's environment—all the other populations with which an organism may interact. These include predators and prey and other living things with which the organism competes for resources.

Density-Dependent Limiting Factors

A **density-dependent limiting factor** is one that varies according to the density of populations. **Population density** is a measure of the number of organisms per unit area. A population of 500 wolves may have a high density or a low density, depending on the size of the area over which the population is spread. Two major density-dependent limiting factors are predation and competition.

Predation

Predation is an ecological relationship in which one animal, the predator, hunts and eats another species, the prey. If the predator population in an area grows too large, there will not be enough prey to support it. Some of the predators will go hungry or produce fewer and smaller litters of offspring, and the predator population will shrink. The graph shows how predator and prey population sizes tend to change together in a continuous cycle. Notice that the predator population size follows the prey population. A peak or dip in a prey population causes a similar change in the predator population a few years later.

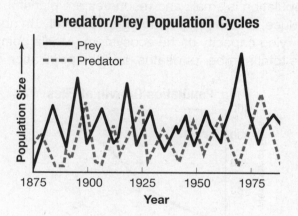

Competition

Competition occurs when organisms try to use the same resource. As a population grows, individuals compete with each other for available resources. A group of trees, for example, may have only so many resources available in the area. When the trees are spread far apart from each other, plenty of soil, sunlight, and water may be available for all of them. As more trees grow, the tree population needs more of those resources. As a result, there is more competition among the trees. Often, seedlings die because they are shaded out by older, larger trees.

Competition may occur between members of the same species. Recall that natural selection depends on competition among members of a population for limited resources. Competition may also take place between populations of different species. For example, wolves compete with coyotes for many of the same prey species. A coyote population will have a larger food supply in ecosystems in which wolves are absent. A diminished food supply may cause coyote deaths to increase and births to decrease. Competition can also cause coyotes to emigrate to areas away from wolves, such as urban areas.

Density-Independent Limiting Factors

Density-independent limiting factors are conditions that limit the growth of a population regardless of a population's density. These factors include climate changes and natural disasters, such as extreme cold or heat, tidal waves, volcanic eruptions, flooding, and drought. These factors often cause a population to experience a major decline. The population may remain small for a long time or eventually return to its previous size.

Carrying Capacity

The largest population that an environment can support over a long period is its **carrying capacity**. The carrying capacity of an environment is different for each species because species' habitats and needs differ. However, two or more species can compete for a resource such as food or nesting sites. For example, an environment may be able to support a limited number of seed-eating birds, regardless of species. If a new seed-eating bird species is introduced to an area, the carrying capacity will limit the growth of both species, which must share and compete for the same resources. If conditions in the environment change, the carrying capacity may also change.

A population stops growing when it reaches the carrying capacity of its ecosystem. The population size then stabilizes, or levels off. The graph below shows the growth of a fly population. Initially, the population is small, and resources are plentiful. As a result, most of the flies survive and reproduce, and the population grows rapidly. In about a month, the fly population reaches the carrying capacity of the ecosystem. At this point, the total number of births is about equal to the total number of deaths, and the population stops growing.

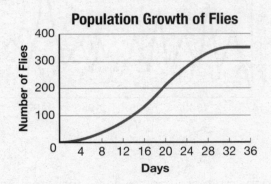

The carrying capacity of an ecosystem depends on the number of organisms living there, the size of the ecosystem, and the available resources. An ecosystem with many resources, such as a tropical rain forest, has a large carrying capacity. In contrast, a desert has a much lower carrying capacity because water is a limiting factor. Knowing an environment's carrying capacity is important to conservationists trying to protect and manage wildlife populations. A healthy population requires enough organisms for genetic variety. Information about carrying capacity can help determine how much habitat must be conserved to sustain healthy wildlife populations.

Discussion Question

Examine the predator-prey graph on the previous page. Is the size of the predator population causing the changes in the size of the prey population, or vice versa? What other factors might affect the prey population?

Lesson Review

1. Increases in which of the following can result in an increase in population size?

    A. emigration and birth rate   C. immigration and birth rate

    B. emigration and death rate   D. immigration and death rate

2. Which is an example of an abiotic limiting factor?

    A. the number of predators in an ecosystem

    B. the amount of nutrients in the soil in an area

    C. the amount of green leaves and grasses available

    D. the number of species that feed on the same food sources

3. Yellow perch are fish that live in freshwater lakes. Yellow perch eat invertebrates and small fish. Rainbow smelts are fish that feed on the same types of prey. If rainbow smelts are introduced into a lake containing yellow perch, how will the yellow perch population **most likely** be affected?

    A. The yellow perch will experience increased predation.

    B. The yellow perch will experience decreased predation.

    C. The yellow perch will experience increased competition.

    D. The yellow perch will experience decreased competition.

4. Which of the following is the **best** definition of carrying capacity?

    A. the maximum rate of growth of a population

    B. the population size that can be sustained by an ecosystem

    C. the number of different species that can inhabit an ecosystem

    D. the minimum number of different species that can compose a food web

5. How will an increase in a predator species affect the population of a prey species?

    A. The birth rate of the prey species will increase.

    B. The death rate of the prey species will increase.

    C. The emigration rate of the prey species will decrease.

    D. The immigration rate of the prey species will increase.

How Human Activities Affect Ecosystems

Key Words • natural resource • deforestation • pollution • groundwater • water table • pesticide • runoff • eutrophication • acid rain • biodiversity • biological magnification • invasive species • global warming

Getting the Idea

The human population of Earth was fairly stable for many millions of years. It then began to grow rapidly at the beginning of the Industrial Revolution, a period from the eighteenth to the nineteenth century. Human activities both add things to and remove things from Earth's land, air, and water, impacting ecosystems and populations.

Natural Resources and Deforestation

As the human population grows, people use more natural resources. A **natural resource** is a product of the environment used by humans or other organisms. Some resources are plentiful and can be replaced or renewed through natural processes. Examples of renewable resources include trees, which can regrow after cutting, and freshwater, which can be purified and recycled repeatedly. By contrast, natural processes cannot replace nonrenewable resources as quickly as they are used. Fossil fuels, for example, are nonrenewable. They formed over millions of years from the remains of organisms beneath Earth's surface and cannot be replenished quickly.

Earth's supply of many natural resources is limited, and people sometimes use more of a resource than they actually need. When humans use large amounts of a resource, it may become unavailable to other organisms. Human use of resources may also physically alter ecosystems. For example, people often clear land and move or fill waterways to make space for buildings and roads. These activities are harmful to the species living there.

Humans rely on trees for wood that is used to build structures such as homes and schools, to make goods such as furniture and paper, and to burn as fuel. **Deforestation** is the complete clearing and destruction of a forest. It is done to obtain wood or to make space available for construction or farming. Forests are vitally important to the global ecosystem because of their role in helping to maintain the proper atmospheric balance of carbon dioxide and oxygen. Forests also moderate temperatures, provide habitats for plants and animals, and reduce soil erosion. Deforestation has many adverse effects on the environment.

Pollution

Pollution is the release of harmful substances, or pollutants, into the environment. Water and soil are polluted when solid wastes are disposed of improperly or chemicals are used recklessly. Oil spills pollute lakes, rivers, and oceans. Pollutants released on land or in water can make an ecosystem unfit for the organisms that normally live there. Pollutants can also make freshwater unusable for drinking, cooking, irrigation, and even manufacturing.

Groundwater and Runoff

One of our most precious natural resources is **groundwater**, which is freshwater stored beneath Earth's surface. Although groundwater makes up only a small percentage of all the water on Earth, it is the largest source of fresh, liquid water available. Most of the freshwater that people use for drinking, household use, and agriculture comes from groundwater.

Groundwater is found in the tiny spaces, or pores, in underground rock and sediment. Water from precipitation seeps into the ground and saturates (fills) these tiny spaces. As the rock fills with water, the top of the zone that holds water rises. This level is called the **water table**. Lakes and ponds occur where the surface dips below the water table.

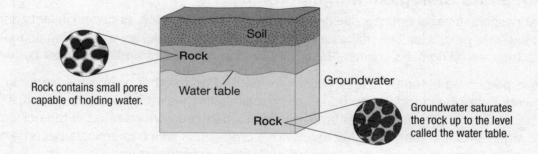

Rock contains small pores capable of holding water.

Groundwater saturates the rock up to the level called the water table.

Pollutants released into the environment at Earth's surface also threaten clean water supplies. Pollutants such as **pesticides** (chemicals designed to kill pest animals), fertilizers, salt, used motor oil, and wastes from industry and mining can seep into and pollute groundwater. Chemicals that are improperly discarded, along with human sewage, can also damage the water supply. Polluted groundwater can harm the health of both humans and wildlife that rely on it for drinking.

Agricultural Runoff and Eutrophication

When rain falls, some water enters the ground. Some water also runs downhill along the surface of the ground, especially in paved areas. This water, called **runoff**, eventually joins a body of water, such as a stream or lake. Runoff can also carry pollution with it.

Lawns, gardens, and farms often use soil fertilizers, which add nutrients to the soil and help plants grow. These nutrients include phosphorous and nitrogen compounds, such as nitrates. Sometimes, fertilizer is overused. When it rains, nutrients dissolve in the rainwater, are carried away by runoff, and enter aquatic ecosystems.

Eutrophication occurs when excess nutrients are released into a body of water, such as a river or lake. The increased nutrient levels can cause an *algal bloom*, in which algae grow much more quickly and in greater numbers than normal. The population of algae may grow past the ecosystem's normal carrying capacity. When the algae die, decomposers use more dissolved oxygen as their activity increases. This can rob fish and other organisms in the water of the oxygen they need. Fertilizer runoff can also damage areas of the ocean. When the oxygen is used up and marine animals die, the area is called a *dead zone*.

Acid Rain

Factories and motor vehicles burn fossil fuels for energy. This releases sulfur dioxide and nitrogen oxide compounds into the air. These pollutants combine with water vapor in the air to form acids, resulting in **acid rain**, which has a lower pH than normal rain. Acid rain increases the acidity (lowers the pH) of the bodies of water that it enters. Altering the pH level of aquatic ecosystems harms the organisms that live in them. Most plants and animals are adapted to a pH level of about 7. Lowering the pH reduces the populations of many species, lowering the biodiversity of lakes and wetlands. **Biodiversity** is the variety of organisms in an ecosystem.

Pesticides and Biological Magnification

Recall that pesticides are chemicals designed to kill pest animals, such as certain insects and rodents. However, pesticides can make an ecosystem unstable by sickening or killing animals other than those they are being used against. Pesticides can be carried into bodies of water by runoff.

Sometimes, pesticides eaten by one organism are passed on to other organisms higher in the food web. Pesticides tend be stored in an organism's tissues rather than eliminated. They are then passed on to predators. Over time, pesticides become concentrated in the cells and tissues of organisms that feed at higher levels. This process, in which chemicals become more concentrated at higher feeding levels, is called **biological magnification**.

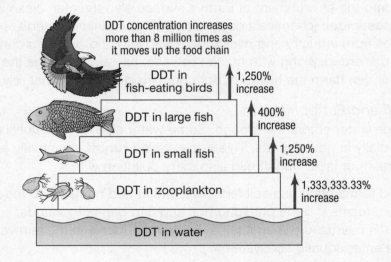

DDT concentration increases more than 8 million times as it moves up the food chain

DDT in fish-eating birds	↑ 1,250% increase
DDT in large fish	↑ 400% increase
DDT in small fish	↑ 1,250% increase
DDT in zooplankton	↑ 1,333,333.33% increase
DDT in water	

In some cases, biological magnification affects the offspring. Populations of predatory birds such as bald eagles and peregrine falcons decreased in the 1960s because of biological magnification of a pesticide called DDT, which made the shells of their eggs brittle. As a result, fewer chicks hatched. The United States has banned the use of DDT as a pesticide.

Invasive Species

Human activities can introduce new species into an environment. This can be intentional or unintentional. For example, insects that get into luggage or rodents that board a ship can be transported from their natural habitats to a new location. Insects have crossed oceans in shipments of wood, bananas, and tires. An **invasive species** harms an environment into which it is introduced. Recall that all species that share an ecosystem compete with each other for resources.

Sometimes, an introduced species has no natural predators in its new ecosystem. Without predators, the new species population may increase rapidly. It competes with native species that need the same resources. If the species is very successful in its new environment, it may even outcompete native species and cause their extinction.

The zebra mussel is an invasive species that was accidentally introduced to aquatic ecosystems in the United States. Zebra mussels may have first come to North America from Europe in water used by ships as ballast. Most scientists think the mussels travel to new ecosystems by attaching themselves to the bottoms of boats. If the boat travels to a new lake or river, a mussel can detach itself and begin living in that body of water. In their new ecosystems, these mussels often have no natural predators, so their populations grow rapidly. The mussels sometimes outcompete native species for resources. In addition, the mussels often live in large numbers in pipes, where they block the flow of water in and out of factories and power plants.

Global Warming

Temperature is an important abiotic factor affecting Earth's ecosystems. Earth's average temperature is the result of both the sun's energy and the atmosphere. The *greenhouse effect* is an effect of the atmosphere that keeps Earth at a temperature that is suitable for life. Much of the sun's energy that reaches Earth's surface is reflected back toward space. As shown in the diagram below, gases in the atmosphere prevent some of this energy from escaping. They trap some of the reflected energy near Earth's surface, in somewhat the same way that a glass greenhouse holds heat. Gases that produce this effect are called greenhouse gases and include water vapor, carbon dioxide, and methane.

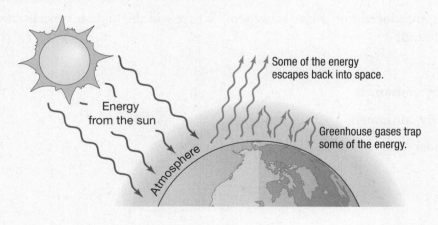

Energy from the sun

Some of the energy escapes back into space.

Atmosphere

Greenhouse gases trap some of the energy.

The greenhouse effect can be increased or decreased by altering the concentration of greenhouse gases, which make up less than one percent of the atmosphere. Most scientists conclude that an increase in greenhouse gases is responsible for **global warming**—the steady increase in average global temperature observed over the past 200 years. (Global warming is discussed further in Lesson 51.) The burning of fossil fuels, for example, releases carbon dioxide into the atmosphere. Humans started burning large quantities of fossil fuels at the beginning of the Industrial Revolution. Deforestation also increases the CO_2 in the air because trees normally remove this gas when carrying out photosynthesis.

A warmer average global temperature can affect populations and ecosystems. For example, fish populations have responded by moving to areas of slightly cooler ocean water. Polar ice caps—large areas near the poles that are covered with ice—are shrinking. As they melt, they add water to the oceans, raising sea levels and threatening organisms that live near shores. Polar bears, which hunt seals from floating sea ice, have become endangered because the ice is disappearing.

Discussion Question

All organisms affect the ecosystems they live in. Why do human activities have a greater impact than those of other species?

Lesson Review

1. Which is a primary cause of eutrophication in aquatic ecosystems?

   A. high biodiversity

   B. high oxygen levels

   C. nutrient-rich runoff

   D. loss of algae in the food web

2. A pesticide is introduced into a lake ecosystem. Where will the highest concentration of pesticide be found?

   A. in producers

   B. in tertiary consumers

   C. in primary consumers

   D. in secondary consumers

3. Rain falls on an area for a long period. What is the effect of the rainfall?

    A. The water table falls, and the groundwater is closer to the surface.

    B. The water table rises, and the groundwater is closer to the surface.

    C. The water table falls, and the groundwater is farther from the surface.

    D. The water table rises, and the groundwater is farther from the surface.

4. What cause the populations of nonnative invasive species to grow faster and larger than those of native species?

    A. fewer prey and more predators

    B. fewer predators and less competition

    C. more prey and fewer predators

    D. more predators and more competition

5. Which of the following environmental changes can result from human activities that increase carbon dioxide in the atmosphere?

    A. deforestation

    B. an ice age

    C. higher sea level

    D. decreased plant growth

Chapter 8 Review

Increasing levels of carbon dioxide in the atmosphere are causing more carbon dioxide to dissolve in ocean waters. The historical average level of this compound is ~400 parts per million (ppm), but current estimates are higher. Carbon dioxide dissociates in water to form carbonic acid, causing a decrease in pH. This increased acidity affects the shells of marine invertebrates, but its effects on vertebrates are less well known. Marine ecologists investigated the effects of pH on the development of the orange clownfish, *Amphiprion percula*. This species is an important member of the coral reef populations around Australia and lives in association with stinging sea anemones. *A. percula* lays eggs outside the anemones. Upon hatching, the miniscule larvae (early-stage fish) swim to open ocean waters, where they feed on phytoplankton. The grown larvae must then settle into an anemone on the reef. *A. percula* larvae use olfactory (smell) cues to locate a suitable habitat and to avoid predation by larger fish.

Ecologists tested the effects of pH level on *A. percula* larvae's responses to olfactory cues. The scientists incubated eggs and larvae in solutions containing different concentrations of dissolved carbon dioxide (400, 500, 700, and 850 ppm). After the eggs hatched, the responses of the larvae were tested using a two-channel flume chamber. This device contains two streams or flumes of water from two different sources flowing side by side. One flume contained water to which the scent of a common predator of the larvae was added. The scientists placed each larva in the chamber and observed where each larva swam. They recorded how long each larva spent in the predator-scented flume. They repeated this process for larvae at 1, 2, 4, 6, and 10 days post-hatching. The results are shown in Figure 1.

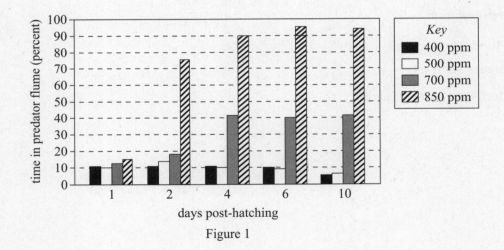

Figure 1

1. Which of the following is the concentration of carbon dioxide used in the control condition?

   A. 400 ppm
   B. 500 ppm
   C. 700 ppm
   D. 850 ppm

2. What is the dependent variable in the experiment described in the passage?

   F. Presence of scent
   G. CO_2 concentration
   H. Time in each flume
   J. Days after hatching

3. Which of the following is a valid conclusion that can be drawn from the experiment?

A. Exposure to 500 ppm CO_2 or greater for ten days after hatching results in reduced ability to avoid predators.

B. Exposure to 700 ppm CO_2 or greater for four days after hatching results in reduced ability to avoid predators.

C. Exposure to 500 ppm CO_2 or greater delays the ability of larvae to detect and avoid predators for 10 days after hatching.

D. Exposure to 700 ppm CO_2 or less delays the ability of larvae to detect and avoid predators for 10 days after hatching.

4. At which age were the larvae exposed to 850 ppm CO_2 most able to use olfactory cues?

F. 1 day

G. 2 days

H. 4 days

J. 6 days

5. Which of the following experiments would be most useful for investigating the hypothesis that a low pH level disrupts multiple functions of the nervous system in *A. percula*?

A. *A. percula* is tested for changes in growth rate and coloration at different CO_2 concentrations.

B. *A. percula* is tested for swimming ability and hearing responses at different CO_2 concentrations.

C. Multiple fish species are tested for olfactory responses at different pH levels.

D. Adult *A. percula* are tested for olfactory responses at different pH levels.

Chapter 9

Earth Science

Earth's Structure

Key Words	• core • mantle • asthenosphere • magma • crust • igneous rock • metamorphic rock • lithosphere • oceanic crust • sedimentary rock • continental crust

Getting the Idea

Picture a hard-boiled egg in its shell. Now, imagine that you cut the egg in half. If you looked at either half, you would see that the egg is made up of distinct sections or layers—the shell, the white, and the yolk. Like a hard-boiled egg, Earth is made up of distinct layers.

Earth's Layers

Earth is not a uniform solid sphere of rock. Instead, it is divided into four main layers, as shown in the diagram. Each layer has distinct characteristics.

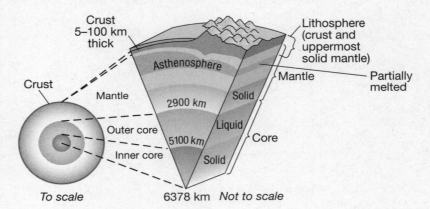

The Inner Core and Outer Core

Earth's innermost layer, the **core**, is composed mostly of iron, with some nickel and small amounts of other elements. The core makes up about 15 percent of Earth's volume. It is divided into a liquid outer core and a solid inner core. The outer core is about 2260 kilometers thick. Although it is liquid, the outer core is probably quite rigid because of high pressure. The flow of material in the outer core is thought to be the source of Earth's magnetic field.

The inner core is probably solid and is estimated to be 1220 kilometers thick. The inner core may be as hot as the sun's surface and is extremely dense. The inner core rotates from west to east like Earth itself, but the inner core rotates slightly faster.

The Mantle and Asthenosphere

The layer above the core is the **mantle**, which is the thickest layer of Earth. It is about 2900 kilometers thick and makes up 84 percent of Earth's volume. It consists of rock that is either solid or partially melted. Scientists cannot access the mantle, but they study it indirectly using earthquake waves, studies of heat flow, magnetic and gravity studies, and experiments on rocks and minerals. Like the core, the mantle consists of different parts. At the deepest part, just above the core, temperatures are highest, but the pressure is so high that it keeps rock from melting. This solid portion is the *lower mantle*. The density of the mantle decreases farther away from the core.

Above the lower mantle is a portion of the mantle called the **asthenosphere**. The temperatures and pressure in the asthenosphere cause the rock in this layer to become viscous and act like a very thick liquid. The rock is hot enough to fold, stretch, compress, and slowly flow without breaking. **Magma**, melted rock beneath Earth's surface, forms in the asthenosphere. Above this, the uppermost layer of the mantle is solid.

The Lithosphere and Crust

Earth's outermost and thinnest layer is the **crust**, which makes up just one percent of Earth's volume. The crust formed as a result of the partial melting and solidification of mantle rock. The crust is composed mostly of igneous and metamorphic rock. **Igneous rock** forms when melted rock cools and solidifies. (Rock formation is discussed in Lesson 46.) Granite, gabbro, and basalt are types of igneous rock that make up the crust. **Metamorphic rock** is rock that has been altered by heat and pressure, such as by being buried deep in Earth's crust.

The crust and the part of the mantle just under the crust form a solid region called the **lithosphere**, which floats on the asthenosphere. The lithosphere is brittle and fractures easily. It has broken into seven large and many smaller tectonic plates that fit together on Earth's surface like the pieces of a jigsaw puzzle. These plates, which you will learn more about in Lesson 44, carry the continents, ocean basins, and islands. Convection currents in the asthenosphere cause movement in the lithosphere. (Convection currents are explained in Lesson 48.) The interaction between the solid lithosphere and the partially melted asthenosphere are responsible for many of Earth's surface features.

Oceanic and Continental Crust

There are two kinds of crust: continental and oceanic. **Oceanic crust** is the layer of rock under the oceans. It is about six kilometers thick and is denser than continental crust. It consists mainly of basalt. In most areas, it is covered by a layer of sediment, which can be as thick as 800 meters. Ocean sediment is made up of rock particles and the shells and skeletons of marine organisms. As these materials pile up on the ocean floor, they form layers. Over millions of years, pressure from the weight of the materials turns the lower layers into **sedimentary rock**. A thin layer of sedimentary rock covers Earth's crust in many places, including about three-fourths of the land surface.

Continental crust is the layer of solid rock that forms the continents. Continental crust is thicker, less dense, older, and more varied than oceanic crust. The continental crust ranges from 30 to 100 kilometers thick and is thickest under large mountain ranges. It is made up mainly of granite but contains many different kinds of rock.

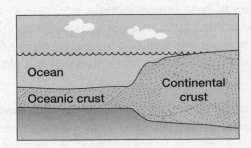

The oldest continental crust is about 4 billion years old. The oldest oceanic crust is about 200 million years old, and new oceanic crust is forming all the time.

The table below provides a summary of Earth's layers and their major characteristics.

Characteristics of Earth's Layers

Layer	Thickness (km)	State	Composition (Major Component)
Continental crust	30–100	Solid	Granite (igneous)
Oceanic crust	5–8	Solid	Basalt (igneous)
Upper mantle	720	Solid and partially melted	Rock
Lower mantle	2170	Solid	Rock
Outer core	2260	Liquid	Iron and nickel
Inner core	1220	Solid	Iron and nickel

Discussion Question

Discuss the changes in density from Earth's crust to its core.

Lesson Review

1. Which of the following covers about three-fourths of Earth's land area in a thin layer?

    A. magma

    B. igneous rock

    C. sedimentary rock

    D. metamorphic rock

2. Which of Earth's layers is made up of metals?

   A. core

   B. crust

   C. mantle

   D. asthenosphere

3. Which of the following is true of Earth's continental crust?

   A. It is older than oceanic crust.

   B. It is denser than oceanic crust.

   C. It is lower than the oceanic crust.

   D. It is thinner than the oceanic crust.

4. The asthenosphere consists of

   A. the entire crust only.

   B. a portion of the crust only.

   C. a portion of the mantle only.

   D. the crust and a portion of the mantle.

5. Earth's layers are labeled 1, 2, 3, and 4 in the diagram.

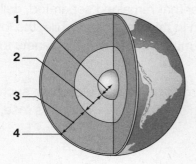

   Which layers are mainly solid?

   A. 1 and 4

   B. 1, 2, and 3

   C. 1, 3, and 4

   D. 2, 3, and 4

Geologic Time

• solar nebula • absolute dating • fossil • relative dating • law of superposition

Getting the Idea

Earth is older than most people can imagine and has undergone many changes since its formation. Earth is estimated to be about 4.6 billion years old. Scientists use various methods to determine the ages of parts of Earth.

The Solar Nebula Hypothesis of Earth's Origin

Most scientists think that the sun, Earth, and the rest of the solar system formed about 4.6 billion years ago from a cloud of dust and gas. This is known as the *solar nebula hypothesis*. Before the solar system formed, hydrogen and helium atoms, along with dust and other matter, existed as a giant cloud or **solar nebula**. Then, this matter began to contract toward the center of the nebula. The contracting nebula began to spiral and flatten, and a large proportion of material concentrated in the center. The loss of gravitational potential energy as matter was pulled toward the center generated large amounts of thermal energy.

Eventually, the sun formed, and the contraction and heating of the nebula ended. The thermal energy at the center was lost, and this cooling caused the matter around the sun to condense into bodies the size of asteroids. Over many millions of years, some of these bodies collided and clumped together to form the four inner, rocky planets (Mercury, Venus, Earth, Mars). Clumps of matter that remained separated, called *meteoroids*, provide evidence that Earth formed in this way. Meanwhile, the lower temperatures farther from the sun allowed four massive low-density planets to form: the gas giants.

Early Earth was hot—so hot that it was largely melted. Heavier elements, such as iron and nickel, sank to the center and formed Earth's core. Lighter elements rose, cooled, and formed the mantle and crust.

Absolute Dating

Scientists use a variety of techniques to determine the order of events and how long ago they happened. These techniques can be classified as *relative* or *absolute*. **Absolute dating** determines the actual age of a rock sample or fossil, often using the decay rates of unstable isotopes. Radioisotope dating, discussed in Lesson 36, is a type of absolute dating.

Radioisotope dating of Earth rocks can be used to estimate the planet's age. However, the technique is not completely reliable because rocks on Earth constantly change through the rock cycle (discussed in Lesson 46). For this reason, scientists have applied radioisotope dating to moon rocks and meteorites, which probably formed at the same time as Earth.

Fossils and Relative Dating

Recall that a **fossil** is the preserved remains or trace of a once-living thing. Most fossils are found in layers of sedimentary rock. Many fossils formed by a process in which an organism died and was covered over by sediment. Over time, the sediment was compacted and cemented into sedimentary rock around the organism's remains. In some cases, the remains of the organism decayed and left a mold, a hollow space in the rock. Some molds became filled with minerals or sediments, forming a fossil called a cast. Trace fossils, such as footprints and imprints of leaves, also formed in this way.

As you learned in Lesson 36, scientists use a fossil's location in a rock layer to determine its age relative to the ages of other fossils. In contrast to absolute dating, **relative dating** describes the age of an object or event in comparison to another object or event. Geologists use rocks and fossils as clues about Earth's geologic history. Often, information from these clues provides only relative ages. Consider a fossil species that existed for only a short period of geologic time but was found in many parts of the world. Scientists may be able to use absolute dating techniques to determine the period during which this species existed. They can then use the known age of the fossil, called an *index fossil*, as a reference for the ages of rock layers or other fossils found around it.

Geologists apply the law of superposition to determine the order in which rock layers and fossils formed. The **law of superposition** states that in undisturbed sedimentary rock layers, older layers of rock lie beneath younger layers. In general, rocks and fossils are about as old as the rock layers in which they are found. A fossil in any rock layer is assumed to be older than the rocks or fossils found in layers above it, and younger than rocks or fossils in deeper layers.

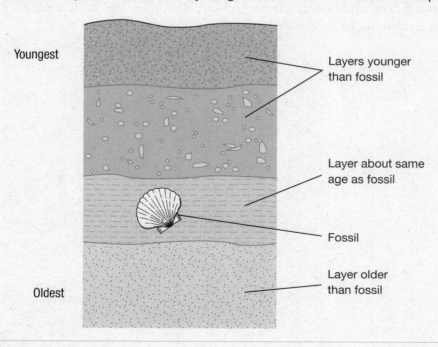

Determining the relative age of rock layers is not always easy. Movements of tectonic plates can disturb rock layers in ways that make their relative ages less apparent. However, the relative ages of these rock layers can be determined by understanding how the layers have changed. The diagrams below show some ways that rock layers can be altered or rearranged.

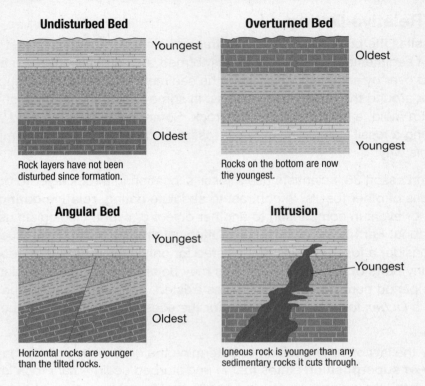

Undisturbed Bed

Youngest

Oldest

Rock layers have not been disturbed since formation.

Overturned Bed

Oldest

Youngest

Rocks on the bottom are now the youngest.

Angular Bed

Youngest

Oldest

Horizontal rocks are younger than the tilted rocks.

Intrusion

Youngest

Igneous rock is younger than any sedimentary rocks it cuts through.

Discussion Question

Why do scientists use both absolute dating and relative dating to determine geologic history? How can the two techniques be used together?

Lesson Review

1. The diagram shows an undisturbed sedimentary rock bed.

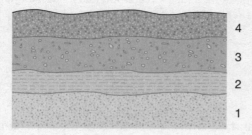

   Which layer in the bed is youngest?

   A. layer 1

   B. layer 2

   C. layer 3

   D. layer 4

2. Radiometric dating is used to find

   A. the locations of index fossils.

   B. the identities of index fossils.

   C. the absolute ages of rocks and fossils.

   D. the relative ages of rocks and fossils.

3. According to the solar nebula hypothesis, Earth formed from

   A. the matter that formed just after the big bang.

   B. melted rock ejected from the newly forming sun.

   C. gas and dust cooling to a mass the size of a planet.

   D. smaller pieces of matter colliding to form a larger mass.

4. Which type of dating depends on the surrounding rocks and fossils?

   A. relative dating

   B. absolute dating

   C. radioisotope dating

Plate Tectonics

Key Words • continental drift hypothesis • theory of plate tectonics • plate boundary • convergent boundary • subduction • trench • volcano • divergent boundary • seafloor spreading • mid-ocean ridge • rift valley • transform boundary

Getting the Idea

Earth's surface is made up of continents and oceans. The shapes of these features have changed over time, as continents have broken apart and new oceans have formed.

The Continental Drift Hypothesis

In 1912, Alfred Wegener noticed that the edges of continents seemed to fit neatly together. He proposed that they were once joined in a single large landmass, called Pangaea, that broke apart, and the pieces then drifted to their current locations. This was the **continental drift hypothesis**. The maps below show stages in the formation of today's continents from the breakup of Pangaea. Although this hypothesis was rejected, it was later supported by a related theory.

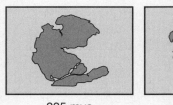      

225 mya   135 mya   Today

mya = million years ago

Theory of Plate Tectonics

Recall that the lithosphere is made up of the crust and the top of the mantle. Earth's lithosphere is broken into large sections or plates that float on a part of the mantle, the asthenosphere. The main plates are shown below.

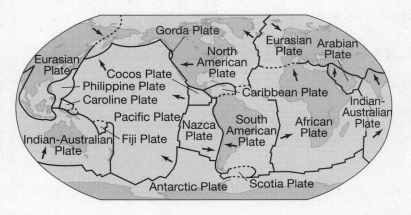

Earth's crust is shaped by interactions of its lithospheric plates as they are carried on the asthenosphere. This idea is the **theory of plate tectonics**. These movements take place slowly, at a rate of only centimeters per year. However, over geologic time (many millions of years), these movements have created mountains and other landforms and continue to reshape Earth's surface.

About seven major plates and many smaller ones make up Earth's surface. The movement of these tectonic plates changes more than just the locations of the continents. It also changes Earth's surface at places where plates meet, called **plate boundaries**. The three main types of plate boundaries are convergent boundaries, divergent boundaries, and transform boundaries.

Convergent Boundaries

Where two tectonic plates move toward each other and collide, they form a **convergent boundary**. Mountain ranges form where two plates carrying continental crust converge. The continental crust on each plate crumples and is uplifted, forming a mountain range. The highest mountain range in the world, the Himalayas, formed where the Indian-Australian Plate converged with the Eurasian Plate. The Alps of central Europe and the Rocky Mountains and Great Smoky Mountains in the United States also formed in this way.

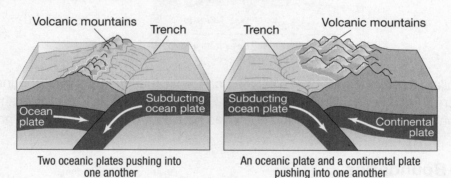

Two oceanic plates pushing into one another

An oceanic plate and a continental plate pushing into one another

Recall that oceanic crust is denser than continental crust. When one of two converging plates is made up of oceanic crust, it is typically pushed underneath the other plate in a process called **subduction**. A **trench**—a long, narrow, steep-sided depression in the ocean floor—forms where the two plates meet. As the edge of the subducted oceanic plate sinks into the hot mantle, the plate begins to melt and form magma. Some newly formed magma rises to the surface of the continental plate and erupts through **volcanoes**, openings in Earth's surface through which magma is released. Subduction can produce chains of volcanic mountains on the edge of the continental plate.

A similar process occurs where two oceanic plates converge. One plate is subducted under the other, and volcanic mountains may develop on the upper plate. Over millions of years, the mountaintops may rise above sea level to form an island arc, such as the Aleutian Islands in the northern Pacific Ocean. (Volcanoes will be covered in Lesson 45.)

Divergent Boundaries

Two tectonic plates move apart at a **divergent boundary**, and melted rock from the mantle flows up to fill the space between the plates. This magma hardens to form new crust. When the diverging plates are oceanic, the process forms new sea floor and is called **seafloor spreading**. Seafloor spreading can widen existing ocean basins and sometimes forms new ocean basins. Long, continuous chains of volcanic mountains, called **mid-ocean ridges**, can form along divergent boundaries between oceanic plates. The Mid-Atlantic Ridge is an example of a mid-ocean ridge. Seafloor spreading at the ridge is causing the Atlantic Ocean to become wider. A deep valley called a **rift valley** runs along the middle of some mid-ocean ridges, including the Mid-Atlantic Ridge.

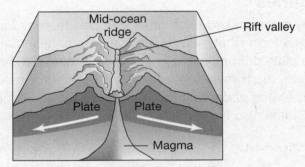

Two oceanic plates moving away from each other

Rift valleys similar to those at mid-ocean ridges can form on land where two continental plates diverge or where one plate is splitting in two. The East African Rift Valley is an example of the first case. Africa's Great Rift Valley, which stretches for about 6000 kilometers, is an example of the second.

Transform Boundaries

At a **transform boundary**, two plates grind past one another mainly in a horizontal direction. The crust at these boundaries is faulted—that is, cracked and deformed. A *fault* is a crack in Earth's crust. Transform boundaries often have long faults. When tectonic plates shift near a fault, large sections of Earth can be pushed upward or sink downward, as shown below. The tallest blocks of crust pushed upward can form fault-block mountains, such as the Sierra Nevada range.

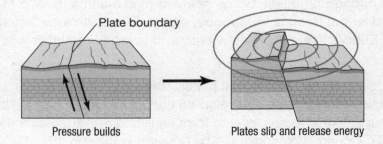

The San Andreas Fault is a well-known transform boundary that separates southwestern California from the North American Plate. Earthquakes are common along transform boundaries.

Evidence for Plate Tectonics

Trenches and mid-ocean ridges are evidence for the theory of plate tectonics. Plate tectonic theory predicts that Earth's oceanic crust should be younger than its continental crust because it is continually recycled. The oldest continental crust is 4 billion years old, while the oldest oceanic crust is only 200 million years old. A good theory predicts and explains many types of evidence. One piece of evidence that puzzled scientists was the pattern of magnetism in the ocean crust on either side of the Mid-Atlantic Ridge. The crust is made up of basalt, which contains traces of iron. This iron is magnetized in opposite directions, resulting in the pattern of bands shown in the diagram below. In addition, the rock closest to the ridge is newer, and its age increases the farther it moves from the ridge.

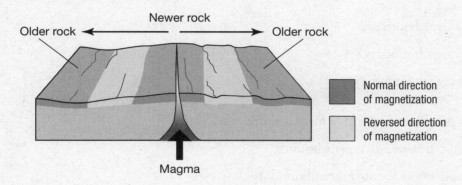

Plate tectonic theory states that the crust near the ridge formed slowly over time from magma. If this is true, it explains the evidence. Earth's core gives it its magnetic field, and the direction of this field reverses periodically over time. When the basalt forms from cooling magma, the iron becomes magnetized by Earth's magnetic field. The magnetic field of the basalt is determined by the direction of Earth's magnetic field when it formed. The increase in age of the basalt with increased distance from the ridge is also consistent with plate tectonics.

Discussion Question

Which tectonic processes form new crust? Which processes destroy existing crust? Is there any oceanic crust or continental crust that formed at Earth's beginnings, 4.6–4.0 billion years ago?

Lesson Review

1. Which type of boundary is shown in this diagram of a plate tectonic process?

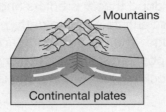

   A. transform boundary

   B. divergent boundary

   C. convergent boundary

2. Which type of boundary may form a subduction zone?

   A. oceanic-oceanic divergent boundary

   B. oceanic-oceanic convergent boundary

   C. continental-continental divergent boundary

   D. continental-continental convergent boundary

3. At which feature is associated with a transform boundary?

   A. faulting   **C.** seafloor spreading

   B. volcanic activity **D.** mountain uplift

4. At which type of boundary does a mid-ocean ridge form?

   A. oceanic-oceanic divergent boundary

   B. oceanic-oceanic transform boundary

   C. continental-oceanic transform boundary

   D. continental-oceanic convergent boundary

5. What do the alternating stripes of magnetic polarity in rock near centers of seafloor spreading indicate?

   A. The rock formed over millions of years.

   B. The rock formed in a single tectonic event.

   C. The rock formed as a result of volcanic activity.

   D. The rock formed from different types of magma.

Earthquakes and Volcanoes

Key Words • earthquake • seismic wave • Mercalli scale • Richter scale • volcano • lava • hot spot

Getting the Idea

Plate tectonic processes cause gradual changes to Earth's surface that are usually not perceptible on a human time scale. However, they can also result in rapid, dramatic, and catastrophic changes. The actions of tectonic plates cause both volcanic eruptions and earthquakes, sudden changes that are easily noticed by humans.

Earthquakes

An **earthquake** is a shaking of Earth's surface. Earthquakes can originate near Earth's surface or far below it. Most earthquakes occur along plate boundaries where many faults are located. Earthquakes can happen at any type of boundary, but they are most common at transform boundaries, such as the San Andreas Fault in California. Pressure builds in rock as plates press together, slide past each other, or move away from each other. Earthquakes occur when the energy stored as pressure is released quickly in the form of seismic waves. A **seismic wave** is a wave of energy that travels through Earth's crust. Seismic waves travel away from the center of an earthquake in all directions and are felt as vibrations in the ground.

A *seismograph*, or seismometer, records and measures seismic waves. The simplest type of seismograph consists of a weighted pen that moves in response to vibrations and records them on a moving strip of paper. The record is called a *seismogram*. A seismograph is shown below.

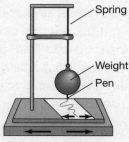

Spring
Weight
Pen
Motion due to earthquake

Earthquakes differ in intensity, from those that are barely perceptible to those that cause widespread and massive damage. The *intensity* of an earthquake is the strength of the shaking at a certain location. It is measured by the effects on people, structures, and the environment. The *magnitude* of an earthquake is a measure of the energy released at the source and is determined from measurements on seismographs. The intensity and magnitude of an earthquake are measured on two different scales: the Mercalli scale and the Richter scale.

The **Mercalli scale** rates the intensity of an earthquake according to the damage and changes that result. A Mercalli scale value of III, for example, corresponds to the sensation of a large truck passing by. A value of IX corresponds to large cracks in the ground, damage to sewer and gas pipes, and shifts in the positions of buildings.

The **Richter scale** measures magnitude. It is based on the amplitude of the largest seismic wave produced by the earthquake. The Richter scale is logarithmic, meaning that each whole-number value represents a magnitude ten times as great as the next value. Therefore, an earthquake measuring 8.6 on the Richter scale is many times more powerful than one measuring 7.2. News reports usually describe earthquakes using the Richter scale.

Volcanoes

A **volcano** is an opening in Earth's surface through which magma is released. Magma in the mantle can move upward and accumulate in underground pools or chambers. As magma builds in these chambers, it can exert enough pressure on the rock above to break through onto Earth's surface. This creates a crater at the opening. Magma that reaches Earth's surface is called **lava**. As it cools and hardens around the crater, it builds and changes the shape of the volcano. The movement of magma in and around a volcano can also trigger an earthquake.

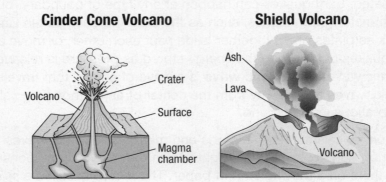

Two types of volcanoes may form, depending on the type of lava and eruptions. If the eruptions are violent and the lava contains water, gases, and silica (a mineral), a *cinder cone volcano* forms. Because the lava shoots straight up, it lands close to the crater to form a mountain with steep sides. In contrast, a *shield volcano* results from slow, steady flows of large amounts of lava, rather than violent eruptions. The lava from shield volcanoes is thicker and contains less water, gases, and silica than lava from cinder cone volcanoes. Shield volcano lava oozes down around the sides of the crater. This produces a flat, broad volcano with gentle slopes.

In contrast to the slow growth of mountains that result from the folding of continental crust, volcanic eruptions can change Earth's surface quickly and noticeably. Most volcanic activity occurs at convergent and divergent boundaries. Convergent boundaries involving oceanic crust lead to the subduction of oceanic rock, turning it into magma that may erupt.

The Ring of Fire and Hot Spots

Scientists have observed that volcanoes cluster in certain geographic locations. For example, a zone of frequent volcanic eruptions that circles the Pacific Ocean basin is called the Ring of Fire. The Ring of Fire contains more than 75 percent of all volcanoes on Earth. As the map shows, many plate boundaries are located along the Ring of Fire. Both volcanoes and earthquakes occur most often at or near plate boundaries.

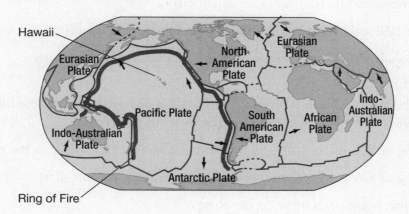

Not all volcanoes are located at plate boundaries, however. Volcanic activity can occur near the middle of a tectonic plate due to a hot spot. A **hot spot** is a region in the upper mantle that produces volcanic activity in the crust above it. Although the hot spot in the mantle remains in one place, the tectonic plate moves over it. As it moves, new volcanoes form behind the existing volcanoes, creating a chain of volcanoes. The volcanoes are no longer active once they are no longer over the hot spot. The Hawaiian Islands are a chain of volcanic islands that formed as the Pacific Plate traveled over a hot spot. The island chain continues to form to this day.

Discussion Question

What structures would you expect to find under the surface of the Pacific Ocean near the Hawaiian Islands? Explain your reasoning.

Lesson Review

1. Which of the following **most** accurately describes the Mercalli and Richter scales?

    A. The Mercalli and Richter scales are qualitative.

    B. The Mercalli and Richter scales are quantitative.

    C. The Mercalli scale is qualitative, and the Richter scale is quantitative.

    D. The Mercalli scale is quantitative, and the Richter scale is qualitative.

2. The rim of the Pacific Ocean is often called the Ring of Fire. Which of the following explains why earthquakes and volcanic eruptions often occur in this region?

    A. The Ring of Fire is the main region where convection takes place in the mantle.

    B. The Ring of Fire is located near the middle of a large tectonic plate.

    C. Many plate boundaries lie along the Ring of Fire.

    D. Many hot spots lie along the Ring of Fire.

3. Which of the following are **not** caused by interactions between tectonic plates?

    A. hot spots

    B. earthquakes

    C. shield volcanoes

    D. cinder cone volcanoes

4. Which of the following produces a seismic wave?

    A. motion of tectonic plates

    B. eruption of magma to the surface

    C. potential energy stored inside rock

    D. kinetic energy of earthquake damage

Rocks and Minerals

Key Words • mineral • rock • igneous rock • magma • lava • sediment • sedimentary rock
• metamorphic rock • rock cycle

Getting the Idea

Earth's oldest rocks are about 4 billion years old. However, most rocks on Earth's surface have changed form many times. This lesson discusses the composition and formation of rocks.

The Composition of Minerals and Rocks

A **mineral** is an inorganic solid that occurs naturally and has a definite chemical composition and structure. Minerals are divided into two groups based on their chemical composition. One group is the silicate minerals, which are made up of silicon bonded to oxygen, along with other elements. Most of the minerals in Earth's crust are made up of only eight elements: oxygen, silicon, aluminum, iron, calcium, sodium, potassium, and magnesium. Silicon and oxygen are the two most common elements in Earth's crust, and silicate minerals make up more than 90 percent of the crust.

The rest of the crust is made up of minerals that lack silicon bonded to oxygen. These minerals are made up of elements such as carbon, fluorine, sulfur, various metals, and oxygen. Pure metals, such as silver and gold, are also considered minerals.

Minerals have a definite chemical composition. For example, the mineral quartz has the chemical formula SiO_2. In feldspar, potassium, aluminum, or calcium is bonded to a silicate. Minerals also form crystals. The particles that make up a mineral determine the shape of a mineral crystal.

Quartz

Rock is a naturally occurring substance that is made up of one or more minerals. Granite is made up mostly of three minerals—quartz, feldspar, and mica—but the amounts of these minerals vary in different types of granite. Rocks can be identified by their color, texture, density, and patterns such as banding. A rock's color is the result of its mineral composition. The size of the mineral crystals, or grains, determines a rock's texture.

Scientists classify rocks into three main groups, depending on how the rocks formed: igneous, sedimentary, and metamorphic.

Igneous Rock

Igneous rock forms when melted rock cools and hardens. Recall that melted rock below Earth's surface is called **magma**. When magma rises to the surface, such as at a divergent plate boundary or volcano, it is called **lava**. The amount of time it takes for the melted rock to cool determines its texture, or the size of its mineral crystals. Obsidian, a black, glassy rock that forms from rapidly cooling lava, contains no crystals.

Igneous rocks can be light or dark in color, depending on their composition. Granite, for example, forms from magma that is rich in light-colored elements such as sodium, aluminum, potassium, and silicon. Basalt forms from lava that is rich in dark-colored elements such as iron, magnesium, and calcium. Granite and basalt also differ in texture. Granite forms when magma cools very slowly beneath Earth's surface. This provides time for the mineral crystals of granite to grow, resulting in a coarse-grained rock. The lava that forms basalt cools quickly at Earth's surface, producing smaller crystals and a fine-grained texture. Basalt forms new oceanic crust at centers of seafloor spreading, such as the Mid-Atlantic Ridge.

Basalt   Granite

Sedimentary Rock

Sediment is made up of rock particles and sometimes the remains of organisms. Sediment sinks to the bottom of oceans and other bodies of water. Over millions of years, layers of sediment build up, and the weight of the layers compacts the sediments at the bottom, pressing them together. Chemical changes also occur, cementing the particles together. These two processes, compaction and cementation, form **sedimentary rock**. Layering is the most distinctive feature of many kinds of sedimentary rock. A single layer of sedimentary rock can extend for large areas over Earth's surface.

Shale   Sandstone

Sedimentary rock exists in a variety of compositions and textures. Shale is a fine-textured sedimentary rock that often contains fossils. Sandstone is a coarse-grained sedimentary rock. Some kinds of sedimentary rock form mainly from organic matter. Coal is a dark-colored, fine-textured rock that forms very slowly from the remains of plants. Limestone is a light-colored rock that consists mostly of calcium carbonate ($CaCO_3$). Limestone forms from the remains of marine organisms with hard, calcium-rich shells.

Sedimentary rock is made up of layers called *beds*. Each bed has distinctive properties that reflect how it formed and can range in thickness from a few centimeters to several meters. Multiple beds in sedimentary rock form stripes called *bedding planes*. Bedding planes are evidence that a rock is sedimentary.

Metamorphic Rock

Metamorphic rock forms when existing rock is exposed to high heat, high temperature, or both and undergoes chemical as well as physical changes. These changes happen mainly deep in Earth's mantle and at plate boundaries. Heat and pressure can alter the size and shape of mineral crystals, sometimes changing the identity of the minerals. Metamorphic rock can form from igneous, sedimentary, or existing metamorphic rock. Each kind of metamorphic rock forms from a particular kind of existing rock. For example, gneiss forms from granite, slate forms from shale, and marble forms from limestone. Metamorphic rocks are often *foliated*, with their mineral arranged in parallel bands.

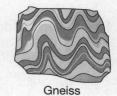

Gneiss

The Rock Cycle

Igneous, sedimentary, and metamorphic rocks melt if the temperature and pressure inside Earth are high enough. Melted rock forms magma. As magma cools, it becomes igneous rock. Such changes are part of the **rock cycle**, a continuous process in which rocks form or change from one type to another. The diagram shows the many pathways of the rock cycle. For example, heat and pressure can change igneous rock into metamorphic rock. An igneous rock can also be weathered, creating sediment that is compacted and cemented to form sedimentary rock. Igneous rock can also melt and then harden again, forming another igneous rock.

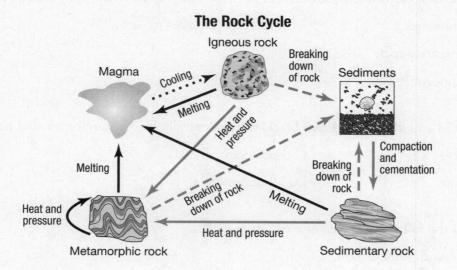

The Rock Cycle

Discussion Question

Can a metamorphic rock become another kind of metamorphic rock? Explain your answer.

Lesson Review

1. Which of these rocks forms when magma cools and hardens?

   A. coal

   B. shale

   C. granite

   D. sandstone

2. Which of these rocks forms from compacted and cemented sediments?

   A. shale

   B. basalt

   C. gneiss

   D. granite

3. What type of rock forms when heat and pressure inside Earth chemically change existing rock?

   A. igneous rock

   B. sedimentary rock

   C. metamorphic rock

4. How would you identify a glossy, black, microscopically fine-textured rock that has no layering?

   A. marble   C. obsidian

   B. granite   D. limestone

5. Which of the following is true of a silicate mineral?

   A. It contains only carbon.

   B. It must contain a metal.

   C. It contains silicon bonded to oxygen.

   D. It can only be found in metamorphic rock.

Weathering, Erosion, and Deposition

Key Words • weathering • mechanical weathering • chemical weathering • soil • erosion • deposition • sediment • alluvium • meander • delta

Getting the Idea

As you have learned, Earth's surface changes due to processes within Earth. Earth's surface also changes due to processes occurring in the oceans and in the atmosphere. Organisms also contribute to these surface changes.

Weathering

Agents such as flowing water, freezing and thawing water, wind, and plant and animal activity constantly break apart rocks on Earth's surface. The process by which rock is broken down into smaller pieces is called **weathering**. There are two types of weathering: mechanical weathering and chemical weathering.

Mechanical weathering breaks rock into smaller pieces by physical means, without changing its chemical composition. Agents of mechanical weathering include water, wind, gravity, glacial movement, changing temperatures, and organism activity. The grinding and wearing away of rock surfaces by contact with other particles is called *abrasion*. Swiftly moving rivers and streams can cause rocks to rub against and abrade each other. Wind causes abrasion by blowing sand and small rock pieces against other rocks. When rocks bump against each other during mass movements such as falls or landslides, gravity is the weathering agent.

Glaciers are large masses of moving ice. As glaciers move across Earth's surface, they pick up and carry weathered rock material. This material scratches and abrades rock surfaces over which the glacier flows. Temperature changes often cause mechanical weathering. As shown in the diagram below, when temperatures drop, water within a crack in a rock can freeze. The frozen water expands and pushes the rock apart on either side of the crack in a process called ice wedging. When the temperature rises, the ice melts, and pressure is released. Over time, the rock weakens and breaks apart by repeated freezing and thawing cycles.

Mechanical Weathering

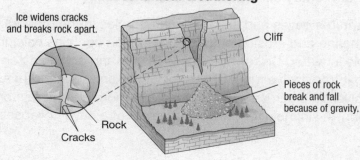

Ice widens cracks and breaks rock apart.

Cliff

Rock

Cracks

Pieces of rock break and fall because of gravity.

Plant and animal activity also break rocks apart. Plant roots growing in tiny cracks in a rock can weaken the rock and cause it to break. Burrowing animals, such as earthworms and moles, can bring rock particles to the surface, where most weathering occurs.

Chemical weathering breaks rocks apart by changing the chemical makeup of rocks and minerals. Common agents of chemical weathering include water, acids, and oxidation. Water can dissolve and wash away some minerals in rocks. Acids produced by fungi or in acid rain (discussed in Lesson 41) can dissolve minerals and change their composition. Oxygen in the air can react chemically with substances (such as iron) in rocks, and these chemical changes contribute to weathering. Lichens are also able to break down rock chemically.

The rate at which a rock weathers depends on several factors. These factors include rock composition, climate, and elevation. Soft rocks, such as limestone, weather faster than harder rocks, such as granite. The surface area of a rock also affects the weathering rate.

Rocks with a larger surface area weather faster than rocks with a smaller surface area. Mechanical weathering occurs faster in wet, cool climates where ice is more likely to form. Chemical weathering occurs faster in wet, warm climates where certain chemical reactions occur faster. Because of their elevation, mountain peaks are exposed to strong winds and ice. Therefore, rocks near the tops of mountains tend to weather mechanically more quickly than rocks at lower elevations.

Soil Formation

Weathering produces soil. **Soil** is the loose, weathered rock and organic material that covers parts of Earth's surface. Soil formation begins with the weathering of rock, known as the parent rock. In some regions, the parent material is bedrock (rock making up the surface) that weathered in one place. In other regions, the parent rock consists of weathered rock transported to a new location by wind, water, and ice. Soil forms as the parent material gradually changes over time. Topsoil is a dark soil layer that contains organic material called *humus*. This material forms from decayed organic matter such as plants.

Erosion

Rock that has been broken down by weathering can then be eroded. **Erosion** is the process by which weathered rock and soil are picked up and moved by wind, water, ice, or gravity. Erosion can be fast or slow. For example, a beach erodes quickly when hurricane waves carry away large amounts of sand. Gravity can quickly pull large amounts of rock and soil downhill during a landslide. Moving river water forms canyons. This takes a long time, as the river first weathers and then erodes the rock over which it travels. One way to prevent topsoil from eroding is to plant vegetation. Plant roots hold topsoil in place, preventing the wind from blowing it away.

Karst landscape features caves and sinkholes (large holes in the ground). Karst results from the chemical weathering and erosion of limestone, which contains calcium carbonate. Calcium carbonate is soluble in water. Dissolved organic matter and acid rain can decrease the pH of the water, allowing it to dissolve more of this mineral. Karst caves form as acidic water flowing underground dissolves and carries away material. As more and more stone is removed, the caves are left behind. A sinkhole forms when the roof of a cave collapses.

Deposition

Weathering and erosion are destructive processes that break down Earth's surface. A constructive process called deposition balances them. **Deposition** is a process in which weathered rock transported by erosion is dropped in a new location. The deposited material, which may include organic matter, is called **sediment**. Agents of deposition include wind, water, glaciers, and gravity. When wind and flowing water slow down, and when glaciers melt, they deposit weathered rock that they are carrying. Gravity overcomes the forces transporting the rock.

Wind deposition leads to the formation of sand dunes and loess. Wind blowing from the ocean toward land picks up sand along the shore and deposits it nearby. Sand dropped by the wind builds up around rocks or plants on the shore, forming dunes. Silt is similar to sand but is made up of smaller particles. Loess is a sediment that forms when wind deposits silt that becomes loosely cemented by calcium carbonate.

Streams and rivers also carry out deposition. When moving water slows, it deposits some of the materials it carries. Sediment deposited by flowing water is called **alluvium**, or an alluvial deposit. When a river floods, it deposits alluvium along the sides of the riverbanks. Alluvium is nutrient-rich and good for farming. River water flows more slowly around inner curves, depositing sediment and deepening the curves. These alluvial deposits produce the **meanders**, or bends, shown below. The grain size of the alluvium that builds up at different regions along a river depends on water speed. Fast-flowing water can carry larger, heavier rock particles than slower-moving water.

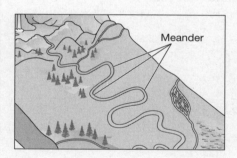

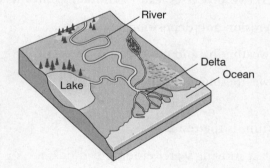

River **deltas** are triangular deposits of sediment at the mouths of rivers. Deltas form because river water slows when it enters the ocean. A delta is often called an alluvial fan because of its shape.

Discussion Question

Describe how vegetation, ice, wind, water, and gravity are agents of both destructive processes and constructive processes.

Lesson Review

1. Which process is responsible for breaking rocks apart on Earth's surface?

   A. compaction

   B. erosion

   C. deposition

   D. weathering

2. Which of these results from deposition by wind?

   A. meander

   B. delta

   C. alluvium

   D. loess

3. Which two processes lead to an increase in the amount of soil?

   A. erosion and deposition

   B. weathering and erosion

   C. weathering and deposition

4. Alluvium is the result of

   A. fast-moving water eroding bedrock.

   B. rivers depositing fine-grained particles.

   C. acidic water chemically weathering limestone.

   D. tall mountain peaks becoming physically weathered.

5. River deltas and meanders form because

   A. faster-moving water can spread over a larger area than slower-moving water.

   B. slower-moving water is less able to carry sediment than faster-moving water.

   C. slower-moving water can carry larger pieces of sediment than faster-moving water.

   D. faster-moving water deposits a greater amount of sediment than slower-moving water.

Winds and Currents

Key Words • radiation • convection current • global wind • jet stream • Coriolis effect • ocean current

Getting the Idea

Heat flows in a predictable way from warmer to cooler materials. Heat may move through empty space, flow from one location to a nearby location, or cause fluids to rise and sink repeatedly. The transfer of heat across Earth's surface causes air and ocean waters to move.

Radiation and Convection

Energy from the sun reaches Earth in the form of electromagnetic waves, which can travel through space. The transfer of electromagnetic energy through space is called **radiation**. Solar radiation is either absorbed by Earth's surface and atmosphere or reflected back into space as heat.

Consider the air above a hot, sandy beach. The air just above the ground warms as heat moves from the sand to the cooler air above it. When a gas such as air gets warmer, its molecules move faster and spread farther apart. This makes the air less dense. On a hot beach, the warm, less-dense layer of air just above the sand moves upward. Higher, cooler air sinks because it is denser and heavier than the warm air. After it sinks, the hot sand warms this cooler air, and it becomes less dense. It rises, cooler air from above sinks to take its place, and the process continues. *Convection* is the transfer of heat by the circulation of a gas or a liquid. A **convection current** is a circular flow of a gas or a liquid caused by temperature differences. The continuous rising of warm air and sinking of cool air is an example of a convection current.

The sun's energy reaches Earth unevenly, and some materials on Earth's surface absorb more sunlight than others do. The temperature differences that result cause global winds and ocean currents that distribute the heat.

Global Winds

Convection in the atmosphere causes all of Earth's winds and weather. The uneven heating of Earth's surface creates wind. Warm air rises. As it rises, it creates a low-pressure area into which cooler air can move. Wind moves from areas of higher pressure toward areas of lower pressure. This situation causes breezes and local wind patterns. It also causes **global winds**, which blow steadily for thousands of kilometers in stable patterns across Earth's surface.

The sun's heat and Earth's rotation create wide belts of global winds. In each hemisphere, there are three belts of global winds. These are the polar easterlies, the westerlies, and the trade winds. These winds push storms and cloud cover in predictable directions.

The *polar easterlies* extend from the poles to 60 degrees latitude. Cold, dense air moves away from the high-pressure areas around the poles and curves west. In the Northern Hemisphere, the polar easterlies bring cold arctic air down over the United States.

Trade winds blow toward the equator from 30 degrees latitude. Warm, rising air at the equator moves upward. Cooler air north and south of the equator moves toward the low-pressure area at the equator. This cooler air makes up the trade winds.

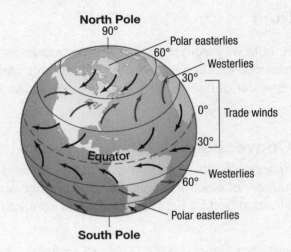

Between the polar easterlies and the trade winds are the westerlies, which lie between latitudes of 30 and 60 degrees. These winds flow from west to east and toward the poles. The westerly wind belt carries storms across the United States.

High in the atmosphere, flowing for thousands of kilometers from west to east, are the **jet streams**. These "rivers of wind" can reach speeds up to 400 kilometers per hour. They do not follow regular paths around Earth, but move north and south over time.

The Coriolis Effect

Earth's rotation plays an important role in wind patterns. You might expect global winds to move straight down from the poles toward the equator, from high-pressure areas into low-pressure areas. However, they do not. Wind paths and ocean currents curve because of Earth's rotation, a phenomenon known as the **Coriolis effect**. In the Northern Hemisphere, winds moving north curve to the east, and winds moving south curve to the west. At every 30 degrees of latitude, the Coriolis effect causes winds to curve in a different direction. It also causes tropical depressions and hurricanes in the Northern Hemisphere to spin in a clockwise direction. In the Southern Hemisphere, tropical depressions spin counterclockwise instead.

Oceans and Ocean Currents

Ocean waters absorb heat from the sun. Water changes temperature much more slowly than air. In other words, once water is warmed, it takes a long time for it to cool. This is one reason why Earth's Southern Hemisphere, which is mostly ocean, has less extreme temperature changes than the Northern Hemisphere, which contains more land.

Water's ability to retain heat allows it to transport heat around the world through currents. An **ocean current** is a flow of water in one direction within the ocean. Two types of currents are surface currents and deep-water currents. A *surface current* flows at or near the water's surface, extending less than 200 meters deep. Surface currents move water hundreds or thousands of kilometers around the globe. Notice that warm-water surface currents flow from warm regions near the equator, while cool-water surface currents flow from cold areas near the poles.

Winds are the main cause of surface currents, as they drag ocean water along with them. One of the most important surface currents is the Gulf Stream, which starts in the Gulf of Mexico and carries warm water north and east through the Atlantic Ocean toward Western Europe. Because of the Gulf Stream, Western Europe is much warmer than other areas at similar latitudes. Similarly, cold-water surface currents can cool the regions they travel past.

Ocean Currents

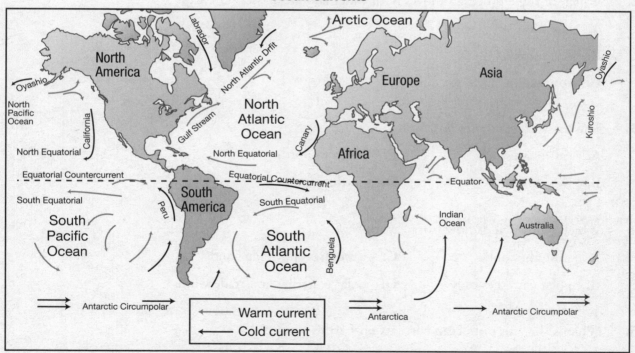

Surface currents do not move in straight paths from north to south. Instead, their paths curve due to the Coriolis effect. Ocean currents traveling north in the Northern Hemisphere curve to the east, while ocean currents traveling south curve to the west.

Currents that form deep in the ocean are called *deep-water currents* or *density currents*. They result from differences in water temperature, salinity, and density. They originate in polar areas, where the water becomes colder, more saline, and denser. This denser cold water sinks and begins to flow under warmer ocean water, forming a deep-water ocean current.

Discussion Question

Identify two general relationships among the temperature, density, and behavior of fluids, and apply those relationships to the natural processes discussed in this lesson.

Lesson Review

1. What causes surface currents to curve rather than move in straight lines?

    A. the rotation of Earth

    B. differences in latitude

    C. temperature differences

    D. changes in water pressure

2. Which of these processes moves both water and air masses on Earth?

    A. radiation

    B. conduction

    C. convection

3. The jet streams usually flow from

    A. east to west.

    B. west to east.

    C. south to north.

    D. north to south.

4. Which global winds flow from east to west?

    A. westerlies only

    B. polar easterlies only

    C. westerlies and trade winds

    D. polar easterlies and trade winds

5. What is the effect of ocean currents on Earth's surface?

    A. to equalize energy differences

    B. to create regional climate differences

    C. to trap the sun's energy on Earth's surface

    D. to make waters uniform in temperature and density

Weather and Climate

Key Words • weather • climate • biome • water cycle • evaporation • transpiration • condensation • precipitation • runoff • humidity • latitude • topography • elevation

Getting the Idea

Weather is the state of the atmosphere at a certain time and place. **Climate** is the average weather of a region over many years. An area's climate tends to be consistent and somewhat predictable. Climate around the globe varies, however, because it results from the transfer of energy and water into, out of, and within the atmosphere.

Climate and Biomes

Each region of Earth has a characteristic climate. Earth's climate variations lead to different biomes. A **biome** is a large group of ecosystems that have similar climatic conditions and organisms. The map shows the locations of the six main terrestrial biomes.

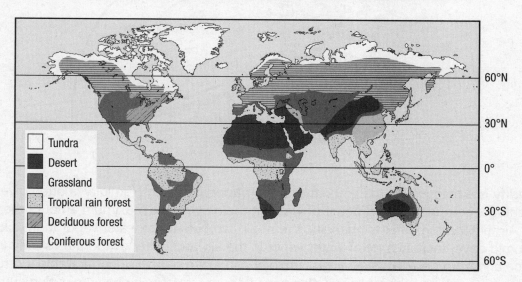

Warm year-round temperatures and high average yearly precipitation in the form of rain or mist characterize the *tropical rain forest* biome, while the *desert* biome receives less than 25 cm of precipitation each year and has very dry conditions. Deserts can be hot or cold or vary in their temperatures. *Grasslands* are regions having warm to hot summers and cool to cold winters. Precipitation in this biome is seasonal, occurring mostly in the spring and fall. The *tundra* is a cold, dry biome characterized by permafrost, a layer of permanently frozen subsoil. *Deciduous forests* have broad-leafed trees, which shed their leaves in the fall and sprout them in the spring. Rainfall and temperatures are moderate. *Coniferous forests* are cold to cool, moderately wet areas located in the northern parts of North America, Europe, and Asia. They are named for the cone-bearing trees that are common there.

Many interacting factors affect a region's climate, including global winds and ocean currents (discussed in the previous lesson), proximity to large bodies of water, height above sea level, and the shape of the land. Both weather and climate result from the transfer of energy into and out of the atmosphere. This energy transfer drives many surface processes.

The Water Cycle and Humidity

For example, the heating of surface water drives the water cycle. Water is a renewable resource that continuously moves through the physical environment and living things in a process known as the **water cycle**. Water in oceans, lakes, and streams heats up and undergoes **evaporation**, forming water vapor in the atmosphere. Plants take in water from the ground and release water vapor through their leaves in the process of **transpiration**. Molecules of water vapor may then undergo **condensation** into microscopic droplets to form clouds. Water moves from clouds back to Earth's surface in the form of **precipitation** (rain, snow, sleet, and hail). Some of this precipitation enters the ground and becomes groundwater (freshwater stored in the earth). **Runoff** is precipitation that moves downhill over surfaces until it reaches a body of water.

The Water Cycle

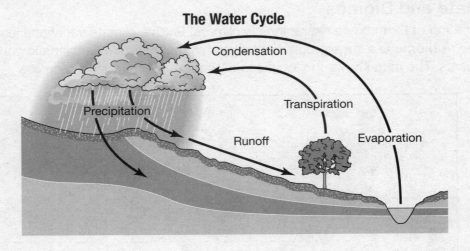

Humidity is a measure of the amount of water vapor in the air. Humidity is often given as a percentage, comparing the amount of water in the air with the maximum amount the air can hold. Air temperature affects humidity. Warm air can hold more water vapor than cold air can. On humid days, there is a lot of water vapor in the air, and water evaporates slowly from Earth's surface and from people's skin. High humidity can make people uncomfortable. Fortunately, areas that have high humidity often also have frequent, brief rain showers during summer. The humidity decreases after these showers.

Bodies of Water

Water heats and cools more slowly than land. Therefore, areas near oceans or other large bodies of water tend to be warmer in the winter and cooler in the summer than areas farther inland. These areas are more temperate. Areas downwind of large bodies of water may also get more precipitation. The winds pick up water vapor from the warmer air over the water. Then, in the cooler air over land, the water vapor condenses, freezes, and falls as snow. By contrast, areas far from large bodies of water tend to be drier. Many deserts are far from the coasts, in the interiors of the continents. The Southern Hemisphere is covered by more water than the Northern Hemisphere. Therefore, regions in the Southern Hemisphere tend to experience fewer variations in temperature over the year than Northern Hemisphere regions do.

Latitude

Latitude is an area's distance north or south of the equator, measured in degrees. In general, regions near the equator have warmer climates than those nearer the poles. At the equator, the sun's rays strike Earth almost directly, so this region receives more solar energy than do areas nearer the poles. This creates an uneven distribution of heat between the equator and the poles.

Global Winds and Ocean Currents

Recall that global wind patterns and ocean currents result from Earth's rotation and the heat imbalance of the planet. These processes transport heat from the equator toward the poles. Other winds and currents transport colder air and water from the poles toward the equator. This global circulation of air and water cools the tropics and warms the polar regions.

Altitude and Topography

Topography, or the shape of the land, affects climate. Large mountain ranges can affect both temperature and precipitation. A location's **elevation** is its altitude, or height above sea level. Areas at high altitude tend to be cooler than areas near sea level. Tall mountains tend to have the types of ecosystems characteristic of cold-climate biomes, such as coniferous forests and tundra.

Mountain ranges also affect precipitation patterns. Winds usually blow toward one side of a mountain, called the windward side. The windward side of a mountain range often has a wetter, cooler climate than the opposite, leeward side. As moist air reaches a mountain range, it rises.

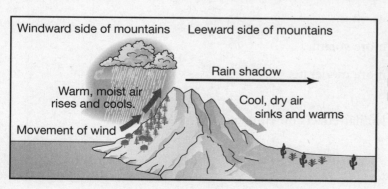

The windward side of a mountain range is the side from which the wind usually blows. The leeward side is the side to which the wind usually blows. The windward side tends to be wetter than the leeward side.

As the air rises, it cools, water vapor condenses, and precipitation falls on the slopes of the windward side. Winds that reach the opposite side of the mountains are drier because they have lost most of their moisture. The leeward side, therefore, receives less precipitation. This effect, known as a *rain shadow*, can cause areas downwind of mountain ranges to have arid climates.

Discussion Question

At what latitudes are most desert biomes located? How does this fit with what you learned about global winds and air pressure in the previous lesson?

Lesson Review

1. Which is a possible sequence of events for a water molecule in the water cycle?

   A. condensation, runoff, evaporation, precipitation

   B. evaporation, precipitation, condensation, runoff

   C. transpiration, evaporation, precipitation, condensation

   D. evaporation, condensation, precipitation, transpiration

2. Which biome is **more likely** to occur at higher elevations?

   A. tundra

   B. desert

   C. grassland

   D. tropical rain forest

3. What effect does a large body of water have on the climate of nearby land?

   A. The climate tends to be colder.

   B. The climate tends to be warmer.

   C. The climate tends to be more volatile.

   D. The climate tends to be more moderate.

4. Which of the following have similar effects on climate?

   A. latitude and elevation

   B. ocean currents and elevation

   C. latitude and major bodies of water

Weather Patterns and Prediction

Key Words air pressure • air mass • front • cloud • weather map

Getting the Idea

Meteorology is the scientific study of weather. Understanding the behavior of air and water vapor in the atmosphere helps meteorologists forecast the weather.

Weather Conditions

Recall that weather is the state of the atmosphere at a certain time and place. Weather conditions include temperature, humidity, precipitation, wind speed and direction, and air pressure. Measurements of these conditions are the data meteorologists use to understand weather patterns and make forecasts.

Air Pressure and Air Masses

Radiant energy from the sun drives Earth's weather. When air at Earth's surface is heated, it expands and becomes less dense. As the density of the air decreases, the air rises, creating an area of low atmospheric or air pressure. **Air pressure** is a measure of the force a column of air exerts on Earth's surface. Meteorologists use a *barometer* to measure air pressure. When air becomes less dense, the particles in the air spread out, and air pressure decreases. When low pressure forms over an area, higher-pressure air in a nearby area can flow in and replace the low-pressure air. Low or decreasing air pressure predicts rainy or stormy weather. By contrast, high or increasing air pressure is associated with fair weather.

An **air mass** is a large body of air whose properties are fairly consistent throughout. The characteristics of an air mass depend on where the air mass formed. Air masses that form near the poles tend to be cool, while air masses that come from the equator tend to be warmer. The moisture content of an air mass also depends on its origin. Air masses that form over water tend to be moist, while air masses that form over land tend to be drier.

Weather Fronts

The boundary formed where two different air masses meet is called a **front**. The colder air mass is denser and moves under the warmer air mass. This pushes the warmer air upward in the atmosphere, where the air cools, and water vapor condenses to form clouds.

There are four types of weather fronts, each associated with a different weather pattern.

- A *warm front* forms when a warm air mass slides over a cold air mass. A warm front brings falling air pressure, clouds, and gentle precipitation. After the warm front passes, warmer temperatures tend to occur.

- A *cold front* forms when a cold air mass overtakes a warm air mass. The dense, cold air rapidly pushes the less-dense, warmer air upward. The temperature drops quickly, and stormy weather often occurs. A cold front is followed by colder temperatures and rising air pressure.

- A *stationary front* forms when two air masses meet and remain in one place. Stationary fronts often have weather patterns similar to warm fronts: clouds and light precipitation.

- An *occluded front* forms when a warm air mass is caught between two colder air masses coming together. When the cooler air masses meet, they force the warmer, less-dense air that lies between them upward. Weather associated with occluded fronts includes heavy rain or snow and cooler temperatures.

Illustrations of the different types of fronts are shown below.

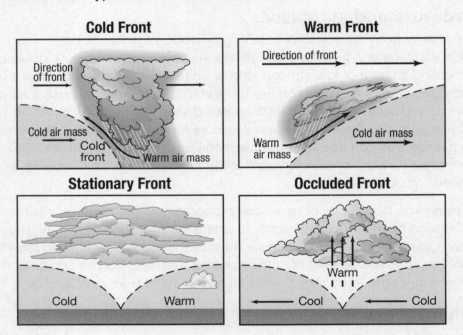

Cold Front

Direction of front

Cold air mass

Cold front

Warm air mass

Warm Front

Direction of front

Warm air mass

Cold air mass

Stationary Front

Cold   Warm

Occluded Front

Warm

Cool   Cold

Clouds and Weather

Clouds are masses of water droplets or tiny ice crystals suspended in the atmosphere. Clouds form when water vapor rises and then cools and condenses around dust particles. Clouds form at different heights and are associated with different kinds of weather.

- *Stratus* clouds are low sheets of gray clouds that cover the sky. Rain or snow sometimes falls from stratus clouds.

- *Cumulus* clouds are puffy white clouds with flat bottoms. They are usually associated with fair weather. Cumulus clouds can become *cumulonimbus clouds*—large dark clouds in which thunderstorms form. Thunderstorms bring heavy rain, hail, lightning, and thunder.

- *Cirrus* clouds are the highest clouds. These thin, wispy clouds usually appear in fair weather, but they sometimes signal that rain is on the way. Cirrus clouds are very cold and are made up of ice particles instead of drops of water.

Stratus clouds   Cumulus clouds   Cirrus clouds

Jet Streams

Recall from Lesson 48 that a jet stream is a fast-moving current of air located about 10–15 km above Earth's surface. Jet streams form where cold air masses from the north meet warm air masses from closer to the equator. The jet stream moves like a river from west to east, often carrying storms and other weather with it. Two jet streams move across the continental United States. The northern jet stream typically has more effect on weather patterns. When it dips south, it brings cooler air from Canada. The farther south it moves, the farther south the cold air travels. When this jet stream remains over Canada, the northern United States has mild winters. The southern jet stream is often south of the United States. However, it can move north and bring warmer temperatures to the southern United States.

Weather Maps

Meteorologists use computers and maps to analyze and display weather data and make weather forecasts. A **weather map** uses symbols to show the weather conditions of specific locations at a certain time. Data are collected at weather stations all over the country. The atmospheric conditions you are likely to see on a weather map include areas of high and low air pressure, cloud cover, types of precipitation, temperature, and fronts. Recall that high pressure (H) brings fair weather and low pressure (L) brings stormy weather. Storms and changeable weather often occur along fronts.

The weather map below shows the continental United States. The shaded bands that stretch across the map are labeled with numbers and show temperature ranges. Here the temperature is shown in degrees Fahrenheit. A different symbol is used for each kind of front. The direction the front is moving is indicated by the direction of the triangles or half-circles. For example, the cold front in the northwestern United States is moving south. It is also moving east due to the jet stream.

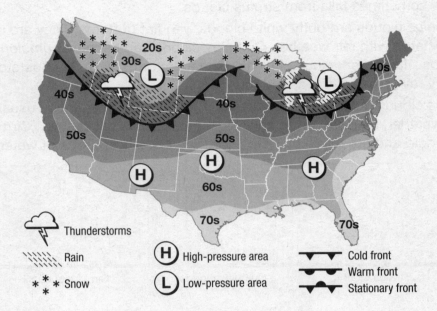

Weather forecasters also use data from satellites that report weather conditions around the world. The data are entered into computers. Computer programs analyze the data and generate models of how the weather in various locations is likely to change.

Discussion Question

Look at the weather map above. What was the weather in the region where you live on the day this map was made? What type of weather did your region experience in the days following?

Lesson Review

Use the diagrams below to answer questions 1 and 2.

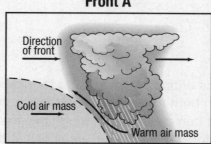

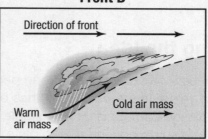

1. What kind of front is Front B?

   A. cold front   **C.** occluded front

   B. warm front   **D.** stationary front

2. What type of cloud is forming in Front A?

   A. stratus   **C.** cumulus

   B. cirrus   **D.** cumulonimbus

3. Which of the following is associated with high or increasing air pressure?

   A. stormy weather   **C.** fair, dry weather

   B. gentle precipitation   **D.** cold, humid weather

4. In which direction do the jet streams over the United States move weather?

   A. west to east

   B. east to west

   C. north to south

   D. south to north

The Atmosphere and Climate Change

Key Words • ice age • axial tilt • orbit • atmosphere • greenhouse effect • global warming

Getting the Idea

Earth's climate can change over long periods of time, from tens, to thousands, to millions of years. In the past, Earth has been both much colder and much warmer than it is today. Climate is usually stable but can change over long time scales. Earth's climate can change due to plate tectonic movements, variations in the tilt of its axis, or changes to the atmosphere.

Plate Tectonics and Climate

An **ice age** is a period in which the average global temperature is cooler, causing the amount of snow and ice that forms each year to be greater than the amount that melts. This leads to the formation and expansion of glaciers over land. The last period in which glaciers covered much of the continents was from about 110,000 to 10,000 years ago. Today, glaciers cover only about 10 percent of continental land mass. What can cause Earth's global climate to change?

Plate tectonics changes Earth's climate over very long periods by changing the shapes and arrangements of the continents. The maps below show how Earth's continents looked at various points in geologic time. When much of the land was located closer to the South Pole, the climate was cooler. Also, when land was clustered in one large continent, ocean currents were less able to equalize the temperature among regions. Land located far from bodies of water experienced more extremes of hot and cold. When the landmass broke into smaller continents, all surrounded by water, they had more moderate temperature ranges.

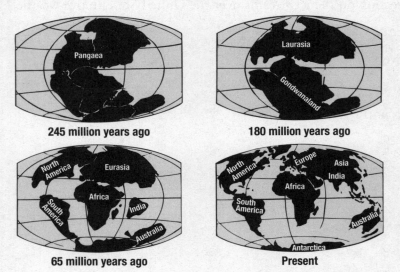

245 million years ago

180 million years ago

65 million years ago

Present

Plate tectonic processes also produce mountains. Over time, these mountains are slowly worn down. Recall that higher-altitude areas tend to be cooler. The formation of tall mountain ranges, therefore, produces cool climate regions. Glaciers begin to form at high altitudes or near the poles. Plate tectonic processes can explain global climate changes over many millions of years.

Earth's Axis and Climate

Earth's seasons are caused by the combination of Earth's 23.5-degree tilt on its axis, or **axial tilt**, and Earth's changing position in its **orbit**, its path around the sun. The Northern Hemisphere experiences summer when it is tilted toward the sun and winter when it is tilted away from the sun. The same is true of the Southern Hemisphere, where seasons occur at opposite times from those in the Northern Hemisphere. However, over tens of thousands of years, Earth's axial tilt and the shape of its orbit change in predictable cycles. These cycles help explain past climate changes and predict such changes in the future.

If you have ever observed a wobbling top, you know that as the top spins, the direction of its axis changes slightly. Like a top, Earth's axial tilt changes its orientation relative to other objects in space, such as stars. It takes nearly 26,000 years for Earth's axis to return to its starting position. The diagram below illustrates this phenomenon.

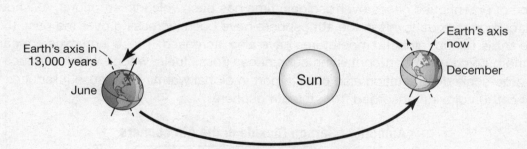

The changing orientation of Earth's axis affects climate because Earth's orbit is not a perfect circle. Rather, it is slightly elliptical, or egg-shaped. Earth is closer to the sun in some parts of its orbit than in others. Currently, Earth is closest to the sun when it is winter in the Northern Hemisphere. Earth is farthest from the sun when it is winter in the Southern Hemisphere. This causes the Northern Hemisphere to have milder winters and summers than the Southern Hemisphere. (However, because the surface of the Southern Hemisphere contains more water and less land, the extreme winters and summers caused by Earth's distance from the sun are moderated.) In 13,000 years, it will be winter in North America when Earth is farthest from the sun. Winters then will be colder in the Northern Hemisphere and milder in the Southern Hemisphere. Similarly, Southern Hemisphere summers will be cooler, and Northern Hemisphere summers will be hotter.

The tilt of Earth's axis also changes relative to the plane of its orbit. The axis is currently tilted at an angle of 23.5 degrees. The degree of tilt affects the difference between seasons. A larger tilt means more extreme summers and winters. Earth's axial tilt shifts from 22.1 to 24.5 degrees and back again over a period of 41,000 years.

Over hundreds of thousands of years, the shape of Earth's orbit changes. At some times, it is more elliptical than at others. A more elliptical orbit causes more extreme seasons. A more circular orbit results in more moderate seasons.

The Atmosphere and Climate

The composition of Earth's atmosphere also affects climate. The **atmosphere** is the mixture of gases that surrounds Earth and maintains temperatures that are suitable for life. Some of the solar radiation that reaches Earth is reflected back into the atmosphere as infrared radiation. A portion of this reflected radiation is absorbed as heat by certain gases in the atmosphere. The greenhouse gases include carbon dioxide, water vapor, and methane. They make up only a tiny percentage of atmospheric gases. Recall that the atmosphere holds the heat in a process known as the **greenhouse effect**, a natural process that keeps the planet at a temperature that is suitable for life. However, high levels of greenhouse gases, such as carbon dioxide, cause the atmosphere to retain too much heat. This, in turn, causes **global warming**, an increase in average temperatures around the world.

Composition of the Atmosphere

| Nitrogen 78% | Oxygen 21% | Others (1%): argon 0.9%, carbon dioxide 0.03%, neon, helium, methane, krypton, nitrous oxide... |

One source of greenhouse gases over geologic time has been volcanic eruptions. As shown in the graph, carbon dioxide levels in the atmosphere have been increasing over the past 150 years. During the same period, global temperatures have also increased. These increases are caused partly by the burning of carbon-containing substances (fossil fuels, wood), which produce carbon dioxide. Large-scale deforestation also plays a part in global warming because it reduces the amount of carbon dioxide absorbed from the atmosphere.

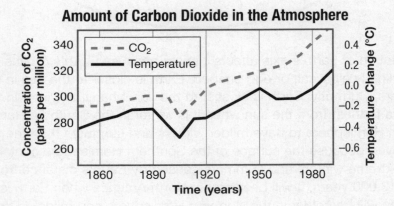

Amount of Carbon Dioxide in the Atmosphere

Global warming is predicted to affect many parts of Earth's surface and ecosystems. The polar ice caps are expected to shrink. Melting ice is expected to cause sea levels to rise as water is added to the oceans. Rising sea levels mean that low-lying coastal areas will experience flooding. Since 60 percent of Earth's human population lives near coastlines, many people may need to be relocated. Because these changes happen rapidly and are significant, they can also lead to extinction of species.

Discussion Question

Which of the processes discussed in this chapter can cause climate to change within a human lifespan? Which changes climate over the longest term? Explain.

Lesson Review

1. The atmosphere is a mixture of gases consisting mostly of

    A. oxygen.

    B. nitrogen.

    C. water vapor.

    D. carbon dioxide.

2. Which change to Earth's surface would result in a cooler global climate?

    A. smaller continents

    B. larger ocean currents

    C. taller mountain ranges

    D. land masses closer to the equator

3. Which is **not** a consequence of increasing the amount of greenhouse gases?

    A. rising sea level

    B. extinction of species

    C. widespread deforestation

    D. increasing average global temperature

4. Which of these is likely to result in more moderate winters and summers in a hemisphere?

    A. Earth being closest to the sun when the hemisphere has summer

    B. more land than water covering the surface of the hemisphere

    C. Earth's orbit becoming less elliptical

    D. Earth's axis tilting at a bigger angle

Chapter 9 Review

The seas surrounding the North Pole are covered in ice. Unlike Antarctica, which is an ice-covered continent, the Arctic sea ice is sensitive to global temperature changes. The sea ice accumulates through the fall and winter, reaching its maximum extent each year in the early spring. During the summer months, sea ice melts faster than it forms, and it reaches its minimum in the late summer or early fall.

In recent years, the sea ice has reached smaller minimums than in the past (Figures 1 and 2). Although there are fluctuations from year to year, the minimum extent of Arctic sea ice has shown an overall declining trend since about 1950 (Figure 3).

Ice has a high albedo, meaning that it reflects much of the light that strikes it. Because water absorbs more of the incident radiation, loss of sea ice leads to an increased amount of solar radiation that is absorbed by Earth's surface. In addition, ice covering the polar seas prevents the evaporation of water into the atmosphere. Increasing the amount of water vapor reinforces the warming trend that leads to the loss of sea ice.

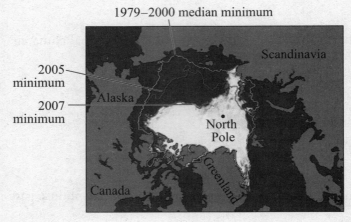

Figure 1

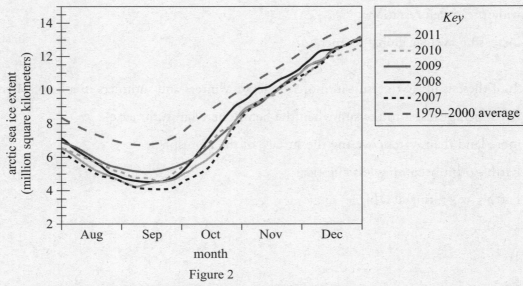

Figure 2

Based on graph from National Snow and Ice Data Center

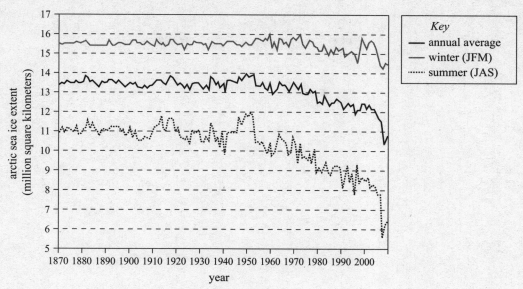

year

Figure 3

1. According to the passage, the main effect of warming global temperature on sea ice has been:

   A. a decrease in the melting rate during summer months.
   B. an increase in the melting rate during summer months.
   C. a decrease in the formation rate of ice in the winter months.
   D. an increase in the formation rate of ice in the winter months.

2. According to Figure 2, in which year was the sea ice minimum the smallest?

   F. 2007
   G. 2008
   H. 2010
   J. 2011

3. According to Figure 3, the change in annual sea ice extent is due mostly to:

   A. increasing winter sea ice.
   B. decreasing winter sea ice.
   C. increasing summer sea ice.
   D. decreasing summer sea ice.

4. The effects of diminished sea ice discussed in the last paragraph of the passage can be characterized as:

   F. positive feedback mechanisms, because they amplify the effect of global warming on sea ice.
   G. negative feedback mechanisms, because they further diminish the amount of sea ice over time.
   H. positive feedback mechanisms, because they counter the effects of having less sea ice in the summer months.
   J. negative feedback mechanisms, because they have the opposite effect on Earth's energy budget and climate as they have on the sea ice.

5. It can be concluded from the passage that:

   A. water vapor in the atmosphere acts as a greenhouse gas.
   B. sea ice increases the amount of water vapor in the atmosphere.
   C. the reflection of solar energy by ice contributes to global warming.
   D. the absorption of solar energy by water reduces global temperature.

Chapter 10 Astronomy

The Origin and Structure of the Universe

Key Words • big bang theory • galaxy • Doppler effect • redshift • cosmic background radiation

Getting the Idea

What does the universe consist of, and how did it form? These questions are discussed in this lesson.

The Big Bang Theory

The most widely accepted theory for the formation of the universe is the **big bang theory**. According to this theory, the universe was once compacted in a tiny, dense volume smaller than an atom. This point was incredibly dense and hot. In an event called the big bang, the tiny, dense point suddenly began to expand greatly. During the first fraction of a second of the big bang, matter and energy were propelled outward in all directions. All energy, space, time, and matter resulted from the big bang. The universe expanded and cooled.

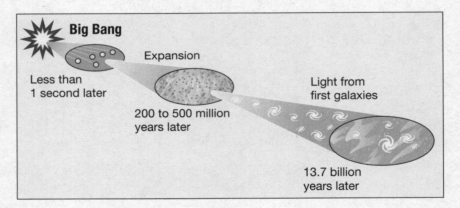

About 200 to 500 million years after the big bang, the first galaxies began to form. A **galaxy** is a very large group of stars held together by gravity.

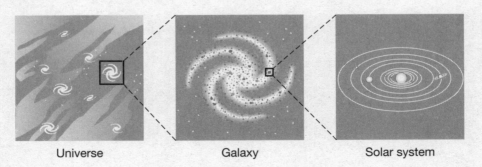

Some galaxies spiral around their centers, like a flat, spinning disk. The Milky Way is the spiral galaxy that contains Earth. Galaxies vary greatly in size and shape. Dwarf galaxies contain 10^7 stars, while the largest galaxies have the square of this number, or 10^{14} stars.

Individual galaxies, in turn, are composed of stars, clouds of dust and gas, black holes, pulsars, and dark matter. Pulsars are described in Lesson 53. Many stars are surrounded by orbiting planets and other bodies, forming solar systems. The solar nebula hypothesis, discussed in Lesson 43, describes how stars and solar systems can form from clouds of gas and dust.

Evidence for the Big Bang

Some evidence suggests that the big bang occurred approximately 13.7 billion years ago. This evidence includes measurements of moving galaxies and radiation levels in space. Studies show that most galaxies are moving away from each other. This observation indicates that the universe is expanding. To understand how the galaxies are moving, look at the diagram below. The balloon on the left is only partly inflated. The dots represent galaxies. As air is added to the balloon, it expands, and the dots move farther apart.

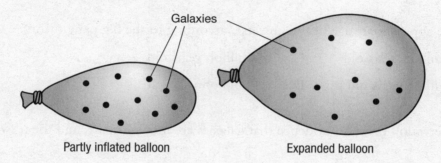

Galaxies

Partly inflated balloon   Expanded balloon

Evidence for the motion of galaxies comes from the light they emit. Recall from Lesson 19 that when the source of a wave is moving away from an observer, the wave has a longer wavelength and a lower frequency. In the case of an emergency siren moving farther away, the pitch of the siren would be lower. This is known as the **Doppler effect**.

The light observed from most galaxies shows evidence of the Doppler effect. It is shifted toward the lower-frequency (red) end of the electromagnetic spectrum, known as the **redshift**. This redshift indicates that the galaxies are moving away from observers on Earth in all directions. This movement is evidence that the universe is expanding. In the 1920s, Edwin Hubble demonstrated that the farther away a galaxy is, the faster it is moving away from Earth and the more the galaxy's light is redshifted.

Another important observation supporting the big bang theory is **cosmic background radiation**. This weak radiation is found to be coming from all directions in the universe, and does not originate from any single point or object. It is thought to be a result of the early expansion of the universe just after the big bang, and is sometimes called *relic radiation* because it provides clues to the past, like a fossil. The universe at the time of the big bang was very hot and gave off large amounts of energy in the form of thermal radiation. As the universe expanded, it cooled. The cosmic background radiation is thought to be the remains of the extremely high-energy radiation from the big bang. Cosmic background radiation has a temperature of only about 3 kelvins and a wavelength of about 1 millimeter. It is long-wavelength, low-energy radiation.

Discussion Question

What evidence supports the big bang theory for the formation of the universe?

Lesson Review

1. What is the approximate age of the universe, according to the big bang theory?

    A. 13.7 million years old   **C.** 137 billion years old

    B. 137 million years old   **D.** 13.7 billion years old

2. Which observation provides evidence that galaxies are moving apart, and the universe is expanding?

    A. the grouping of galaxies into clusters

    B. the cosmic background radiation from galaxies

    C. a shift in light from galaxies toward lower frequencies

    D. a shift in light from galaxies toward shorter wavelengths

3. From where do scientists think cosmic background radiation originates?

    A. the initial expansion of the big bang

    B. nuclear fusion reactions in distant stars

    C. gravitational attraction between galaxies

    D. the motion of galaxies away from Earth

4. The greatest distances in the universe occur between

    A. stars.   **C.** solar systems.

    B. galaxies.   **D.** planets.

The Evolution of Stars

Key Words • nebula • protostar • nuclear fusion • stellar equilibrium • main sequence • red giant • planetary nebula • white dwarf • black dwarf • supernova • neutron star • pulsar • black hole

Getting the Idea

Most stars exist for billions of years. During that time, a star changes many times. The pattern of these changes is called the star life cycle. A star's life cycle depends on its mass.

Life Cycle of Stars

A star is a massive ball of hot gases that gives off its own light. Stars are composed primarily of hydrogen and helium. According to the solar nebula theory, a star forms inside a cloud of gas and dust called a **nebula**. Gravity pulls particles of gas and dust together to form a dense, rotating sphere. The cloud becomes hotter as it gets smaller. The gravitational potential energy of the particles first changes into kinetic energy and then into heat. As it gets hot, the cloud starts to glow. This glowing, hot sphere of dust and gas is a beginning star called a **protostar**.

When a protostar becomes hot enough, nuclear fusion begins. **Nuclear fusion** is the joining of small atomic nuclei to form a larger atomic nucleus. In young stars, hydrogen nuclei combine to form helium nuclei. Nuclear fusion releases huge amounts of energy. The nuclear fusion reactions in the sun, for example, produce the energy that reaches Earth as electromagnetic radiation. In later phases of a star's life cycle, the helium may fuse to produce heavier elements, such as carbon and oxygen. These elements may later fuse to form even heavier elements.

A star's mass determines how much gravity pulls inward on the gases making up the star. The more massive a star, the greater is the force of gravity. The inward pull of gravity is opposed by outward pressure from nuclear fusion and energy radiation. If gravity is stronger, the star contracts. If the outward pressure is stronger, the star expands. When the star reaches a point where gravity and the outward pressure are equal, it does not change size. The stable state in which a star is neither expanding nor contracting is called **stellar equilibrium**.

The initial mass of a star determines the star's temperature, its luminosity (brightness), and its diameter. Luminosity is a measure of the energy released from the surface of a star each second. The apparent brightness of a star depends on its luminosity and its distance from the observer.

The temperature and brightness of stars are plotted on the Hertzsprung-Russell diagram, shown below. Note that our sun lies in the middle of the band connecting the brightest and hottest stars with the dimmest and coolest. This band represents the main-sequence stage, the first and longest stage of a star's life cycle. Most main-sequence stars are medium-mass stars—stars with masses similar to the sun. Massive stars are found to the upper left of the main sequence. Low-mass stars are located in the lower right. **Main sequence** stars use hydrogen in their cores as fuel for nuclear fusion. The fusion process continues until the hydrogen runs out and the star enters the next phase of its life cycle.

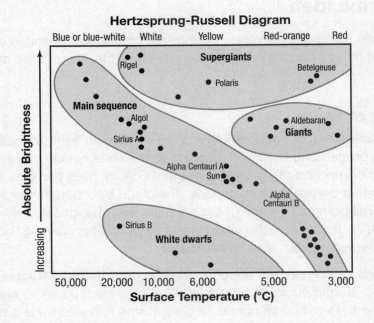

Life Cycles of Medium-Mass Stars

When the hydrogen in a star's core is used up, the star's outer layers expand and it becomes a large, cool **red giant**. Hydrogen in the red giant's outer layers continues to form helium by fusion. When this hydrogen is used up, and fusion stops, the outer layers of the red giant expand outward and form a glowing shell of gas called a **planetary nebula**. The planetary nebula name is very misleading. Astronomers named these objects in the late 1700s when they were first discovered. Through the telescopes of that time, these objects looked round and greenish like the planet Uranus. We now know the nebulae have nothing to do with planets. The remaining core of the star forms a small, hot object called a **white dwarf**. A white dwarf does not produce energy. It glows from its remaining thermal energy as it slowly cools. When it has too little energy to glow, it becomes a **black dwarf**.

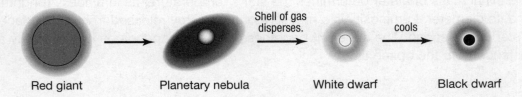

Life Cycles of Low-Mass Stars

A *low-mass star* is a star whose mass is less than one-half the mass of the sun. Low-mass stars use up their hydrogen fuel slowly. The cores of these stars never get hot enough for helium to fuse into heavier elements. As a result, these stars do not become red giants. When the hydrogen in the core of a low-mass star is used up, the star collapses and forms a white dwarf. In time, the white dwarf cools to form a black dwarf.

Life Cycles of Massive Stars

Massive stars are those with masses at least three times the mass of the sun. Because the force of gravity is so great, a massive star must undergo fusion at a faster rate to counterbalance the inward pull of gravity. These stars, therefore, use up their fuel quickly and have fairly short life spans. Massive stars also carry out fusion reactions in stages. The first stage involves the fusion of hydrogen to form helium. Later stages of fusion reactions include the formation of carbon, oxygen, nitrogen, and other chemical elements. Many of the elements in the universe were formed in these later stages of massive stars. A massive star may expand to form a red giant or supergiant at the end of each reaction stage. Fusion of iron into heavier elements requires too much energy to take place in the core of the star. Formation of an iron core is the last stage in a star's life cycle. If a massive star loses enough mass, it may become a white dwarf, and then a black dwarf.

Some massive stars die in huge explosions called **supernovas**. The explosion is hot enough to form heavier elements than iron, such as gold and iodine. Large amounts of matter are flung into space by supernova explosions. If the original massive star is less than three times the mass of the sun, it can form a neutron star after the supernova. A **neutron star** consists of neutrons rather than ordinary matter. Neutron stars are smaller and denser than white dwarfs and may be as small as Earth. Some neutron stars emit a beam of radiation in one direction. Because these stars also rotate, the beam is detected on Earth as a repeating pulse. These stars are called **pulsars**.

If the mass remaining after a supernova explosion is more than three times the mass of the sun, it collapses to form a black hole. A **black hole** is a small, extremely dense object whose gravitational pull is so strong that not even light can escape it. Only the most massive stars are thought to form black holes.

Discussion Question

The sun is a medium-mass star. Betelgeuse is a supergiant. How will the sun's life cycle differ from that of Betelgeuse?

Lesson Review

1. What forms after all the hydrogen has been exhausted in the core of a medium-mass star?

   A. red giant

   B. black hole

   C. neutron star

   D. white dwarf

2. What develops after the supernovas of the most massive stars?

   A. black hole

   B. neutron star

   C. black dwarf

   D. planetary nebula

3. What property of a star determines the stages it will go through during its life cycle?

   A. mass

   B. position

   C. diameter

   D. brightness

4. Which list shows the correct sequence of elements that are used as fuels form in the cores of massive stars?

   A. iron, hydrogen, helium, carbon, and oxygen

   B. helium, hydrogen, oxygen, carbon, and iron

   C. carbon, hydrogen, helium, oxygen, and iron

   D. hydrogen, helium, carbon, oxygen, and iron

5. What element is formed in the core of a massive star just before the star explodes in a supernova?

   A. iron

   B. silicon

   C. carbon

   D. helium

The Sun

Key Words • photosphere • chromosphere • corona • solar wind • sunspot • solar prominence • solar flare • ionosphere • aurora

Getting the Idea

All life on Earth depends on the sun's energy. Recall that this star produces energy when hydrogen nuclei fuse together in its core. This lesson describes the sun's structure and features.

The Sun's Structure and Atmosphere

The sun is a hot, dense sphere of gas and plasma. Like other main-sequence stars, the sun consists of hydrogen and helium with traces of other elements. The sun's innermost core is where nuclear fusion of hydrogen takes place to form helium. Fusion releases large amounts of energy. This energy travels from the core through the sun's interior before entering its atmosphere. From there, it radiates into space in the form of electromagnetic radiation.

The sun has several layers surrounding its core, which are in turn surrounded by an atmosphere. The **photosphere** is the innermost, thickest layer of the sun's atmosphere. The sun's visible light comes from the photosphere, which is what you see when you look at an image of the sun.

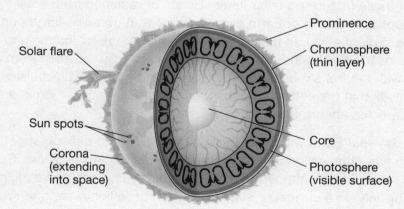

Solar flare

Sun spots

Corona (extending into space)

Prominence

Chromosphere (thin layer)

Core

Photosphere (visible surface)

The photosphere is surrounded by the **chromosphere**, the middle layer of the sun's atmosphere. It is thinner and hotter than the photosphere, but emits only red light. The outermost layer of the sun's atmosphere is the **corona**. The corona is very thin and very hot, and extends for millions of kilometers into space.

Solar Features

The sun's corona is the source of the solar wind. The **solar wind** is a constant stream of charged particles that escape the sun's gravity because the corona is so hot. The solar wind consists of fast-moving ions that shower the entire solar system. Huge bubbles of gas can suddenly erupt from the corona and flow out into space. These bursts are called *coronal mass ejections* (CMEs). CMEs can produce gusts of solar wind that move at up to 1.6 million kilometers per hour.

Dark spots, called sunspots, can be observed on the photosphere. **Sunspots** are regions that are cooler than the surrounding areas. Sunspots appear dark because a cool gas does not give off as much light as a hotter gas. Although they look small when seen against the sun, some sunspots are larger than our entire planet. Sunspots are temporary features that appear and disappear over days, weeks, or months. Their movement across the photosphere is evidence that the sun rotates.

Sunspots are related to other features of the photosphere—solar prominences and solar flares. **Solar prominences** are large loops or arcs of gas that link different areas of sunspots. Some solar prominences are powerful enough to blast material from the sun into space. **Solar flares** are sudden, intense eruptions on the sun's surface. Flares occur when loops of gas near sunspots suddenly connect and release large amounts of energy. A solar flare can release a tenth of the energy of the entire sun. This energy includes both radiation and subatomic particles.

Effects of the Sun on Earth

You have read that the sun is the primary source of energy for Earth. This energy drives ecological processes such as photosynthesis and the water cycle. Energy from the sun is also vital to maintaining temperatures on Earth that can sustain life.

The sun also affects Earth by producing space weather. Several features of the sun cause space weather. One of these features is solar flares. Blasts of radiation from solar flares are absorbed by Earth's **ionosphere**, a layer of Earth's atmosphere that contains large numbers of charged particles, or ions. Solar flares can block shortwave radio communication and disrupt satellite navigation systems (GPS). When Earth's atmosphere absorbs radiation from a solar flare, the protons collide with neutral atmospheric gases, creating more ions. Satellites normally send and receive radio waves that travel through the ionosphere. Communication is disrupted because the extra charged particles absorb those radio waves.

The solar wind showers Earth with ions. Earth's magnetic field deflects most of these particles, trapping them in two rings called the Van Allen belts that circle the planet. Some of the particles that manage to reach Earth's atmosphere produce **auroras**, or displays of light in the night sky. An aurora may appear as a curtain or streak of light. These lights are often red or fluorescent green in color. Auroras are seen most often in latitudes near the poles.

When gusts of solar wind pass Earth, they disrupt Earth's magnetic field and interfere with electrical grids, spacecraft operations, radio communication, and satellite navigation.

Discussion Question

Compasses are navigation tools that can be affected by the solar wind. Why would the solar wind affect a compass?

Lesson Review

1. What are the three layers of the sun's atmosphere, in order from innermost to outermost?

    A. chromosphere, corona, photosphere

    B. chromosphere, photosphere, corona

    C. photosphere, chromosphere, corona

    D. photosphere, corona, chromosphere

2. Sunspots are dark areas on the surface of the sun. Why do they appear darker than the areas around them?

    A. They are areas of gas that are hotter than the surrounding areas.

    B. They are areas of gas that are cooler than the surrounding areas.

    C. They are craters that formed from space debris crashing into the sun.

3. Which solar feature causes auroras?

    A. sunspots   C. the solar wind

    B. solar flares   D. solar prominences

4. Which of the following **best** describes why solar flares can block shortwave radio communication?

    A. They damage the equipment that receives radio waves.

    B. They remove the charged particles that transmit radio waves.

    C. Their charged particles absorb the radio waves outside the atmosphere.

    D. They add charged particles to Earth's atmosphere that absorb radio waves.

5. Which layer of Earth's atmosphere absorbs blasts of radiation from the sun that damage communication and navigation systems?

    A. corona   C. lithosphere

    B. ionosphere   D. hydrosphere

The Solar System

• planetary system • asteroid • orbit • comet • ellipse • Kepler's laws • tide

Getting the Idea

Like many stars, our sun is surrounded by a system of orbiting planets and other bodies. Recall from Lesson 43 that most scientists believe the solar system formed by collapsing from a cloud of dust and gas about 4.6 billion years ago—the solar nebula theory. In this lesson, you will learn about the solar system.

Our Solar System

Recall that the solar nebula theory describes how the solar system formed from a cloud of dust and gas. As the particles in this nebula moved around, they bumped into each other. Gravity began to pull some of the particles closer together. Over time, gravity drew the particles in the nebula together to form the sun, planets, moons, and other bodies in the solar system.

Shortly after the sun formed, the remaining particles of the nebula formed a flat disk rotating around the sun. This disk became the planets, their moons, and other bodies of the solar system. The rocky *inner planets*—those nearest the sun—formed mostly from substances that do not evaporate at high temperatures. These planets include Mercury, Venus, Earth, and Mars. The gaseous *outer planets*—Jupiter, Saturn, Uranus, and Neptune—formed mostly from hydrogen and helium. A system made up of a star and surrounding bodies is called a **planetary system**.

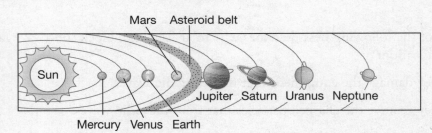

The solar system, including Earth, formed about 4.6 billion years ago.

Asteroids are small, irregular rocks in orbit around the sun. Recall from Lesson 51 that an **orbit** is the path that a planet or other space body takes as it revolves around another, more massive body. Most of the asteroids are in the asteroid belt, a region between the inner and outer planets. Jupiter's gravity keeps the asteroids in this region. The diagram above shows the arrangement of the planets and the asteroid belt.

Gravity and Motion in the Solar System

Gravity is the force responsible for the motions of the planets, asteroids, **comets** (bodies that are made up of ice and rocky dust particles and that orbit the sun), and moons in the solar system. Recall that gravity is an attractive force that works to pull objects together. Since gravity works to pull objects toward each other, what keeps the planets from crashing into the sun, or the moon from crashing into Earth? Newton's first law of motion states that all matter has *inertia*, or the tendency to resist a change in its motion. Inertia keeps moving objects in motion along a straight path. The more mass the object has, the greater its inertia.

The diagram shows how inertia and gravity work together to keep the moon orbiting Earth. First, the moon's inertia pushes it to travel continuously in a straight line. At the same time, Earth's gravity is pulling the moon toward Earth. These combined forces cause the moon to move in a curved path around Earth.

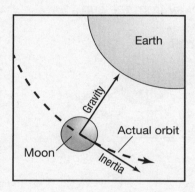

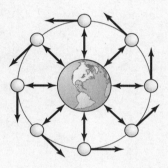

Kepler's Laws and Planetary Orbits

All the planets orbit the sun. In the early seventeenth century, the German mathematician and astronomer Johannes Kepler concluded that the planets' orbits are not perfect circles, but **ellipses**, or ovals. He also developed other descriptions of the orbits. These descriptions are known as **Kepler's laws** of planetary motion. Kepler's three laws are summarized here:

- First law: The orbit of each planet is an ellipse with the sun at one focus. (There are two points called *foci* inside an ellipse.)
- Second law: A planet moves faster in its orbit when it is closer to the sun, and slower when it is farther from the sun.
- Third law: The farther a planet is from the sun, the longer its period of revolution is.

Kepler developed his laws from carefully recorded observations, kept over many years, by the Danish astronomer Tycho Brahe. When Brahe recorded the motions of visible planets such as Mars, the telescope had not yet been invented. Brahe did not analyze his observations. It was Kepler who closely studied Brahe's data and used it to formulate his laws. Science makes progress when scientists draw testable conclusions from observations.

According to Kepler's laws, the planets farthest from the sun should move more slowly. Because their orbits are so large, they also take much longer. For example, Neptune takes ~165 Earth years to make a complete revolution around the sun. In contrast, Mercury takes only 88 days.

Earth's orbit is almost a perfect circle, but it is slightly elliptical. That is why winter is a little longer than summer in the Northern Hemisphere. A planet's gravity can change the orbits of comets, asteroids, and meteoroids. These changes in orbit can cause these bodies to collide with planets or moons, creating craters on impact or burning up in the atmosphere. A *meteoroid* is a piece of rock in space. Once it enters the atmosphere, it burns and is perceived as a *meteor*.

Comets

A comet is a body made up of ice and rocky dust particles that orbits the sun in an extremely elliptical orbit, many taking hundreds of years. Comet ice is made up of gases such as methane in solid form. The main part of a comet is called the head. The elliptical orbits of some comets bring them into the inner solar system. As a comet approaches the sun, the ice vaporizes, causing the comet to lose mass and produce a spectacular streak or tail that can be more than 100 million kilometers long. Solar wind causes a comet's tail to always point away from the sun, whether the comet is moving toward the sun or away from the sun.

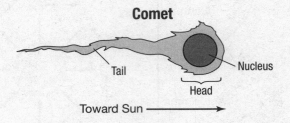

Comet

Tail

Nucleus

Head

Toward Sun ⟶

Tides

Tides are daily changes in the height of the ocean surface. Tides are caused by the gravitational pull of the moon and sun on Earth. The moon's gravity pulls on Earth's surface water, causing the oceans to bulge on the side of Earth nearest to the moon (A). At the same time, the moon's gravity pulls Earth toward the moon, leaving behind a bulge of ocean on the opposite side (B). This produces high tides on opposite sides of Earth. The water level is highest at high tide.

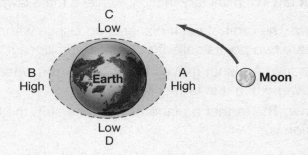

C
Low

B
High — Earth — A
High

Moon

Low
D

Areas between the two high-tide regions experience low tides (C and D). At any time, there are two regions of Earth experiencing high tides and two regions experiencing low tides. On any given coast, the ocean rises and falls about every 12.5 hours. The sun's gravity also affects tides. But the effect of the sun's gravity is about half as strong as the moon's, because the sun is much farther away. The tides are stronger than usual at new and full moon, when the sun and moon pull in the same direction. They are weaker when the sun and moon pull at right angles to each other.

Discussion Question

Mercury travels at a mean velocity of about 173,000 km/h around the sun. Explain how the planet is able to remain in orbit without falling into the sun or speeding off into space.

Lesson Review

1. Which is the **best** explanation for why the moon orbits Earth rather than Earth orbiting the moon?

   A. Earth has less mass than the moon.

   B. Earth has more mass than the moon.

   C. Earth rotates faster than the moon rotates.

   D. The moon has no gravitational pull on anything.

2. According to Kepler's laws, what is the relationship between the size of a planet's orbit and the speed with which it moves around the sun?

   A. As the size of a planet's orbit increases, the speed of the planet decreases.

   B. As the speed of a planet increases, the time required to complete on orbit increases.

   C. As a planet's distance from the sun increases, the speed of the planet also increases.

3. How does gravity affect a planet's orbit around the sun?

   A. Gravity causes a planet to leave its orbit and travel away from the sun.

   B. Gravity creates an orbit by pushing the planet into an elliptical motion.

   C. Gravity creates an orbit by constantly pulling the planet toward the sun.

   D. Gravity causes a planet's inertia, making it more likely to travel away from the sun.

4. Which of the following **best** describes a comet?

   A. large mass of burning hot gas

   B. body of ice and dust that orbits the sun

   C. large rocky ball with a tail that points toward the sun

   D. small rocky object that burns up in Earth's atmosphere

5. The smallest differences between high and low tides occur

   A. when the sun and moon are in the same direction from Earth.

   B. when the sun and moon are in opposite directions from Earth.

   C. when the sun and moon form a right angle with each other and Earth.

Chapter 10 Review

A student understands that ocean tides are caused by the gravitational interaction between the moon and Earth. The student decided to conduct the following experiments to examine the effect, if any, of the sun on tides.

Experiment 1

For the first experiment, the student wanted to determine if the beach where her study would be conducted had diurnal tides (one high and one low tide per day) or semi-diurnal tides (two high and two low tides per day). The student designed a water level measuring device that contained a floating ball in a pipe open to the water. As the water level moved up and down with the tides, the floating ball moved with the water level. The pipe was connected to a recording device that collected water level data every hour. The student collected water levels over a 3-day period. The results are shown in Figure 1.

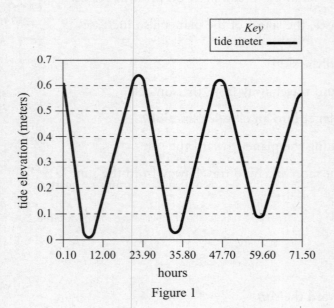

Key
tide meter ———

Figure 1

Experiment 2

For the next experiment, the student wanted to determine if the gravitational interaction of the sun and Earth could be detected by measuring tides. The student knew that during the new moon, the moon was between Earth and the sun, and that during the first and third quarter moon phases, the moon was perpendicular to the sun as viewed from Earth. She reasoned that if the sun also had an influence on the tides, the tidal range should be greatest when the gravitational force of the moon and the sun worked together (during the new moon) and the tidal range should be smallest when the moon and the sun's gravitational force canceled each other out (during the first or third quarter moon). Therefore, she measured the low and high tide for the new moon and first quarter moon for five months. The results are shown in Table 1.

Table 1				
	Measurement (meters)			
Month	High tide	Low tide	Tidal range	Average range
New moon				
January	0.71	−0.50	1.21	0.82
February	0.62	−0.43	1.05	
March	0.34	0.00	0.34	
April	0.56	0.09	0.65	
May	0.71	−0.012	0.84	
First quarter moon				
January	0.37	−0.09	0.47	0.58
February	0.47	−0.22	0.68	
March	0.56	−0.12	0.68	
April	0.50	−0.03	0.53	
May	0.50	−0.03	0.53	

1. What was the measured independent variable in Experiment 1?

   A. Time
   B Tide elevation
   C. Difference between high and low tide
   D. Moon phase

2. When the water level measuring device was installed in the water, the tide was between low and high tide for that day. The student decided to set the measuring device to 0.0 meters and base all other measurements on this setting. What would happen if she set the measuring device during high tide?

   F. The measurements would be invalid, because she did not properly calibrate the device.
   G. Most measurements would be negative numbers, but the calculated differences between high and low tides would not change.
   H. Most measurements would be positive but the calculated differences between high and low tides would not change.
   J. The measurements and results would all be higher.

3. Which of the following factors would be most likely to have affected the tide elevation measurements in these experiments?

   A. Choice of beach for the study area
   B. Water temperature
   C. Storms
   D. Ocean current speeds

4. Which of the following statements is best supported by the results shown in Figure 1 and Table 1?

   F. The tides are diurnal and tidal ranges are greatest during new moons.
   G. The tides are semi-diurnal and tidal ranges are greatest during new moons.
   H. The tides are diurnal and tidal ranges are greatest during first quarter moons.
   J. The tides are semi-diurnal and tidal ranges are greatest during first quarter moons.

5. If Experiment 2 were repeated using tide measurements from the third quarter moon, what would be the expected differences in the results?

   A. The tidal ranges would have been more than double the ranges of the first quarter moon.
   B. The tidal ranges would be approximately one half that of the first quarter moon.
   C. The tidal ranges would be about the same as the ranges for the new moon.
   D. None, since the tidal range would be roughly the same as the ranges for the first quarter moon.

6. Using the results presented in Table 1, which of the following statements best describes the variation in tidal ranges for new and first quarter moons?

   F. New moon tidal ranges were more variable, but always greater than ranges for first quarter moons.
   G. New moon tidal ranges were less variable, but always greater than ranges for first quarter moons.
   H. New moon tidal ranges were more variable, and sometimes less than ranges for first quarter moons.
   J. New moon tidal ranges were less variable, and sometimes less than ranges for first quarter moons.

Glossary

abiotic factor a nonliving aspect of an organism's environment (Lesson 40)

absolute dating a method of determining the actual age of a rock sample or fossil, often using the decay rates of unstable isotopes (Lesson 43)

absolute zero the point at which particles have no motion at all; a temperature of $-273°C$ or 0 K (Lesson 14)

accelerated reference frame a reference frame that is accelerating relative to other objects or reference frames (Lesson 20)

acceleration a change in an object's velocity over time (Lesson 20)

accuracy a measure of how close a measurement is to the true value (Lesson 4)

acid any substance that releases or donates hydrogen ions (H^+) in solution; a solution with a pH below 7 (Lesson 12)

acid rain precipitation with a lower pH level than normal (Lesson 41)

action-reaction forces a pair of equal and opposite forces produced according to Newton's third law of motion (Lesson 21)

activation energy the energy required to allow a chemical reaction to proceed (Lessons 11, 28)

active transport the movement of particles into or out of a cell against a concentration gradient, which requires a cell to use energy (Lesson 27)

adaptation a trait that increases an organism's chance of survival and becomes more common in a population through natural selection (Lesson 35)

adaptive radiation the evolution of many new species from a single ancestor species (Lesson 36)

aerobic requiring oxygen (Lesson 29)

aerodynamic having to do with a force in a moving fluid, such as air (Lesson 24)

air mass a large body of air that has about the same properties throughout (Lesson 50)

air pressure the combined force of all the molecules in the air on anything within the atmosphere; a measure of the force a column of air exerts on Earth's surface (Lessons 24, 50)

alkali metal any of the elements in Group 1 of the periodic table, which are very reactive (Lesson 7)

alkaline earth metal any of the elements in Group 2 of the periodic table, which are very reactive (Lesson 7)

alleles different forms of a gene (Lesson 32)

alluvium deposit sediment deposited by flowing water (Lesson 47)

amino acid a small molecule that is a building block of proteins (Lesson 31)

amplitude the distance from the midpoint of a wave to either its highest or lowest point (Lesson 18)

anaerobic not requiring oxygen (Lesson 29)

analyze to study and interpret a set of data or observations in order to form a conclusion (Lesson 1)

angle of incidence the angle at which a wave strikes a surface (Lesson 19)

angle of reflection the angle at which a wave reflects, or bounces back, from a surface (Lesson 19)

annelid a member of the phylum that includes segmented worms, such as earthworms (Lesson 38)

anticodon the three exposed bases of a tRNA molecule that pair with an mRNA codon during translation (Lesson 31)

arthropod a member of the phylum that includes crustaceans, insects, and spiders; an organism with a segmented body, jointed appendages, and an exoskeleton (Lesson 38)

asteroid a small, irregular rock in orbit around the sun, usually found in the asteroid belt (Lesson 55)

asthenosphere the soft layer of the mantle underneath the lithosphere (Lesson 42)

atmosphere the mixture of gases surrounding Earth (Lesson 51)

atom a basic building block of matter, consisting of a nucleus surrounded by an electron cloud (Lesson 6)

atomic number the number of protons in the nucleus of an atom of an element (Lesson 6)

ATP (adenosine triphosphate) a small molecule used as a cell's primary energy carrier (Lesson 29)

aurora a display of light in the night sky, usually seen in higher latitudes and caused by the solar wind (Lesson 54)

autosome a non-sex-determining chromosome (Lesson 34)

average atomic mass the average mass of all the isotopes of an element that are found in nature (Lesson 6)

Avogadro's number 6.02×10^{23}; the number of particles in a mole (Lesson 11)

axial tilt the degree to which the imaginary line connecting Earth's north and south poles is shifted from vertical (Lesson 51)

balanced equation a chemical equation in which each side of the equation (reactants and products) has the same number of atoms of each element (Lesson 11)

bar graph a graph that compares data using bars of different heights or lengths (Lesson 3)

base a substance that accepts hydrogen ions and/or releases hydroxide ions (OH^-) in solution; a solution with a pH greater than 7; also called alkali (Lesson 12)

bias a personal prejudice, unfair preference, or slanted point of view that leads to an incorrect conclusion (Lesson 4)

big bang theory the idea that the universe began as a tiny, dense, hot volume that expanded and propelled matter and energy outward in all directions (Lesson 52)

binomial nomenclature a system that gives each species a two-part name consisting of a genus name and a species name (Lesson 37)

biodiversity the variety of organisms living on Earth or in a specific area, as indicated by the number of species (Lessons 36, 41)

biological magnification a process in which chemicals consumed by organisms become more concentrated in the tissues of animals at higher feeding levels (Lesson 41)

biome a large group of ecosystems having similar climatic conditions and organisms (Lesson 49)

biotic factor the biological or living aspects of an organism's environment (Lesson 40)

black dwarf a small, dark object that results when a white dwarf uses up its thermal energy (Lesson 53)

black hole a small, extremely dense object, resulting from the supernova of a larger massive star, whose gravitational pull is so strong that not even light can escape it (Lesson 53)

boiling the process in which bubbles of gas form throughout a liquid and rise to the surface (Lesson 13)

Boyle's law the principle that if the temperature of a gas remains constant, decreasing the volume will cause the pressure to increase, and vice versa (Lesson 14)

buffer a substance that tends to neutralize acids and bases in solution (Lesson 28)

buoyancy the tendency of an object to float due to the force that the surrounding fluid, such as water, exerts on it (Lesson 24)

carrier an individual with normal phenotype who is heterozygous for a recessive gene (Lesson 34)

carrying capacity the largest population of one or more species that an environment can support over a long period (Lesson 40)

catalyst a substance that increases the rate of a chemical reaction without itself being changed by the reaction (Lesson 28)

cell the smallest unit that can carry out all the functions of life; the basic unit of structure and function in all living things (Lesson 26)

cell membrane a thin, flexible layer that surrounds, protects, and supports the rest of the cell, controlling the substances that may enter or leave (Lesson 26)

cell wall a rigid structure that surrounds the cell membrane and gives the cell additional protection and support (Lesson 26)

cellular respiration a biochemical process that breaks the chemical bonds of glucose to release energy (Lesson 29)

charge a property of matter that causes it to experience a force when it is near other charged matter (Lessons 6, 25)

Charles's law the principle that the volume of a gas increases as temperature increases, and vice versa, when pressure is held constant (Lesson 14)

chemical bond the forces, caused by interactions between valence electrons, that hold atoms together in a compound (Lesson 8)

chemical energy the energy that is stored in the bonds that hold together atoms and that is released in chemical reactions (Lesson 15)

chemical equation an equation that shows how a chemical reaction takes place; includes the chemical formulas for reactants on the left side and the formulas for the products on the right side (Lesson 10)

chemical formula an abbreviation that uses chemical symbols and subscripts to show the number of atoms of each element in a molecule of a compound, or the ratio of atoms in an ionic compound (Lessons 8, 10)

chemical reaction a change in the arrangements of atoms in substances, yielding one or more new substances (Lesson 10)

chemical symbol a one- or two-letter abbreviation representing an element (Lesson 6)

chemical weathering a process that breaks rock into smaller pieces as a result of chemical reactions (Lesson 47)

chlorophyll a pigment that gives plants their green color and absorbs light energy (Lesson 29)

chloroplast an organelle that captures the energy of sunlight and uses it for photosynthesis (Lessons 26, 29)

chordate an animal with a hollow dorsal nerve cord and a long, flexible notochord at some stage in development; includes both vertebrate and invertebrate chordates (Lesson 38)

chromosome a structure inside the nucleus of a cell consisting of a molecule of DNA wound around proteins and tightly coiled (Lesson 30)

chromosphere the middle layer of the sun's atmosphere (Lesson 54)

circle graph a graph, consisting of a divided circle, that shows how parts relate to the whole (Lesson 3)

cladogram a diagram that shows evolutionary relationships among different groups of organisms (Lesson 37)

class a taxonomic group smaller and more specific than a phylum, containing one or more orders (Lesson 37)

climate the average weather of a region over many years (Lesson 49)

cloud a mass of water droplets or tiny ice crystals suspended in the atmosphere (Lesson 50)

cnidarian a member of the phylum that includes jellyfish, sea anemones, corals, and hydras (Lesson 38)

codominance a condition in which two different alleles of a gene are both expressed in the same organism (Lesson 34)

codon a nucleotide triplet that codes for a specific amino acid (Lesson 31)

coefficient the numbers in a chemical equation that show how many of each type of molecule are present in a chemical reaction (Lesson 10)

comet a body made up of ice and rocky dust particles that orbits the sun, usually in an extremely elliptical orbit (Lesson 55)

compound a pure substance made up of two or more elements joined chemically (Lesson 8)

compression a region in which particles are temporarily pressed closer together by a longitudinal wave (Lesson 18)

concentration the amount of solute in a given quantity of solvent or solution (Lesson 12)

concentration gradient a difference in the concentration of a solution between two regions (Lesson 27)

conclusion a statement that explains whether the results of an experiment support the hypothesis (Lessons 1, 2, 4)

condensation the change of a gas to a liquid (Lessons 13, 49)

conductor a material or substance that electric current flows through easily (Lesson 17)

constant a factor that is kept the same in all conditions, groups, or treatments in an experiment (Lesson 2)

consumer an organism that obtains its energy and nutrients by ingesting (consuming) other organisms; a heterotroph (Lesson 39)

continental crust the thick, lower-density layer of rock forming Earth's landmasses, consisting mostly of granite (Lesson 42)

continental drift hypothesis the idea that the continents were once joined in a single large landmass that broke apart and that the continents have drifted to their current locations (Lesson 44)

control group the group, treatment, or condition in which the independent variable is set to zero or left out (Lesson 2)

convection current a circular flow of a gas or liquid caused by temperature differences (Lesson 48)

convergent boundary a region where two tectonic plates collide (Lesson 44)

core Earth's deepest, innermost layer (Lesson 42)

Coriolis effect the curvature of the paths of winds and ocean currents due to Earth's rotation (Lesson 48)

corona the outermost layer of the sun's atmosphere; very thin and hot and extends for millions of kilometers into space (Lesson 54)

cosmic background radiation weak radiation coming from all directions in the universe and thought to be a result of the early expansion of the universe (Lesson 52)

covalent bond a bond formed when atoms share valence electrons to gain a more stable electron structure (Lesson 8)

crest the highest point of a wave (Lesson 18)

crossing-over the meiotic process in which homologous chromosomes exchange segments of DNA, resulting in sister chromatids that are genetically unique (Lesson 33)

crust Earth's thinnest, outermost layer (Lesson 42)

crystal a solid made up of ions, atoms, or molecules arranged in a regular, repeating pattern (Lesson 9)

culture cells, tissues, or small microorganisms grown and maintained under laboratory conditions (Lesson 5)

cytoplasm the thick, jelly-like material that holds a cell's internal structures (Lesson 26)

data measurements or observations that are systematically recorded (Lesson 2)

data table a table that organizes related data into rows and columns, with the independent variable in the first column and one or more dependent variables in columns to the right (Lesson 3)

decibel (dB) a unit measuring the intensity or loudness of a sound (Lesson 18)

decomposer an organism that obtains energy and nutrients by breaking down organic wastes, returning unused compounds to the environment (Lesson 39)

deforestation the complete clearing and destruction of a forest to obtain wood or make space available for construction or farming (Lesson 41)

delta a triangular deposit of sediment in a flat, shallow area where a river empties into a body of water (the river's mouth) (Lesson 47)

density a measure of the mass of a substance per unit volume (Lesson 14)

density-dependent limiting factor a limiting factor that varies according to the density of a population (Lesson 40)

density-independent limiting factor a factor that limits the growth of a population regardless of its density (Lesson 40)

dependent variable the variable that is measured in an experiment; the factor that is expected to be influenced by the independent variable (Lesson 2)

deposition the process in which erosion transports sediments and drops them in new locations (Lesson 47)

dichotomous key a tool, consisting of sets of paired statements, that helps scientists identify organisms that they encounter in nature (Lesson 37)

diffraction the spreading of waves as they pass through an opening or move around an obstacle (Lesson 19)

diffusion the spreading of gas particles until they are evenly distributed throughout a space (Lesson 14); the movement of particles from an area of higher concentration to an area of lower concentration (Lesson 27)

diploid number the number of chromosomes in a somatic cell (Lesson 33)

displacement the net change in an object's position as a result of motion (Lesson 20)

distance a measure of how far an object moves, regardless of direction (Lesson 20)

divergent boundary a region where two tectonic plates are moving away from each other (Lesson 44)

DNA (deoxyribonucleic acid) the nucleic acid that transmits genetic information from parent to offspring and encodes the instructions for cellular activity and the formation of proteins (Lesson 30)

dominant (describing an allele or trait) always expressed in an organism (Lesson 32)

Doppler effect the change in the apparent frequency of a wave due to its source moving toward or away from the observer (Lessons 19, 52)

double helix the twisted ladder shape of a double-stranded DNA molecule (Lesson 30)

earthquake a shaking of Earth's crust caused by the release of potential energy stored in rock at plate boundaries (Lesson 45)

echinoderm a member of the phylum that includes sea stars, sea urchins, sand dollars, and sea cucumbers; an animal with five-fold radial symmetry and tiny, fluid-filled tube feet (Lesson 38)

ecological succession a natural process in which one community of organisms gradually replaces another after a disturbance (Lesson 39)

ecosystem a system made up of all the populations of organisms in an area and their nonliving environment (Lesson 39)

electric current the continuous flow of electric charge through a material (Lesson 17)

electrical energy the energy of moving electrical charges (Lesson 15)

electrical force a universal force that exists between any two charged objects; can attract or repel (Lesson 25)

electromagnet a temporary magnet made by passing an electric current through a coil of wire wound around an iron core (Lesson 17)

electromagnetic energy energy that can travel through empty space in the form of waves (Lesson 15)

electromagnetic induction the generation of an electric current in a conductor by the motion of a magnetic field (Lesson 17)

electromagnetic wave a wave that can transfer energy through a vacuum (Lesson 18)

electron a subatomic particle with a negative charge and nearly zero mass, found in the electron cloud region of an atom (Lesson 6)

electron cloud the region of an atom where electrons are found (Lesson 6)

electron transport the third stage of cellular respiration, in which a series of reactions produces ATP from the electron carrier molecules made in the Krebs cycle (Lesson 29)

electrostatic force the attractive force between opposite charges; the force holding ions together in an ionic compound (Lesson 9)

element a pure substance that cannot be broken down into a simpler substance by ordinary chemical means (Lesson 6)

elevation a location's height above sea level (Lesson 49)

ellipse the shape of planetary orbits; a slightly elongated circle or oval (Lesson 55)

emigration the movement of organisms out of an area or population (Lesson 40)

endocytosis a process in which a cell surrounds and takes in material from its environment (Lesson 27)

endoplasmic reticulum a network of membranes and sacs that surrounds the nuclear membrane (Lesson 26)

endothermic reaction a chemical reaction that absorbs energy; a reaction in which the products contain more energy stored in their bonds than the reactants (Lesson 11)

energy the ability to change matter or do work (Lessons 15, 23)

energy level a region in an atom in which electrons having similar amounts of energy are likely to be located (Lesson 6)

entropy energy that cannot be used to do useful work; the amount of disorder in a system (Lesson 16)

enzyme a biochemical catalyst that increases the rate of a specific chemical reaction in the body (Lesson 28)

equilibrium a state in which a solution has the same concentration in all areas (Lesson 27)

erosion the process by which weathered rock and soil are picked up and moved by wind, water, ice, or gravity (Lesson 47)

eukaryote an organism whose cells contain a distinct nucleus and other membrane-bound organelles (Lesson 26)

eutrophication the addition of excess nutrients, such as nitrogen and phosphorus-containing compounds, to an aquatic ecosystem, which leads to algal blooms and oxygen depletion (Lesson 41)

evaporation the change of a liquid to a gas at the surface of the liquid (Lessons 13, 49)

evolution the change in species over time (Lesson 35)

exocytosis a process in which a cell removes waste by fusing a vacuole containing the waste to the cell membrane (Lesson 27)

exothermic reaction a chemical reaction that releases energy; a reaction in which the products contain less energy stored in their bonds than the reactants (Lesson 11)

experiment a procedure that tests a hypothesis (Lesson 1)

experimental group the group, treatment, or condition in which the independent variable is set to some quantity (Lesson 2)

extinction the permanent loss of a species (Lesson 36)

facilitated diffusion a type of diffusion that allows specific ions or molecules to enter a cell through protein channels embedded in the cell membrane (Lesson 27)

family a vertical column in the periodic table; also called a group (Lesson 7); a taxonomic group smaller and more specific than an order, containing one or more genuses (Lesson 37)

field study an investigation conducted outside a laboratory (Lesson 5)

fitness the ability of an organism to survive and reproduce in its environment (Lesson 35)

flatworm a flat, simple worm that exchanges gases directly with the environment without specialized organs (Lesson 38)

flow the movement of a fluid through or around objects (Lesson 24)

fluid dynamics the branch of science that studies the behavior of fluids (gases and liquids) (Lesson 24)

food web the interconnected food chains in an ecosystem (Lesson 39)

force a push or pull on an object (Lesson 21)

formula a mathematical equation that describes a relationship between variables (Lesson 3)

fossil the preserved remains or trace of an organism that lived in the past (Lessons 36, 43)

frame of reference the place or viewpoint from which motion is measured (Lesson 20)

freezing the change of a liquid to a solid (Lesson 13)

frequency the number of repetitions of a wave at a given point in one second, measured in hertz (Lesson 18)

front the boundary formed where two different air masses meet (Lesson 50)

galaxy a very large mass of matter, such as star systems and nebula, held together by gravity (Lesson 52)

gamete a sex cell (sperm or egg), containing a haploid number of chromosomes (Lesson 33)

gas a substance that has neither a definite shape nor a definite volume (Lesson 13)

gene a section of DNA that encodes information for assembling a protein or proteins (Lesson 30)

gene expression the process by which the information carried by genes is used to synthesize proteins (or noncoding RNA) (Lesson 33)

gene flow the exchange of alleles between gene pools that occurs when members of different populations breed and produce offspring (Lesson 36)

gene pool all the alleles carried by members of a population, whether or not they are expressed (Lesson 35)

genetic recombination the breaking and rejoining of DNA strands to form new molecules with different information (Lesson 33)

genetic variation the range of different phenotypes in a population due to differences in genes (Lesson 33)

genetics the study of how genes are passed from parents to offspring (Lesson 30)

genotype the set of alleles for a particular gene in an individual organism (Lesson 32)

genus a taxonomic group smaller and more specific than a family, containing one or more species (Lesson 37)

geographic isolation a condition in which a physical barrier prevents members of a population from breeding with individuals outside the population (Lesson 36)

global warming an increase in average global temperatures observed over the past 200 years (Lessons 41, 51)

global wind a wind that blows steadily for thousands of kilometers in stable patterns across Earth's surface (Lesson 48)

glycolysis the first stage of cellular respiration, in which a small amount of energy is released by breaking one molecule of glucose into two molecules of pyruvic acid (Lesson 29)

Golgi apparatus a system of membranes that modifies proteins and lipids according to where they will be used in the cell (Lesson 26)

gradualism the idea that evolutionary change occurs slowly and steadily over a long period of time (Lesson 36)

gravitation an attractive force that every mass in the universe exerts on every other mass (Lesson 21)

greenhouse effect a natural process by which heat is absorbed by gases in the atmosphere, keeping Earth's temperatures suitable for life (Lesson 51)

groundwater freshwater stored beneath Earth's surface (Lesson 41)

group a vertical column in the periodic table; also called a family (Lesson 7)

half-life the period of time required for one-half of an unstable isotope sample to decay into the stable form (Lesson 43)

halogen any of the elements in Group 17 of the periodic table, which are very reactive (Lesson 7)

haploid number the number of chromosomes in a gamete, equal to half the diploid number for the species (Lesson 33)

heat the transfer of thermal energy between objects or substances at different temperatures (Lesson 16)

hertz (Hz) the number of cycles per second (Lesson 18)

heterozygous having two different alleles for a gene (Lesson 32)

homeostasis a stable internal environment (Lesson 26)

homologous chromosomes paired chromosomes (one from each parent) containing the same genes but not necessarily the same alleles (Lesson 33)

homozygous having two matching alleles for a gene (Lesson 32)

hot spot an area where the mantle under the crust is hotter than normal, melting the bottom of the crust and forcing magma upward to form volcanic islands (Lesson 45)

humidity a measure of the amount of water vapor in the air (Lesson 49)

hydraulics the study of forces in fluids in closed containers (Lesson 24)

hypertonic having a higher concentration of solute compared to that within a cell (Lesson 27)

hypothesis a possible explanation or answer to a scientific question; a testable prediction of what will happen if something is altered in a certain way (Lesson 1)

hypotonic having a lower concentration of solute compared to that within a cell (Lesson 27)

ice age a period in which the average global temperature is cooler, causing the formation and expansion of glaciers over land (Lesson 51)

ideal gas a gas in which particles take up almost no volume compared to the volume of the space occupied by the gas and exert no significant forces on each other (Lesson 14)

igneous rock rock that forms when melted rock cools and solidifies (Lessons 42, 46)

immigration the movement of organisms into an area or a population (Lesson 40)

inclined plane a sloped or slanted surface (Lesson 23)

incomplete dominance a condition in which the resulting trait in the offspring is a blend of the phenotypes seen in the parents (Lesson 34)

independent assortment the random separation of homologous chromosomes into different cells in meiosis I (Lesson 33)

independent variable the variable that is deliberately changed or manipulated by the experimenter (Lesson 2)

index of refraction the ratio of the speed of light in a vacuum to its speed in a particular medium (Lesson 19)

indicator a substance that changes color in response to a change in pH (Lesson 12)

inert having a tendency not to react with other elements (Lesson 7)

inertia the tendency of an object at rest to remain at rest and for an object in motion to continue moving at the same speed and in the same direction (Lesson 21)

inertial reference frame a reference frame with a constant velocity relative to other objects or reference frames (Lesson 20)

insulator a material or substance that electric current does not flow through easily (Lesson 17)

intensity (of a sound) the amount of energy per unit area delivered by a sound wave and perceived as loudness or volume (Lesson 18)

interference the interaction of two or more waves that intersect, resulting in an amplitude increase (constructive) or decrease (destructive) (Lesson 19)

invasive species a species that harms an environment into which it is introduced because of unchecked population growth (Lesson 41)

inverse square law a mathematical relationship in which one quantity decreases as the square of a second quantity increases (Lessons 21, 25)

invertebrate an animal that lacks a dorsal nerve cord surrounded by bony vertebra; may be a chordate (Lesson 38)

ion an atom with a net positive or negative charge (Lessons 6, 8, 9)

ionic bond a bond formed when one atom transfers its valence electrons to the outer energy level of another atom (Lesson 8)

ionosphere a layer of Earth's atmosphere that contains large numbers of ions (Lesson 54)

isotonic having the same concentration of solute as that within a cell (Lesson 27)

isotopes forms of an element that have different numbers of neutrons and therefore different atomic masses (Lessons 6, 43)

jet stream a "river of wind" high in the atmosphere, flowing for thousands of kilometers from west to east (Lesson 48)

joule (J) a unit of energy equal to one newton-meter (Lesson 23)

Kepler's laws the principles describing how planets move in elliptical orbits around the sun (Lesson 55)

kinetic energy energy due to the motion of an object (Lesson 15)

kinetic molecular theory the principle that particles of matter are always moving in a random fashion (Lesson 13)

kingdom the largest taxonomic group below domain (Lesson 37)

Krebs cycle the second stage of cellular respiration, in which pyruvic acid is broken down into carbon dioxide in a series of energy-releasing reactions (Lesson 29)

laboratory report a written account of the purpose, procedure, results, and conclusions of an experiment (Lesson 1)

latitude a location's distance north or south of the equator (Lesson 49)

lava magma that reaches Earth's surface (Lessons 45, 46)

law of conservation of energy the principle that while energy can be transformed from one form to another, it can never be created or destroyed; the first law of thermodynamics (Lessons 15, 16)

law of conservation of matter the principle that during a chemical reaction, matter cannot be created or destroyed but can be changed into a different form (Lesson 11)

law of conservation of momentum the principle that the total momentum in a system of objects does not change (Lesson 22)

law of independent assortment the principle that the alleles for different genes separate independently of each other when gametes form (Lesson 32)

law of reflection the principle that the angle of reflection of a wave is equal to its angle of incidence (Lesson 19)

law of segregation the principle that alleles separate when gametes are formed, so each gamete contains only one allele of each gene (Lesson 32)

law of superposition the principle that in undisturbed sedimentary rock layers, older layers of rock lie beneath younger layers (Lesson 43)

lever a simple machine consisting of a bar that pivots on a fixed point called a fulcrum (Lesson 23)

limiting factor any aspect of the environment that can limit the size of a population (Lesson 40)

line graph a graph that uses plotted points and lines to show relationships between variables (Lesson 3)

linked genes genes that are located close together on the same chromosome and tend to be inherited together (Lesson 34)

liquid a substance that has a definite volume but no definite shape (Lesson 13)

lithosphere the solid layer formed by the crust and the part of the mantle just under the crust (Lesson 42)

longitudinal wave a wave in which the particles of the medium are displaced parallel to the path of the wave (Lesson 18)

lysosome a small, spherical organelle that uses enzymes to digest complex molecules (Lesson 26)

magma melted rock beneath Earth's surface (Lessons 42, 46)

magnetic field the space around a magnet in which it exerts a magnetic force (Lesson 17)

main sequence a category of stars that use hydrogen in their cores as fuel for nuclear fusion (Lesson 53)

mantle Earth's largest layer, located above the core (Lesson 42)

mass extinction the extinction of very large numbers of species in a fairly short period of time (Lesson 36)

mass number the number of protons plus the number of neutrons in the nucleus of an atom (Lesson 6)

matter anything that has mass and volume (Lesson 6)

mean the statistical average resulting from adding together all the values in a data set and dividing the sum by the number of items in the data set (Lesson 3)

meander a bend in a river caused by the slowing of water and deposition of sediment at the inner curve (Lesson 47)

mechanical advantage a measure of how much a simple machine multiplies a force; the ratio of the output force to the input force (Lesson 23)

mechanical energy the energy of position and motion; kinetic and gravitational potential energy combined (Lesson 15)

mechanical wave a wave, such as a sound wave, that requires a medium to travel through (Lesson 18)

mechanical weathering a process that breaks rock into smaller pieces by physical means, without changing its chemical compostion (Lesson 47)

median the middle value in a data set when all the values are arranged from least to greatest (Lesson 3)

medium a material through which a wave travels (Lesson 18)

meiosis a process by which the number of chromosomes per cell is cut in half; the process by which four genetically distinct, haploid gametes are produced from a diploid cell (Lesson 33)

melting the change of a solid to a liquid (Lesson 13)

Mercalli scale a scale describing the intensity of an earthquake according to the damage and changes that result (Lesson 45)

messenger RNA (mRNA) RNA that forms during transcription and carries the instructions for making proteins from the nucleus to the cytoplasm (Lesson 31)

metallic bond a chemical bond that holds the atoms of a solid metal together, caused by the attraction between positive ions and negative electrons (Lesson 8)

metalloid an element that has properties between those of a metal and those of a nonmetal (Lesson 7)

metamorphic rock rock that forms when existing rock is exposed to high heat, high temperature, or both and undergoes chemical as well as physical changes (Lessons 42, 46)

mid-ocean ridge a long, continuous chain of volcanic mountains that forms along a divergent oceanic boundary (Lesson 44)

mineral an inorganic solid that occurs naturally and has a definite chemical composition and structure (Lesson 46)

mitochondria organelles that carry out cellular respiration (Lesson 26)

mitosis the separation of replicated chromosomes and the formation of two new, identical nuclei in eukaryotic cells (Lesson 33)

mixture matter made up of two or more substances that are combined physically (Lesson 8)

mode the most frequently occurring value in a data set (Lesson 3)

model a simplified representation of the natural world that helps scientists understand it (Lesson 37)

mole a quantity equal to 6.02×10^{23} atoms or molecules; a number of particles equal to Avogadro's number (Lesson 11)

molecule the smallest unit of a compound that has all the properties of the compound (Lesson 8)

mollusk a member of the phylum that includes oysters, clams, snails, slugs, octopuses, and squids (Lesson 38)

momentum the product of an object's mass and its velocity (Lesson 22)

motion change in the position of an object over time (Lesson 20)

multiple alleles three or more alleles for a single gene, of which any individual can inherit only two (Lesson 34)

natural resource a product of the environment used by humans or other organisms (Lesson 41)

natural selection the process by which organisms with favorable variations for their environment survive and reproduce, passing those variations on to the next generation (Lesson 35)

nebula a cloud of gas and dust in space (Lesson 53)

negative an electrical charge marked with a minus (−) sign; the type of charge on an electron (Lesson 25)

net force the sum of all the forces acting on an object (Lesson 21)

neutral neither acidic nor basic; having a pH of about 7 (Lesson 12); having neither a positive nor a negative charge (Lesson 25)

neutralization reaction a chemical reaction in which an acid and a base combine to form water and a salt, making the pH of the solution more neutral (closer to 7) (Lesson 12)

neutron a subatomic particle with a neutral charge and a mass of 1 amu, found in the nucleus of an atom (Lesson 6)

neutron star a small star consisting of neutrons that forms after the supernova of a smaller massive star (Lesson 53)

Newton's first law of motion the principle that an object at rest will remain at rest and an object traveling at a constant speed in a straight line will continue to do so unless an unbalanced force acts on it (Lesson 21)

Newton's second law of motion the principle that a force acting on an object is equal to the product of its mass and its acceleration ($F = ma$) (Lesson 21)

Newton's third law of motion the principle that when one object exerts a force on a second object, the second object exerts an equal but opposite force on the first object (Lesson 21)

noble gas any of the elements in Group 18 of the periodic table, which are very unreactive (Lesson 7)

nonmetal an element that does not have the properties of a metal; found on the right side of the periodic table, in Groups 13–18 (Lesson 7)

normal line an imaginary line perpendicular to a surface (Lesson 19)

nuclear energy the energy stored in the nuclei of atoms (Lesson 15)

nuclear fusion the joining of small atomic nuclei to form a larger atomic nucleus, accompanied by a release of energy (Lesson 53)

nucleic acid a macromolecule made up of nucleotides (Lesson 30)

nucleotide the building block of DNA and RNA, made up of three parts: a five-carbon sugar, a phosphate group, and a nitrogen base (Lesson 30)

nucleus the dense center of an atom containing positively charged protons and uncharged neutrons (Lesson 6); the eukaryotic organelle that controls most cellular activities and contains the cell's genetic material (chromosomes) (Lesson 26)

observation information gathered through the senses or by using scientific instruments (Lesson 2)

ocean current a flow of water in one direction within the ocean (Lesson 48)

oceanic crust the layer of rock under the oceans (Lesson 42)

orbit the path that a planet or other space body takes as it revolves around another, more massive body (Lessons 51, 55)

order a taxonomic group smaller and more specific than a class, containing one or more families (Lesson 37)

organelle a specialized structure inside a cell (Lesson 26)

osmosis the diffusion of water molecules through a selectively permeable membrane from an area of lower solute concentration to an area of higher solute concentration (Lesson 27)

passive transport the movement of substances into or out of a cell without the use of energy (Lesson 27)

period a horizontal row in the periodic table (Lesson 7)

periodic table a chart that organizes and displays information about all the known elements (Lesson 7)

periodicity the repeating pattern of properties of elements throughout the periodic table (Lesson 7)

pesticide a chemical substance that is designed and used to kill pest animals (Lesson 41)

pH scale a quantitative scale from 0 to 14 that describes how acidic or basic a solution is (Lesson 12)

phenotype a trait that results from a particular genotype, or allele combination (Lessons 32, 35)

photosphere the innermost, thinnest layer of the sun's atmosphere, which emits visible light (Lesson 54)

photosynthesis a biochemical process that uses energy from sunlight to convert carbon dioxide and water into glucose and oxygen gas (Lesson 29)

phylum a taxonomic group smaller and more specific than a kingdom, containing one or more classes (Lesson 37)

planetary nebula a red giant's outer layers that expand outward and form a glowing shell of gas, produced when the star forms a white dwarf (Lesson 53)

planetary system a system made up of a star and surrounding planets, asteroids, and comets (Lesson 55)

plasma a state of matter that forms when high temperatures remove electrons from their atoms; a mixture of electrons, ions, and neutral atoms (Lesson 13)

plate boundary the location on Earth's surface where the edges of tectonic plates meet (Lesson 44)

pollution the release of harmful substances into the environment (Lesson 41)

polyatomic ion a charged, covalently bonded molecule that acts like a single atom in forming ionic bonds with other atoms (Lessons 9, 12)

polygenic trait a trait controlled by two or more genes (Lesson 34)

population a group consisting of all the organisms of the same species that live in an ecosystem at the same time (Lesson 40)

population density a measure of the number of organisms per unit area (Lesson 40)

positive an electrical charge marked with a plus (+) sign; the type of charge on a proton (Lesson 25)

potential difference the difference in electrical potential energy between two locations (Lesson 17)

potential energy the energy an object has because of its position or composition (Lesson 15)

precipitation water that falls from clouds, in the form of rain, snow, sleet, or hail (Lesson 49)

precision a measure of how close repeated measurements are to each other; the number of significant figures in a measurement (Lesson 4)

prediction a statement about what is likely to happen under certain conditions (Lesson 1)

pressure the amount of force exerted per unit area (Lesson 14)

probability the mathematical chance that an event will occur (Lesson 32)

procedure a written, step-by-step plan for carrying out an experiment (Lesson 1)

producer an organism that captures energy and stores it in the chemical bonds of glucose and other simple molecules, usually through photosynthesis; an autotroph (Lesson 39)

product a substance formed as a result of a chemical reaction (Lessons 10, 28)

prokaryote an organism whose cells lack a nucleus and membrane-bound organelles (Lesson 26)

protein a large organic molecule made up of smaller molecules called amino acids (Lessons 28, 30)

protein synthesis the process by which cells make proteins (Lesson 31)

proton a subatomic particle with a neutral charge and a mass of 1 amu, found in the nucleus of an atom (Lesson 6)

protostar a glowing, hot sphere of nebular dust and gas that will eventually become a star (Lesson 53)

pulley a simple machine consisting of a grooved wheel that holds a rope or cable (Lesson 23)

pulsar a neutron star that emits a beam of radiation in a single direction (Lesson 53)

punctuated equilibrium the idea that evolution occurs in spurts of rapid speciation between periods of little change (Lesson 36)

Punnett square a diagram used to show possible combinations of dominant and recessive alleles that can be inherited by offspring based on the parents' genotypes (Lesson 32)

qualitative data information or observations that are described in words (Lesson 3)

quantitative data measurements or observations in the form of numerical values (Lesson 3)

radiation the transfer of electromagnetic energy through space (Lesson 48)

radioactivity the spontaneous release of particles and/or energy from the nucleus of an atom of an unstable isotope (Lesson 7)

radioisotope dating a method of finding the age of a fossil or rock sample by measuring the amount of a radioactive isotope present in the sample (Lesson 36)

rare earth element an element in the lanthanide series (elements 57–71) or scandium or itrium (Lesson 7)

rarefaction a region in which particles are temporarily spread farther apart by a longitudinal wave (Lesson 18)

reactant a substance present at the beginning of a chemical reaction (Lessons 10, 28)

reactive tending to combine with other atoms of other elements in a chemical reaction (Lesson 7)

recessive (describing an allele or trait) expressed in an organism only in the absence of a dominant allele (Lesson 32)

red giant a large, cool star formed when the hydrogen in the core of a main-sequence star is used up (Lesson 53)

redshift the Doppler shift toward the lower-frequency (red) end of the electromagnetic spectrum of light from objects that are moving away (Lesson 52)

reflection the bouncing back of a wave when it strikes the surface of a medium (Lesson 19)

refraction a change in the direction of waves as they pass from one medium to another (Lesson 19)

relative dating a method of estimating the age of a fossil or rock by comparing it to other fossils or surrounding material (Lessons 36, 43)

replicate to repeat someone else's experiment and obtain similar results (Lessons 1, 2)

replication the process by which a cell's DNA makes a copy of itself before dividing (Lesson 30)

reproductive isolation a condition in which some members of a population do not breed with other members (Lesson 36)

ribosomal RNA (rRNA) the RNA that, along with proteins, makes up a ribosome and helps translate mRNA into a polypeptide (Lesson 31)

ribosome a cell structure in which proteins are assembled (Lesson 26)

Richter scale a logarithmic scale based on the amplitude of the largest seismic wave produced by an earthquake (Lesson 45)

rift valley a deep valley that runs along the middle of some mid-oceanic ridges or on land where tectonic plates are diverging (Lesson 44)

ring of fire a zone of frequent volcanic eruptions that circles the Pacific Ocean basin and consists of tectonic plate boundaries (Lesson 45)

RNA (ribonucleic acid) the nucleic acid that is responsible for copying the information for protein production from DNA and transporting it to ribosomes (Lesson 31)

rock a naturally occurring substance that is made of one or more minerals (Lesson 46)

rock cycle a continuous process in which rocks are formed or changed from one type to another (Lesson 46)

roundworm a cylindrical worm surrounded by a cuticle (Lesson 38)

runoff water from precipitation that runs downhill over the ground surface, eventually reaching and joining a body of water (Lessons 41, 49)

science the study of anything related to the structure and function of the natural world (Lesson 1)

scientific ethics principles of conduct that scientists should follow (Lesson 5)

scientific inquiry the process of posing a scientific question and then using a variety of scientific techniques to find the answer to that question (Lesson 1)

screw a simple machine consisting of an inclined plane wound around a pointed cylinder or shaft that changes the direction of force from one that rotates the cylinder to one that points in the same direction as the cylinder (Lesson 23)

seafloor spreading the process in which magma flows up to fill the space between diverging plates, hardening to form new oceanic crust (Lesson 44)

sediment rock particles and organic matter deposited by wind and water (Lesson 46)

sedimentary rock rock that forms from layers of sediment that become compacted and cemented together (Lessons 42, 46)

seismic wave a wave, produced during an earthquake, that travels through Earth's crust (Lesson 45)

selectively permeable allowing only some substances, and not others, to pass through (Lesson 27)

semiconductor a material with conductive properties between those of conductors and insulators (Lesson 17)

sex chromosome an X or a Y chromosome (Lesson 34)

sex-linked determined by a gene on the X chromosome (Lesson 34)

significant figures the meaningful, reliable numbers in a measurement (Lesson 4)

simple machine a device that makes work easier by changing the size and/or direction of the input (applied) force (Lesson 23)

slope the angle or slant of a graphed line (Lesson 20)

soil the loose, weathered rock and organic material that covers parts of Earth's surface (Lesson 47)

solar flare a sudden, intense eruption on the sun's surface formed when loops of gas near sunspots connect and release large amounts of energy (Lesson 54)

solar nebula the hypothetical cloud of dust and gas that condensed to form the denser matter that makes up the solar system, including Earth and the sun (Lesson 43)

solar prominence a large loop or arc of gas that links different areas of sunspots (Lesson 54)

solar wind a constant stream of charged particles (ions) from the corona that escapes the sun's gravity (Lesson 54)

solid a substance with a definite shape and volume (Lesson 13)

solute the substance that dissolves in a solution (Lesson 12)

solution a mixture in which the particles of a dissolved substance (solute) are evenly distributed throughout a second substance, the solvent (Lesson 12)

solvent the substance in which the solute dissolves to form a solution (Lesson 12)

somatic cell a body cell, containing a diploid number of chromosomes (Lesson 33)

sound energy the energy of vibrating matter that creates waves of pressure (Lesson 15)

sound quality the characteristics of a sound, such as timbre (Lesson 18)

specialization the process by which cells take on specific structures and functions in a developing organism (Lesson 33)

speciation the formation of one or more new species from an existing species (Lesson 36)

species a group of similar organisms that can breed and produce fertile offspring; the smallest and most specific taxonomic classification (Lessons 35, 37)

speed the distance an object moves in a certain amount of time (Lesson 20)

sponge a nonmoving filter feeder that is the simplest type of animal, lacking specialized tissues (Lesson 38)

state change the physical change of a substance from one state to another (Lesson 13)

state of matter a physical form in which matter exists, such as solid, liquid, gas, or plasma (Lesson 13)

stellar equilibrium a stable state in which a star is neither expanding due to fusion nor contracting due to gravity (Lesson 53)

subduction a process in which an oceanic plate at a convergent boundary is pushed beneath the edge of a second plate (Lesson 44)

sublimation the change of a solid directly to a gas (Lesson 13)

subscript the small, lower-set number in a chemical formula that shows how many atoms of an element are in the substance (Lesson 10)

substrate a reactant in an enzyme-catalyzed reaction (Lesson 28)

sunspot a region on the sun's surface that is cooler and darker than the surrounding areas (Lesson 54)

superconductor a material that gains very high conductivity when its temperature drops below a certain point (Lesson 17)

supernova the explosion of a massive main-sequence star that has used up its fuel (Lesson 53)

taxonomy the field of biology that deals with classifying organisms (Lesson 37)

theory of plate tectonics the theory that lithospheric plates float on the asthenosphere and that plate interactions shape and form Earth's surface features (Lesson 44)

thermal energy the energy of the randomly moving particles that make up all matter (Lessons 15, 16)

thermodynamics the study of how heat moves between and within systems (Lesson 16)

tide a daily change in the height of the ocean surface caused by the gravitational pull of the moon and sun on Earth's water (Lesson 55)

topography the shape and features of land (Lesson 49)

trait a characteristic an organism inherits from its parents (Lesson 30)

transcription the process that uses DNA as a template to make a complementary strand of messenger RNA (mRNA) (Lesson 31)

transfer RNA (tRNA) an RNA molecule that contains an anticodon and delivers an amino acid to a new polypeptide chain on a ribosome (Lesson 31)

transform boundary a region where two plates grind past one another in a mainly horizontal direction (Lesson 44)

transition metal any of the elements in Groups 3–12 of the periodic table, which are highly ductile and malleable and good conductors of heat and electricity (Lesson 7)

translation the process that converts the information in mRNA into a sequence of amino acids that makes up a protein (Lesson 31)

transpiration the process by which plants release water vapor through their leaves (Lesson 49)

transverse wave a wave in which the particles of the medium are displaced perpendicular to the path of the wave (Lesson 18)

trench a long, narrow, steep-sided depression in the ocean floor, formed by the subduction of oceanic crust (Lesson 44)

trial a repetition of an experimental procedure in the course of an experiment (Lesson 2)

trough the lowest point of a wave (Lesson 18)

vacuole an organelle that stores water and other important materials and that helps support heavy structures in plants (Lesson 26)

valence electron an electron in an atom's outermost energy level (Lesson 7)

vaporization the change of a liquid to a gas (Lesson 13)

variable a factor that can affect the outcome of an experiment (Lesson 2)

velocity a description of both the speed and the direction of an object (Lessons 20, 22)

vertebrate an animal with a dorsal nerve cord surrounded by bony vertebrae (Lesson 38)

virus a particle consisting of genetic material enclosed in a protein shell (Lesson 26)

volcano an opening in Earth's surface through which magma is released (Lessons 44, 45)

voltage the difference in electrical potential energy between two locations, resulting in a current (Lesson 17)

water cycle the continuous movement of freshwater through the physical environment and living things (Lesson 49)

water table the top level of a zone of saturated rock that holds groundwater (Lesson 41)

wave a disturbance that transfers energy through matter or space (Lesson 18)

wavelength the distance over which a wave repeats (Lesson 18)

weather the state of the atmosphere at a certain time and place (Lesson 49)

weather map a map that uses symbols to show the weather conditions of specific locations at a certain time (Lesson 50)

weathering the process by which rock is broken down into smaller pieces (Lesson 47)

wedge a simple machine, consisting of two inclined planes placed back to back, that splits things apart by changing the direction of the input force to produce a perpendicular force (Lesson 23)

wheel and axle a simple machine that transfers force from the larger outer wheel to the smaller inner axle (Lesson 23)

white dwarf a small, hot, glowing object that remains after a red giant star releases a planetary nebula (Lesson 53)

work a measure of the energy transferred when a force moves an object over a distance in the direction of the force (Lesson 23)

Pretest

Name: _____

DIRECTIONS: There are seven passages in this test. Each passage is followed by several questions. After reading a passage, choose the best answer to each question and fill in the corresponding bubble on your answer sheet. You may refer to the passages as often as necessary.

You are NOT permitted to use a calculator on this test.

Passage I

When ionic solutes dissolve in water, they *dissociate* (separate) to form ions with opposite charges. A substance that dissociates to form positively charged hydrogen ions (H^+), or protons, is an acid. The relative amounts of hydrogen ion and hydroxide ion (OH^-) in a solution determine its pH. The equation below shows the dissociation of an acid. The acid dissociates into protons and the *conjugate base* of the acid. The original acid can be thought of as a *protonated* conjugate base.

$$HNO \rightarrow H^+ + NO^-$$
$$Acid \rightarrow Hydrogen\ ion + Conjugate\ base$$

The pH level of a solution is a measure of the concentration of hydrogen ions. The equation below shows that pH is equal to the negative logarithm of the *molar* (M) concentration of hydrogen ions. (Concentration expressed in molarity refers to moles of solute per liter of solution). The relationship between pH and hydrogen ion concentration is depicted in Figure 1.

$$pH = -\log[H^+]$$

A pH indicator is a compound that exists in a protonated or unprotonated state, depending on the pH of the solution. Equation (1) below shows how an indicator changes from its protonated to its unprotonated state. The symbol "In" stands for *indicator*. Dissociation occurs when the concentration of hydrogen ions in the solution falls below a specific level. When the hydrogen ion concentration increases and surpasses this level, the opposite reaction, (2), takes place. The addition of an indicator contributes an insignificant amount of hydrogen ions, and so does not affect the pH of the solution.

$$(1)\ HIn \rightarrow H^+ + In^-$$

$$(2)\ H^+ + In^- \rightarrow HIn$$

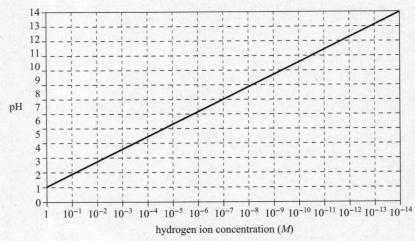

Figure 1

GO ON TO THE NEXT PAGE.

Figure 2 shows the pH ranges for different indicators. The dashed lines indicate the pH level at which each indicator exists in equal concentrations of the protonated and unprotonated forms.

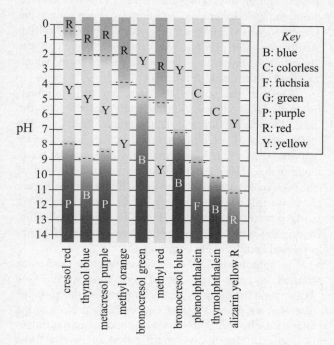

Figure 2

1. Compared to the molar concentration of hydrogen ions at pH 11, the molar concentration of hydrogen ions at pH 9 is:

A. twenty times less.

B. twenty times greater.

C. one hundred times less.

D. one hundred times greater.

2. Phenolphthalein is colorless at pH levels below 9 and fuschia, or bright pink, at pH levels above 9. Which describes the state of this indicator as the concentration of hydrogen ions increases past the color change range?

F. Phenolphthalein exists in protonated form, which appears pink.

G. Phenolphthalein exists as a conjugate base, which appears pink.

H. Phenolphthalein exists in protonated form, which appears colorless.

J. Phenolphthalein exists as a conjugate base, which appears colorless.

3. A solution contains hydrogen ions in a concentration of $1 \times 10^{-5} M$. When the indicator metacresol purple is added to this solution, it will appear:

A. red.

B. blue.

C. purple.

D. yellow.

4. A solution of unknown pH is placed in three test tubes. Each tube is tested with one of the indicators listed in the table below. The result of each test is shown.

Indicator	Result
Phenolphthalein	Colorless
Cresol red	Yellow
Methyl orange	Red

Based on the results shown in the table, what could be the pH of the tested solution?

F. 2   **H.** 8

G. 5   **J.** 11

5. Cresol red, thymol blue, and metacresol purple each have two color shifts and equilibrium points. Unlike the other indicators in Figure 2, these compounds:

A. exist as both acids and conjugate bases.

B. are capable of donating two hydrogen ions.

C. exist in a dissociated and an undissociated form.

D. are capable of donating both hydrogen and hydroxide (OH^-) ions.

6. The equation below shows the dissociation of the indicator bromocresol green (HBG) in solution.

$$HBG \rightarrow H^+ + BG^-$$

At a pH of 4.8, a solution containing bromocresol green (HBG) will have equal concentrations of:

F. hydrogen ions and hydroxide ions.

G. dissociated and undissociated indicator.

H. dissociated indicator and hydrogen ions.

J. undissociated indicator and hydrogen ions.

GO ON TO THE NEXT PAGE.

Passage II

The water in North America's Great Lakes is not uniform. Rather, it is *stratified* into layers with differences in temperature (Figure 1) and density. Figure 2 shows the relationship between water temperature and density. The uppermost layer is the *epilimnon*. This layer contains the most dissolved oxygen, which is provided both by photosynthesis and by the atmosphere. Surface current mixes the water within the epilimnon.

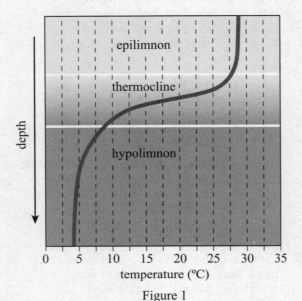

Figure 1

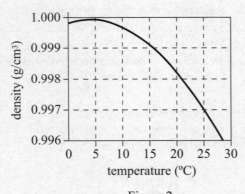

Figure 2

The *thermocline* is the next, relatively thin, layer characterized by a relatively rapid drop in temperature as depth increases. The bottommost layer is the *hypolimnon*. Not enough light reaches this layer to allow phytoplankton to photosynthesize. Because it is isolated from the atmosphere, no additional oxygen enters the hypolimnon. As summer progresses, bottom-dwelling detritivores and decomposers consume oxygen in the hypolimnon. Hypoxic (low-oxygen) zones form, which can lead to the death of lake fish.

Through the spring and summer, the epilimnon in each lake expands and extends deeper into the lake. Decreasing autumn temperatures then cool the epilimnon. As the temperature and density of this water approach that of the hypolimnon, the layers of the water column mix. This event is known as the "turning over" of the lake, and it brings oxygen to the lower depths. Figure 3 shows this sequence of events. In winter, the lake's surface water turns to ice. There is little stratification during this time. After the spring thaw, the lake becomes stratified and the cycle begins again.

In autumn of 2001, an unusually large dead zone formed in Lake Erie, one of the Great Lakes. One explanation for this may be the temperature increase due to global warming. Warmer temperatures mean that the lake ice melts earlier in the spring, and autumn turnover is delayed. This allows stratification to persist for a longer period, causing the level of dissolved oxygen in the hypolimnon to drop to lower levels.

GO ON TO THE NEXT PAGE.

| spring | early summer | late summer | fall |

Figure 3

7. Compared to the epilimnon, the hypolimnon is:

A. denser and colder.
B. denser and warmer.
C. less dense and colder.
D. less dense and warmer.

8. According to Figure 2, at which of the following temperatures is the density of liquid water the greatest?

F. 0°C
G. 5°C
H. 15°C
J. 25°C

9. Which of the following processes contribute to hypoxia in the hypolimnon?

I   respiration
II photosynthesis
III decomposition
IV atmospheric mixing

A. I and II
B. I and III
C. II and IV
D. III and IV

10. According to Figures 1 and 2, what is the relationship between water density and depth in the Great Lakes?

F. Water density increases as depth increases.
G. Water density decreases as depth increases.
H. Water density decreases and then increases as depth increases.
J. Water density increases and then decreases as depth increases.

11. According to the passage, warmer temperatures lead to hypoxia by:

A. causing the hypolimnon to mix with the epilimnon earlier.
B. causing the epilimnon to have a lower density than the hypolimnon.
C. keeping the hypolimnon separate from the epilimnon for longer periods.
D. delaying the beginning of stratification into an epilimnon and hypolimnon.

12. In winter, most of the water in large lakes remains at 4°C, with the exception of a thin layer that is between 0°C and 4°C. Where is this layer located?

F. Just below the ice
G. Below water that is 4°C
H. Above water that is 0°C
J. At the bottom of the lake

GO ON TO THE NEXT PAGE.

Passage III

Microscopic fossil organisms, dating from between 551 and 635 million years ago, were discovered in the Doushantuo rock formation in China. Scientists disagree as to whether the fossils are embryos of multicellular organisms or free-living unicellular protists.

Scientist 1

Examination of the Doushantuo fossils suggests they are embryos of primitive *metazoans* (animals). The fossils share many features with the early blastula-stage embryos of existing animals. For example, animal embryos usually consist of cell numbers equal to a power of 2 (such as 4, 8, 16, or 32). Most of the Doushantuo fossils consist of cells numbering a power of 2, suggesting that the organism formed from division of a single cell. Each cell has about an equal volume, and the cells are large. In addition, many of the fossils show a thin membrane around the cells; animal embryos have a similar protective membrane.

Although most of the fossils consist of similar-sized cells, some have asymmetrical cells. Figure 1 shows three early embryos, two with *polar lobes*. Formation of a polar lobe results from unequal division into one larger cell and one smaller cell. This is a sign that the embryo will develop into a complex animal with specialized cells. Polar lobes are observed in the embryos of mollusks.

A microscopic analysis of the fossils showed that each cell was shaped to fit snugly with adjacent cells, as in animals. However, the larger Doushantuo fossils differ from animal embryos of that size in one major respect: they lack *epithelialization*, the formation of sheets of cells during early development. All metazoans and sponges share this characteristic. These sheets eventually form specific tissues and organs in the animal. The absence of this trait in the fossil embryos indicates that these animals were extremely primitive.

In addition, the existence of blastula-stage embryos suggests that gastrula- and neurula-stage embryos should also be found among the fossils. In the gastrula stage, embryonic cells change in position in preparation for differentiating into specialized tissues. However, even in known species, these later stages are rarely preserved in the conditions that lead to fossilization.

Scientist 2

The evidence does not support the hypothesis that the Doushantuo fossils are early-stage embryos of primitive animals. Some of the fossils resemble the polar-lobe embryos of some complex animals. However, this early asymmetry is not preserved in the later stages, as it is in animal embryos. All of the higher-cell-number fossils consist of equal-sized cells. In addition, some of the supposed embryos, particularly those consisting of hundreds or thousands of cells, are peanut-shaped. This is unusual and is not seen in embryos of existing animals. A more likely alternative is that the fossils are not animal embryos but protists. These single-celled protists would periodically undergo rapid cell division and form a cyst or capsule around the dividing cells. Eventually, the cyst would open and release the spores. If so, the Doushantuo fossils represent organisms outside of the metazoan clade. The cleavage patterns seen in this stage of the life cycle places this organism within the clade Holozoa, which includes metazoans and the most closely related protists, the choanoflagellates (Figure 2).

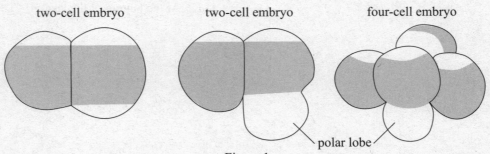

two-cell embryo   two-cell embryo   four-cell embryo

polar lobe

Figure 1

GO ON TO THE NEXT PAGE.

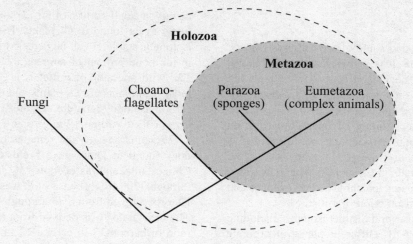

Figure 2

13. Which feature of the fossils suggests that they are animal cells, rather than protists?

    A. Each cell fits snugly against adjacent cells.

    B. The cells in each fossil have equal volumes.

    C. Some of the fossils have unusual "peanut" shapes.

    D. No fossils show cells forming into sheets.

14. According to Figure 2, which clade includes all multicellular animals only?

    F. Parazoa

    G. Holozoa

    H. Metazoa

    J. Eumetazoa

15. Which observation is best explained by Scientist 2's hypothesis?

    A. The higher-cell-number Doushantuo fossils consist of cells that are identical in size.

    B. The Doushantuo fossils consist of clusters of cells numbering a power of 2.

    C. Many of the Doushantuo fossils include a membrane around the cells.

    D. Some of the Doushantuo fossils consist of asymmetrical cells with polar lobes.

16. According to Scientist 1, at which point would the line representing the Doushantuo fossil organisms branch off from the cladogram below?

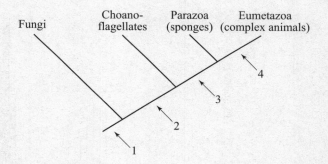

    F. Point 1

    G. Point 2

    H. Point 3

    J. Point 4

17. Which of the following conclusions would Scientist 2 support?

    A. Cell division is part of both the reproduction of protists and animal development.

    B. The later-stage embryos of the Doushantuo organisms did not survive fossilizing conditions.

    C. The Doushantuo organisms are more closely related to Eumetazoa than sponges are.

    D. The formation of cells into sheets places the Doushantuo organisms in the clade Metazoa.

GO ON TO THE NEXT PAGE.

Passage IV

Scientists have found some of the earliest evidence of agriculture in China. It is known that an agricultural system based on rice developed in southern China and that agriculture based on a grain called millet developed in northern China. Dogs and pigs were also domesticated in China, but the exact timing of their domestication is not known. A group of scientists has developed a new method to test archeological claims about the domestication of animals in China. The scientists tested human and animal remains for stable carbon isotopes that would indicate the consumption of millet.

Carbon occurs as several distinct isotopes, including carbon-12 and carbon-13. Different plants incorporate different amounts of these two isotopes. For example, C_4 grasses use a special type of photosynthesis metabolism that increases the proportion of carbon-13 that is taken up by the plant. Therefore, although carbon-13 makes up only a small portion of the carbon on Earth, it is more likely to be found in C_4 plants. Because the carbon-13 isotope is stable, it can be detected in greater abundance in the bone protein of animals that consume C_4 plants. The wild ancestor of millet is a C_4 grass. In contrast, most wild plants are C_3 plants and do not have the same carbon isotope signature. Figure 1 shows the ratio of carbon-13 to carbon-12 in C_3 and C_4 plants.

Scientists tested the remains of humans, pigs, and dogs found at Didiwan, a prehistoric site in northern China. Didiwan was occupied by humans around 7900 through 7200 BCE (Phase 1). It was then abandoned and later reoccupied from 6500 through 4900 BCE (Phase 2). The measure $\delta^{13}C$ is derived from a formula relating the ratio of carbon-13 to carbon-12 in the bone samples to the isotope ratio in a standard. Less negative values of $\delta^{13}C$ indicate a higher proportion of carbon-13, as shown in Figure 2.

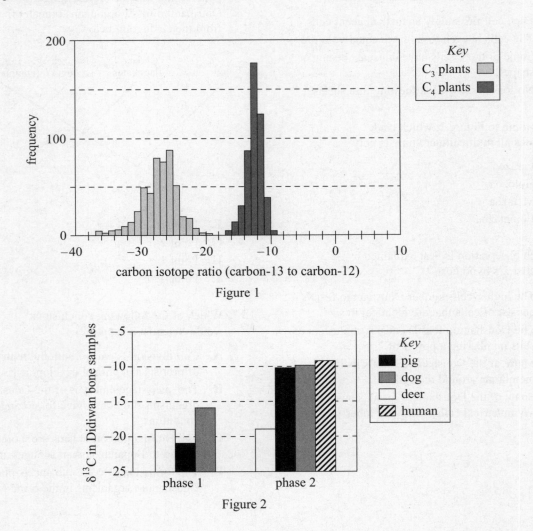

Figure 1

Figure 2

GO ON TO THE NEXT PAGE.

18. According to Figure 2, which bone samples had the highest ratio of carbon-13 to carbon-12?

F. Pigs in Phase 1
G. Dogs in Phase 1
H. Deer in Phase 2
J. Humans in Phase 2

19. Which of the following statements is supported by the information in Figure 1?

A. The mode isotope ratio in C_4 plants is -12.
B. The mean isotope ratio in C_3 plants is -30.
C. The median isotope ratio in C_4 plants is -18.
D. The median isotope ratio in C_3 plants is -24.

20. According to the passage, what is one assumption scientists made?

F. The bones of domesticated pigs and dogs have carbon isotope ratios similar to those of deer.
G. Bones from wild pigs that were hunted and eaten have a different carbon isotope ratio than bones from domesticated pigs.
H. The bones of agricultural prehistoric humans have a different carbon isotope ratio than the bones of any domesticated animals prehistoric humans kept.
J. Bones from wild dogs have carbon isotope ratios similar to bones from domesticated pigs.

21. Why did the isotope ratios found in the remains of deer remain similar in Phases 1 and 2?

A. Deer consumed mostly C_3 plants in both phases.
B. Deer consumed mostly C_4 plants in both phases.
C. Deer consumed mostly domesticated millet in both phases.
D. Deer consumed plants with a high proportion of carbon-13 in both phases.

22. Which hypothesis is consistent with the data presented in Figure 2?

F. The pig bones found at Didiwan in Phase 2 were from feral (wild) pigs.
G. Dogs, but not pigs, were beginning to become domesticated in Phase 1.
H. Domesticated pigs were present at Didiwan in Phase 1 but not in Phase 2.
J. Both domesticated dogs and domesticated pigs were present at Didiwan in Phase 1.

GO ON TO THE NEXT PAGE.

Passage V

Students in a physics lab wanted to determine the force of friction between various surfaces. The force of friction opposes motion. According to Newton's first law, an object will remain at rest or in constant motion unless an unbalanced force acts on it. To determine the force of friction, the students measured the force needed to move an object from rest and the force needed to keep the object in constant motion once it is moving.

Experiment 1

The students used four blocks that had the same dimensions. The blocks were made of different materials and so had different surfaces. The students placed each block on a smooth, flat metal track. A digital force meter was attached to the block with a rope. A cable from the force meter sent data to a computer, which recorded the force used over time. This setup is shown in Figure 1.

A student pulled on the force meter, starting with minimal force and increasing the applied force until the block moved. The students performed multiple trials for each of the four blocks. Table 1 shows the average results for the trials.

Table 1			
Block	Mass (kg)	Force (N)	Coefficient of static friction (μ_S)
1	0.45	2.8	0.62
2	0.68	3.2	0.47
3	0.39	1.6	0.41
4	0.55	2.8	0.51

The students calculated the coefficients of static friction between the metal track and each of the four blocks. The force of friction is a product of the coefficient of friction (μ) between the surfaces in contact and the normal force (N). The equations for the force of friction (1) and the normal force (2) are given below (g is estimated as 10.0 m/s²).

$$(1)\ F_f = \mu N$$

$$(2)\ N = mg$$

Experiment 2

The students repeated Experiment 1, determining the force needed to keep the object in constant motion. To do this, each student pulled the force meter until the computer display showed a straight, horizontal line. Students estimated the force required for constant motion by averaging the values for the straight-line portion of the graph from each trial. They calculated the coefficients of kinetic friction. Table 2 shows the results.

Table 2			
Block	Mass (kg)	Force (N)	Coefficient of kinetic friction (μ_K)
1	0.45	2.1	0.47
2	0.68	1.8	0.26
3	0.39	1.4	0.39
4	0.55	2.5	0.45

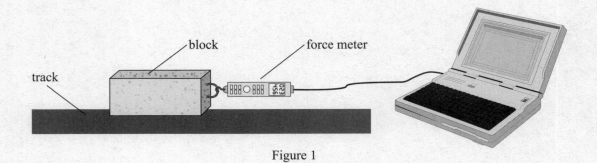

Figure 1

GO ON TO THE NEXT PAGE.

23. In the students' experiments, which of the following is the independent variable?

A. the mass of each block
B. the volume of each block
C. the composition of each block
D. the force exerted on each block

24. Which of the following are constants in these experiments?

F. block material and track surface
G. block volume and track surface
H. force exerted and block mass
J. force exerted and track surface

25. Based on Table 1, which statement is correct?

A. Block 1 generated the same force of friction as Block 2.
B. Block 2 generated a greater force of friction than Block 3.
C. Block 3 generated a greater force of friction than Block 2.
D. Block 4 generated a smaller force of friction than Block 3.

26. A constant force is applied to a block, keeping it in motion at constant velocity. Which of the following best describes the forces acting on the block?

F. The forces are balanced; a constant force is a balanced force.
G. The forces are unbalanced; a constant force causes the block to accelerate.
H. The forces are balanced; the applied force opposes and cancels the force due to friction.
J. The forces are unbalanced; the applied force exceeds the force of friction, resulting in motion.

27. Which of the following expressions can be used to determine the coefficient of kinetic friction between the surface of Block 4 and the metal track?

A. $F \div (m \times g)$
B. $(m \times g) \div F$
C. $m \div (F \times g)$
D. $(F \times m) \div g$

28. Which describes the direction of the force of friction on the block as it is pulled to the right along the track?

F. Upward
G. Downward
H. To the right
J. To the left

29. According to Tables 1 and 2, which conclusion can be reached about friction?

A. More force is required to keep a moving object in motion than to move it from rest.
B. Less force is required to keep a moving object in motion than to move it from rest.
C. The coefficient of static friction is greater for objects with more mass.
D. The coefficient of kinetic friction is greater for objects with more mass.

GO ON TO THE NEXT PAGE.

Passage VI

A catalyst is a chemical that speeds up a chemical reaction without being altered itself by the reaction. Enzymes are catalysts, usually proteins, that facilitate and speed up specific reactions in living systems. Amylase is an enzyme excreted by the pancreas and salivary glands that facilitates the breakdown of starches. A pharmaceutical researcher is developing a synthesized form of amylase to help people who are deficient in natural amylase. Figure 1 shows the rate of breakdown of starch for naturally formed amylase and for the researcher's synthetic amylase at normal human body temperature (37°C).

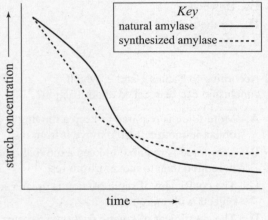

Figure 1

The effect of an enzyme on a reaction rate is often governed by the presence of an activator, a substance that increases the rate of an enzyme reaction but is not itself an enzyme. Chloride ions (Cl⁻) are known to be an important activator for amylase. For this reason, the researcher evaluated the effect of Cl⁻ concentrations (between 0.002 and 0.010 mole NaCl) on both natural and synthetic amylase reaction rates. The results are shown in Figure 2.

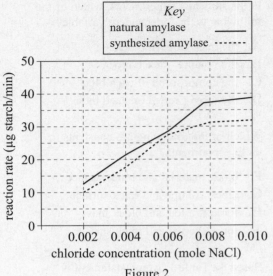

Figure 2

Knowing that pH often affects enzyme performance, the researcher also wanted to look at the effect of pH and chloride concentrations together. The results of four trials using NaCl concentrations between 0.004 and 0.010 mole are shown in Figure 3.

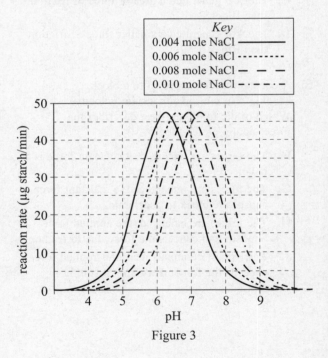

Figure 3

GO ON TO THE NEXT PAGE.

30. Based on Figure 1, which of the following best summarizes the differences between natural amylase and the researcher's synthetic amylase?

F. The synthetic amylase breaks down starch at a rate that is comparable to natural amylase, but it tends not to complete the breakdown of starch.

G. The synthetic amylase initially breaks down starch much slower than natural amylase, but eventually reduces starch concentrations to below that of natural amylase.

H. Natural amylase is able to break down all the starch before the synthetic amylase has broken down half of the starch.

J. The two forms of amylase are good at producing starch in a short amount of time.

31. At which NaCl concentration are the reaction rates for the natural and synthetic amylase most similar?

A. 0.002 mole NaCl

B. 0.004 mole NaCl

C. 0.006 mole NaCl

D. 0.010 mole NaCl

32. Using the results shown in Figure 2, which of the following statements is true?

F. Starch concentrations increase as chloride concentrations increase.

G. Starch concentrations increase as chloride concentrations decrease.

H. Starch is digested faster as chloride concentrations increase.

J. Starch is digested faster as chloride concentrations decrease.

33. At a pH of 6, what is the approximate reaction rate of starch digestion when the concentration of NaCl is 0.006 mole?

A. 20 g starch/min

B. 35 g starch/min

C. 40 g starch/min

D. 45 g starch/min

34. The normal pH of human saliva is approximately 7.4. Based on this information and the results presented in Figure 3, adding table salt (NaCl) to starch-rich foods:

F. speeds up starch digestion, because reaction rates at a pH of 7.4 are fastest with high salt concentrations.

G. slows starch digestion because it takes longer for the reaction to be completed at higher salt concentrations.

H. does nothing to change the rate of starch digestion because the reaction rates are all about the same at a pH of 7.4.

J. will cause the breakdown of starch to be delayed, but it will all get digested by the time pH reaches 9.

GO ON TO THE NEXT PAGE.

Passage VII

Thrust is the upward force that a rocket experiences as gas is expelled from the fuel cylinder. The amount of thrust generated by solid fuel rockets depends on the surface area of fuel burning at a given time. Within the fuel cell of solid fuel rockets, a core is drilled out to create an inner wall that combusts at takeoff. Figure 1 shows three solid fuel cylinders with different inner openings.

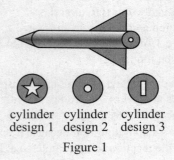

cylinder   cylinder   cylinder
design 1   design 2   design 3

Figure 1

Experiment 1

Some physics students conducted experiments on the three fuel cylinder designs shown in Figure 1. The initial thrust from a test rocket (two seconds after ignition) was measured for each cylinder design. Three trials were conducted for each design. The results of the trials are shown in Table 1.

Table 1					
		Initial thrust (newtons)			
Cylinder	Inner surface area	trial 1	trial 2	trial 3	average
1	45 cm²	244	239	220	234
2	15 cm²	205	194	199	199
3	25 cm²	218	222	221	220

Experiment 2

The students then evaluated the thrust through the entire burn of each fuel cylinder to determine if the shape of the inner surface area affected the thrust over time. The three figures below show the thrust over time for each cylinder design.

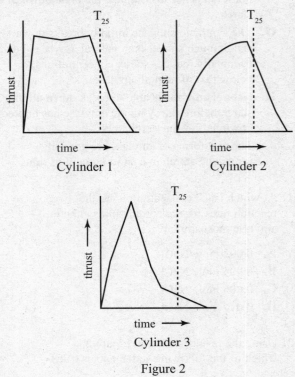

Figure 2

35. The results of Experiment 1 support the hypothesis that the amount of initial thrust generated by a fuel cylinder:

  A. decreases with surface area.
  B. increases with surface area.
  C. is independent of initial surface area.
  D. changes with time.

36. A student wishes to design a rocket that produces its greatest thrust during the initial stages of its launch. Which fuel cylinder design is best suited for that objective?

  F. Cylinders 1 and 2
  G. Cylinder 2
  H. Cylinder 3
  J. Cylinders 2 and 3

GO ON TO THE NEXT PAGE.

37. Based on the thrust curve shown for Cylinder 1, the amount of thrust:

   A. is constant throughout the launch.

   B. gradually increases through the entire launch, with the greatest thrust just before the fuel runs out.

   C. increases rapidly at first, then remains relatively constant before running out of fuel.

   D. increases rapidly at first, then gradually decreases.

38. Which of the following factors would create the most potential bias in these experiments?

   F. Each launch trial was conducted at different times of the day.

   G. A different rocket design was used for each fuel cylinder type.

   H. The number of trial launches for each cylinder design was increased from three to six.

   J. The burn time for the three fuel cylinder designs was found to vary.

39. In order for the rocket to make lift-off and fly upward, the thrust must be greater than any opposing forces acting on the rocket. Which of the following are opposing forces acting on the rocket as it begins lift-off?

   A. Gravity only

   B. Gravity and air resistance only

   C. Gravity, air resistance, and mass

   D. Mass only

40. As the rocket launch proceeds, fuel is consumed. Based on this information, which of the following must continuously decrease throughout the rocket launch?

   F. The rocket's velocity

   G. The rocket's total mass

   H. The rocket's thrust

   J. The rocket's altitude

END OF TEST

STOP!

Posttest

Name: _____

DIRECTIONS: There are seven passages in this test. Each passage is followed by several questions. After reading a passage, choose the best answer to each question and fill in the corresponding bubble on your answer sheet. You may refer to the passages as often as necessary.

You are NOT permitted to use a calculator on this test.

Passage I

The surface temperatures of planets in the solar system can be predicted from the balance of incoming solar radiation and planetary reflection. Incoming radiation is measured as electromagnetic radiant *flux* from the sun, which spreads out with distance (Figure 1).

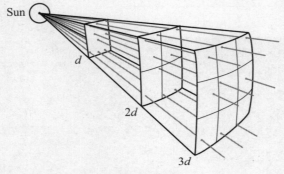

Figure 1

Flux is equal to the amount of energy emitted per unit area and is measured in watts (W), or joules per second. The *luminosity* of an object is the flux multiplied by its surface area.

All objects emit electromagnetic radiation in a spectrum of wavelengths, with a peak at a characteristic wavelength. This peak depends on the temperature of the object, with hotter objects emitting more shorter-wavelength radiation than cooler objects (Figure 2).

Not all the radiation reaching a planet is absorbed. Some is reflected back into space. The amount of solar radiation that is reflected is a function of a planet's *albedo* (proportion of incoming light that a surface reflects). For a planet in energy equilibrium, the amount of incoming energy is equal to the amount of energy emitted into space. The equations below show this relationship.

$$(\text{energy received}) - (\text{energy emitted}) = 0$$

$$(\text{energy received}) = (\text{energy emitted})$$

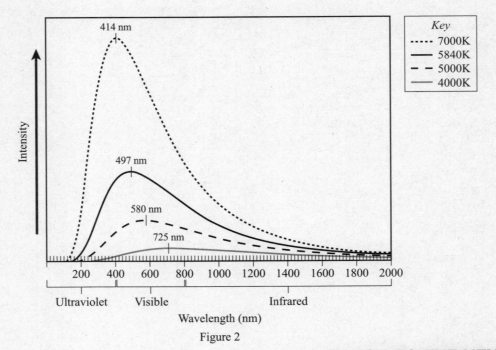

Figure 2

GO ON TO THE NEXT PAGE.

Table 1 shows the temperatures predicted for the four inner planets, along with their observed surface temperatures.

Table 1		
Planet	Predicted temperature (K)	Observed temperature (K)
Mercury	433	533
Venus	231	753
Earth	255	288
Mars	210	218

The observed temperatures of the inner planets are higher than the predicted temperatures due to atmospheric greenhouse gases. Incoming radiation reaches the ground, where it is absorbed and re-emitted outward. Greenhouse gas molecules in the atmosphere re-absorb some of this energy and reflect it back toward the ground.

1. According to Table 1, what is the effect of Earth's greenhouse gases on its surface temperature?

   A. Earth's greenhouse gases increase its surface temperature by 33 kelvins.
   B. Earth's greenhouse gases decrease its surface temperature by 33 kelvins.
   C. Earth's greenhouse gases increase its surface temperature by 288 kelvins.
   D. Earth's greenhouse gases decrease its surface temperature by 255 kelvins.

2. Greenhouse gases affect the energy balance of a planet by:

   F. reducing the amount of energy emitted.
   G. reducing the amount of energy received.
   H. increasing the amount of energy emitted.
   J. increasing the amount of energy received.

3. According to Table 1 and the information in the passage, which planet has the greatest concentration of greenhouse gases in its atmosphere?

   A. Mars
   B. Earth
   C. Venus
   D. Mercury

4. According to Figure 2 and the information in the passage, what is the peak wavelength of the energy emitted by Earth's surface?

   F. Less than 497 nm
   G. Between 497 and 580 nm
   H. Between 580 and 725 nm
   J. Greater than 725 nm

5. Which of the following is indicated by global warming?

   A. Earth is in energy equilibrium.
   B. The wavelengths of energy emitted by Earth are getting longer.
   C. The amount of greenhouse gases in Earth's atmosphere is decreasing.
   D. Earth's ratio of energy received to energy emitted is increasing.

6. What is the effect of increasing a planet's albedo?

   F. The amount of energy emitted increases.
   G. The amount of energy emitted decreases.
   H. The amount of incoming energy increases.
   J. The amount of incoming energy decreases.

Posttest

GO ON TO THE NEXT PAGE.

Passage II

Since all machines lose some amount of energy due to friction, the amount of work put into a simple machine never equals the amount of work produced. A frictionless machine, also called a perfect machine, would have an efficiency of 100 percent. Machine efficiency is defined as

$$\text{Work}_{in} / \text{Work}_{out} \times 100 = \text{machine efficiency}$$

An automotive engineer is testing two gear designs for a transmission component. Due to design constraints, she must choose a gear design that has the highest machine efficiency possible. She is also interested in determining which of three metal alloys produces the highest efficiency with these designs, because the transmission temperatures can vary widely and many alloys have narrow temperature-range requirements. Figure 1 shows the two gear designs: bevel gears and worm gears.

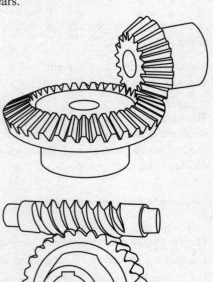

Figure 1

Table 1 shows the results of the machine efficiency trials of three versions of the bevel gear design at four different temperatures. The three versions included one each made of zinc-, titanium-, and nickel-based alloys. Each version was tested at 0°C, 100°C, 500°C, and 1000°C. The worm gear design was tested under the same conditions. Table 2 shows the trial results for the efficiency of the worm gear design.

Table 1: Bevel Gear Efficiency				
	Temperature			
Alloy type	0°C	100°C	500°C	1000°C
Zinc-based	97 %	91 %	88 %	No data
Titanium-based	94 %	94 %	93 %	91 %
Nickel-based	93 %	92 %	92 %	90 %

Table 2: Worm Gear Efficiency				
	Temperature			
Alloy type	0°C	100°C	500°C	1000°C
Zinc-based	89 %	82 %	79 %	No data
Titanium-based	85 %	85 %	92 %	81 %
Nickel-based	85 %	84 %	81 %	79 %

7. Which of the following statements about the machine efficiency is consistent with the results of the two trials?

   A. Regardless of the alloy, the worm gear design loses the least amount of energy due to friction.

   B. Regardless of the alloy, the worm gear design loses the greatest amount of energy due to friction.

   C. Regardless of the gear type, the gears made with zinc-based alloys lose the least amount of energy due to friction.

   D. Regardless of the gear type, the gears made with nickel-based alloys lose the least amount of energy due to friction.

8. Energy loss due to friction was most affected by temperature in which of the alloys?

   F. Zinc-based alloy

   G. Titanium-based alloy

   H. Nickel-based alloy

   J. Friction is not affected by the type of matter, so they must all be the same.

GO ON TO THE NEXT PAGE.

9. In both trials, the gear made with the zinc-based alloy began to fracture and fall apart as temperatures reached 800°C. Based on these results, which of the following conclusions is the scientist likely to make with regard to the zinc-based alloy?

A. The zinc-based alloy is an inferior material for transmission gears, but it is an excellent choice for low-temperature applications such as sewing machines.

B. The zinc-based alloy is a good material for transmission gears, but the transmissions will need to have cooling units installed to avoid structural damage to the gears.

C. Using zinc-based alloys is not recommended for gears of any type due to their poor machine efficiencies and low melting points.

D. The hypothesis regarding the efficiencies of various metals cannot be answered in this experiment because there is no data for the zinc alloy at 1000°C.

10. Which of the following conclusions about machine efficiencies and gear types can be made from the two trials in this experiment?

F. The most efficient gear type is the worm gear and the most efficient material is the titanium-based alloy.

G. The most efficient gear type is the worm gear and the most efficient material is the nickel-based alloy.

H. The most efficient gear type is the bevel gear and the most efficient material at all temperatures is the titanium-based alloy.

J. The most efficient gear type is the bevel gear and the most efficient material at most temperatures is the titanium-based alloy.

11. When the efficiency of a gear is less than 100%, what happens to the lost energy?

A. It is converted to work.

B. It is lost from the system as heat energy.

C. It is lost from the system as magnetic energy.

D. It is converted to the potential energy of the gear.

GO ON TO THE NEXT PAGE.

Posttest

Passage III

Primary succession is the biological colonization of dead or sterile areas following a disturbance. The progression from old glacial lake beds, formed by retreating glaciers, to coniferous forests is a well-studied example of ecological succession. As slowly decomposing aquatic plants build up in glacial lakes, different species are able to colonize. These plants, such as sphagnum moss, then form deeper peat soils, which allows tree species to colonize (see Figure 1).

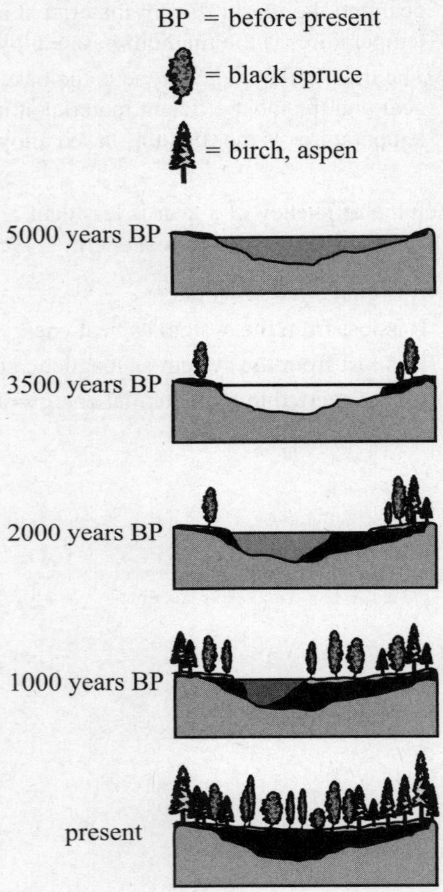

BP = before present
= black spruce
= birch, aspen
5000 years BP
3500 years BP
2000 years BP
1000 years BP
present

Figure 1

Changes in vegetation communities over long periods of time cannot be measured directly because succession occurs over hundreds or, in the case of bogs, thousands of years. However, vegetation can be measured along a gradient from open water to forested wetlands to infer successional relationships. The following figure shows the vegetation cover of four community types and the age of the peat soil based on radiocarbon dating.

70
60
50
40
30
20
10
0
percentage of cover (%)
1
15
25
50
100
200
years
birch, aspen trees
black spruce trees
sphagnum/shrubs
floating sedge mats
vegetation type

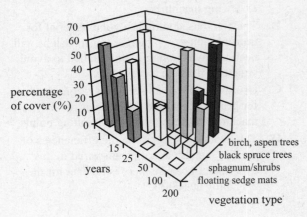

Figure 2

GO ON TO THE NEXT PAGE.

Once the glacial lake has completely filled in with peat soil, the wetland typically becomes dominated by black spruce. With time and the absence of wildfire, balsam fir may out-compete the black spruce (see Figure 3). Note that the land measures are given in hectares. One hectare is equivalent to 10,000 square meters, or 2.47 acres.

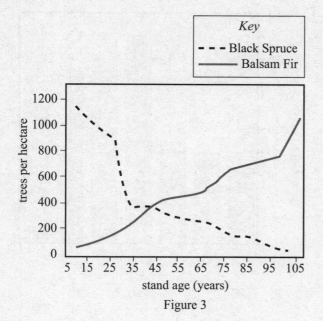

Figure 3

12. Based on the data presented in Figure 2, approximately 200 years after formation of the glacial lake, the dominant vegetation type would be:

F. floating sedge mats.

G. birch/aspen.

H. black spruce.

J. balsam fir/white cedar.

13. According to the tree density data presented in Figure 3, estimated average density of balsam fir trees 75 years after bog formation would be approximately:

A. 100 trees/hectare.

B. 400 trees/hectare.

C. 600 trees/hectare.

D. 800 trees/hectare.

14. The density data shown in Figure 3 indicate that the total tree density after 100 years is approximately 900 trees per hectare. What is the predicted total density of trees after 25 years?

F. 1000 trees/hectare

G. 100 trees/hectare

H. 300 trees/hectare

J. 1200 trees/hectare

15. Figure 1 depicts the process of peat soil formation in glacial lakes as plant biomass accumulates in the lake. What is the original source of the carbon making up this organic soil?

A. Internal recycling from many generations of plants

B. Conversion of atmospheric carbon dioxide via photosynthesis

C. Sediment buildup from the erosion of glaciers

D. Accumulation of carbon from plant respiration

16. According to the plant cover data shown in Figure 2, the progression of plant community types following lake formation is:

F. Birch/aspen → black spruce → sphagnum/shrub → sedge mats

G. Sedge mats → sphagnum/shrub → black spruce → birch/aspen

H. Birch/aspen → sphagnum/shrub → black spruce → sedge mats

J. Sphagnum/shrub → black spruce → birch/aspen → sedge mats

GO ON TO THE NEXT PAGE.

Posttest

Passage IV

Trichloroethylene (TCE) was once used widely in the dry cleaning and airline industries. Today, it is a major pollutant in groundwater. Standard clean-up methods require pumping out the groundwater, treating it, and then pumping the water back into the ground. A novel method for cleaning groundwater underground is being tested. Scientists install cleaning cells deep underground where TCE will react with H_2 and a patented catalyst (PLD-3A) to form less toxic byproducts (ethane and hydrochloric acid).

$$C_2HCl_3 + H_2 \xrightarrow{\text{PLD-3A}} C_2H_6 + 3HCl$$

Figure 1 shows the percentage reduction of TCE with increasing amounts of the catalyst PLD-3A.

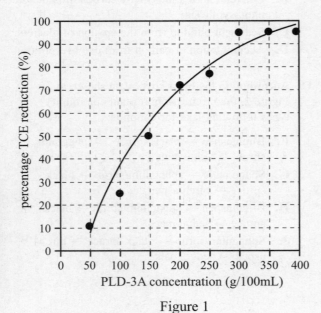

Figure 1

In order to test the effectiveness under different environmental conditions, several laboratory trials were conducted. Figure 2 shows the percentage reduction of TCE from groundwater samples at different pH levels, and Figure 3 shows similar trials at different temperatures.

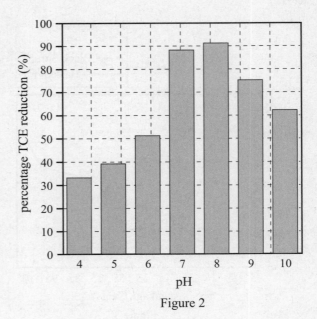

Figure 2

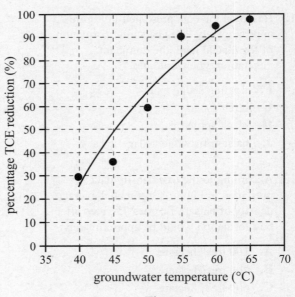

Figure 3

GO ON TO THE NEXT PAGE.

The scientists then examined the TCE reduction reaction using a pH buffer (pH=8) and again using no buffer. The two reaction series are shown in Figure 4.

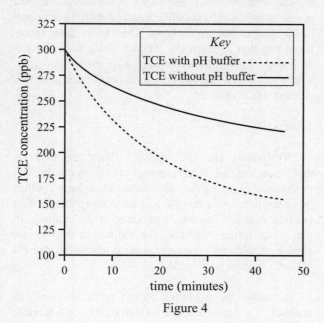

Figure 4

17. Based on the results presented in Figure 1, the appropriate concentration of PLD-3A to catalyze the reaction is:

   A. 50 g/100 mL.
   B. 200 g/100 mL.
   C. 300 g/100 mL.
   D. 400 g/100 mL.

18. Which of the following best explains the observed relationship between temperature and reaction rate?

   F. As the temperature increases, the catalyst's binding point becomes larger, allowing for easier bond formation with TCE.
   G. Hydrogen crystallizes when temperatures fall below 50°C, which keeps the molecules from bonding.
   H. As temperature increases, pH increases; the higher the pH, the greater the reaction rate.
   J. Higher temperatures cause greater molecular movement, which increases the likelihood of the reactants making contact with the catalyst.

19. Considering all the results presented, the best environmental conditions for maximizing TCE reduction would be:

   A. temperatures near 65°C and acidic.
   B. temperatures near 65°C and slightly alkaline.
   C. temperatures near 50°C and slightly alkaline.
   D. temperatures near 65°C and very acidic.

20. Which of the following conclusions can be drawn based on the reaction series shown in Figure 4?

   F. The concentration of TCE increases over time regardless of whether the pH buffer is present.
   G The concentration of TCE decreases over time only in the presence of the pH buffer.
   H. The reaction rate decreases over time regardless of whether the pH buffer is present.
   J. The reaction rate stays the same over time only in the presence of the pH buffer.

21. Which of the following best explains the effect of the addition of the pH buffer?

   A. As the reaction proceeds, the solution becomes more acidic, which reduces the effectiveness of the catalyst. The buffer minimizes this effect.
   B. As the reaction proceeds, the solution becomes more alkaline, which reduces the effectiveness of the catalyst. The buffer is used to keep the pH below 8.
   C. The reaction must be endothermic. As the reaction proceeds, heat is absorbed and the temperature decreases, causing the catalyst to slow down.
   D. The concentration of the catalyst decreases as the reaction proceeds. The buffer helps to maintain a steady concentration of PLD-3A, allowing for reaction to continue.

22. Which of the following design modifications would most likely improve the performance of the TCE removal cell under normal operating conditions (30 meters below the ground)?

   F. A built-in heating element that could warm the water to 65°C
   G. A pH meter that could maintain the pH below 8
   H. A filter to collect the TCE once the reaction was complete
   J. A rubber inner casing to reduce the conductivity of the cell

GO ON TO THE NEXT PAGE.

Posttest

Passage V

Turtles (*testudines*) are classified as reptiles, but their exact evolutionary lineage is disputed. Two hypotheses about the evolution of turtles and their ancestors are described below.

Scientist 1

Turtles belong to the group of reptiles called *anapsids*, of which all other members are extinct. Anapsids lack openings in the sides or top of the skull. This distinguishes them from *diapsids*, which have two pairs of openings, and *synapsids*, the group that includes mammals and has only one pair of openings (Table 1). The morphology (structure) of the turtle skull clearly places them within anapsids (Figure 1).

Table 1		
Category	Pairs of Side Skull Openings	Organisms
Anapsid	0	extinct early reptiles, testudines (turtles)
Synapsid	1	mammals
Diapsid	2	archosaurs (dinosaurs, crocodiles, and birds); lepidosaurs (snakes, lizards)

Anapsids included reptile-like vertebrates common in the Permian period (300–250 million years ago). The probable ancestors of testudines were large, broad-bodied reptiles called *pareiasaurs*. Some pareiasaurs had plates or spikes of a bonelike material called *osteoderm* in the skin of the upper body. Over time, these plates fused together to form the modern turtle shell. Fossils such as the 215-million-year-old *Chinlechelys tenertesta*, which has a thin shell covering its neck, back, and tail, support this evidence.

Scientist 2

Testudines are not anapsids. They are diapsids that have lost the side openings of the skull through evolution. Figure 2 shows the correct cladogram. Turtles share similarities in muscle and bone morphology with existing diapsids (snakes, birds, and other reptiles). In particular, turtles resemble the extinct *sauropterygia*, aquatic reptiles that were common in the Mesozoic era (250–65 million years ago).

Consider the evolution of the turtle shell, which consists of a rigid *carapace* (upper shell) and a flexible *plastron* (lower shell). Fossil testudines show that the plastron evolved before the carapace. Almost all extinct anapsids were *terrestrial* (living on land). Terrestrial reptiles would not benefit from a plastron because their lower bodies would be protected by the ground. Aquatic reptiles, in contrast, can be attacked from either above or below. A plastron would be adaptive in protecting the lower side of the body from attack. A recently discovered turtle species, *Odontochelys semitestacea*, had only a plastron and no carapace.

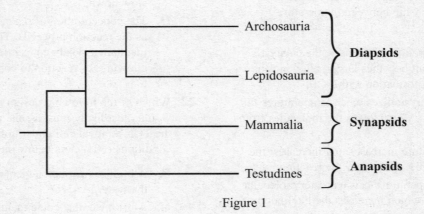

Figure 1

GO ON TO THE NEXT PAGE.

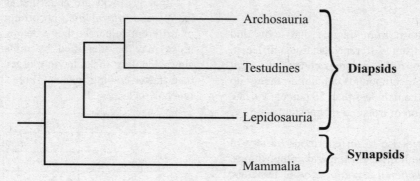

Figure 2

23. According to Table 1, which of the answer choices indicates the number of pairs of side skull openings in the organisms listed?

	Mammals	Birds	Lizards
A.	0	1	2
B.	1	2	0
C.	1	2	2
D.	2	1	0

24. According to Figure 2, turtles are most closely related to:

F. birds.
G. snakes.
H. lizards.
J. mammals.

25. According to Scientist 1:

A. pareiasaurs were anapsids.
B. modern turtles are diapsids.
C. primitive turtles were diapsids.
D. sauropterygia are primitive turtles.

26. Scientist 2 would most likely classify *Odontochelys semitestacea* as:

F. a diapsid.
G. an anapsid.
H. a synapsid.
J. a pareiasaur.

27. Which observation, if true, would best support Scientist 2's hypothesis?

A. The fossil species *Chinlechelys tenertesta* is a synapsid.
B. Fossils of sea turtles from the late Mesozoic are common.
C. The fossil species *Odontochelys semitestacea* is an anapsid.
D. Fossils of pareiasaurs were found to be the same age as turtle fossils.

GO ON TO THE NEXT PAGE.

Posttest

Passage VI

Igneous rocks form from magma that cools and solidifies. Magmas from different locations differ in chemical composition. *Felsic* magmas consist of a high percentage of silicates, compounds containing the group SiO_2. *Mafic* magmas contain less than 50 percent silicate and a higher proportion of iron and magnesium.

Magmas can give rise to an enormous variety of igneous rock, each with different mineral compositions. This is due to the *fractional crystallization* of minerals. Minerals crystallize (solidify) and separate from the remaining melted rock at different temperatures. This changes the mineral composition of rock according to the temperature and rate of cooling during formation.

Bowen's reaction series shows the temperatures at which different minerals crystallize (Figure 1). Plagioclase is a type of mineral that varies in the proportion of sodium (Na) and calcium (Ca) it contains.

Igneous rocks are classified as *felsic*, *intermediate*, *mafic*, and *ultramafic*, according to the percentage of different minerals they contain (Figure 2). Igneous rocks may be identified by mineral grain size, with slower-cooling rocks having larger, more visible grains than faster-cooling rocks. Table 1 lists examples of igneous rocks.

Table 1		
	Grain Size	
Rock Type	coarse	fine
Felsic	gabbro	basalt
Intermediate	diorite	andesite
Mafic	granite	rhyolite
Ultramafic	peridotite	komatiite

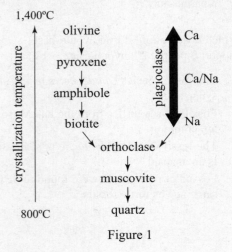

Figure 1

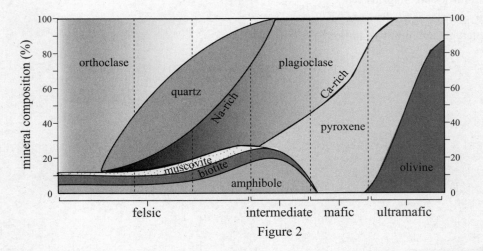

Figure 2

GO ON TO THE NEXT PAGE.

28. According to Table 1 and Figure 2, which mineral is granite most likely to contain?

F. Quartz
G. Olivine
H. Pyroxene
J. Orthoclase

29. According to Figure 1, which of the following minerals remains in the liquid state at the lowest temperature?

A. Olivine
B. Muscovite
C. Sodium-rich plagioclase
D. Calcium-rich plagioclase

30. Which of the following rock types formed from magma with the slowest rate of cooling?

F. Basalt
G. Gabbro
H. Rhyolite
J. Komatiite

31. A rock sample has the mineral composition shown below.

Mineral	% Composition
Plagioclase	30%
Quartz	30%
Amphibole	20%
Orthoclase	10%
Muscovite	5%
Biotite	5%

According to Figure 2, this rock is most likely classified as:

A. felsic.
B. mafic.
C. ultramafic.
D. intermediate.

32. A geologist finds a rock sample and determines that it contains grains of orthoclase, muscovite, biotite, and amphibole. In which order would the grains have formed during the rock's formation?

First → Last

F. Amphibole, biotite, orthoclase, muscovite
G. Biotite, amphibole, muscovite, orthoclase
H. Muscovite, orthoclase, biotite, amphibole
J. Orthoclase, muscovite, amphibole, biotite

33. Which of the following rock types contains the highest proportion of silicate?

A. Basalt
B. Diorite
C. Granite
D. Peridotite

GO ON TO THE NEXT PAGE.

Posttest

Passage VII

Most mammals have two types of photoreceptors in the retina of the eye, resulting in *dichromatic* vision. Old World primates (Old World monkeys, gibbons, and great apes, including humans) are unusual among mammals in possessing *trichromatic* color vision, the perception of color through three different photoreceptor types. Each type expresses a different light-sensitive *opsin* protein in its cell membrane. Trichromatic vision allows the organism to make finer distinctions among different colors. Figure 1 shows the responsiveness of the three opsins (S, M, and L) to light of different wavelengths.

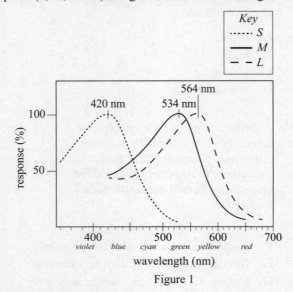

Figure 1

In Old World primates, the M and L opsin genes arose by *gene duplication* of an original M/L gene, creating two separate and distinct genes located close together on the X chromosome. The S opsin gene is located on an autosome. Figure 2 shows the relationship of New World monkeys and Old World primates.

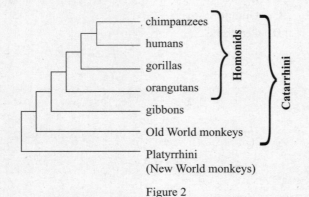

Figure 2

Color-blind people are, except in rare cases, dichromats. By far the most common type of human color blindness is red-green color blindness, a sex-linked trait. Incorrect alignment and crossing-over of the X chromosome causes the gene for the M or L opsin to be lost or nonfunctional. About 95 percent of people with this type of color blindness are male.

Some New World monkeys also have trichromatic vision. This is due to the existence of different alleles of the single M/L gene, in addition to the S gene. Monkeys with two different alleles of the M/L gene are able to distinguish among the longer wavelengths. However, their color vision differs from that of Old World primates. Table 1 compares the wavelength sensitivities and amino acid sequences of the New World M/L alleles and the Old World M and L genes.

Table 1		
Clade	Allele/ Gene	Peak sensitivity (nm)
New World	M/L–1	535
New World	M/L–2	550
New World	M/L–3	563
Old World	M	534
Old World	L	564

34. According to Figure 1, which has the greatest sensitivity to light with a wavelength of 474 nanometers?

  F. S opsin
  G. M opsin
  H. L opsin
  J. M and L opsins

35. In a dichromatic individual with red-green color blindness, which opsins may be affected?

  A. S or L opsins
  B. S or M opsins
  C. M or L opsins
  D. S, M, or L opsins

GO ON TO THE NEXT PAGE.

36. Light with a frequency of 550 nm hits the retina of a person with normal trichromatic color vision. Which of this person's photoreceptors will be activated by the light?

```
        S M L
F.      + − −
G.      − + +
H.      − + −
J.      + − +
```

37. The cladogram below shows four locations marked with arrows.

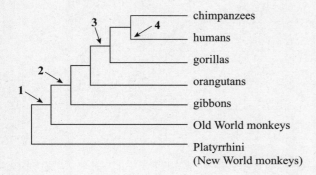

Which arrow shows where the gene duplication event leading to the *M* and *L* genes occurred?

A. Arrow 1   C. Arrow 3
B. Arrow 2   D. Arrow 4

38. According to the passage, which of the following conclusions is true?

F. All male Old World primates have dichromatic vision.

G. All female New World monkeys have trichromatic vision.

H. Only male Old World primates can have dichromatic vision.

J. Only female New World monkeys can have trichromatic vision.

39. According to Table 1, which alleles in New World monkeys are most similar to the M and L genes in Old World monkeys?

A. M/L-1 and M/L-2
B. M/L-2 and M/L-3
C. M/L-1 and M/L-3
D. M/L-3 only

40. Which of the following shows a likely combination of photoreceptor sensitivities in a New World monkey?

F.

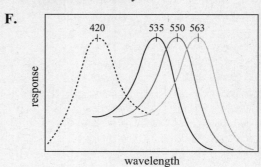

G.

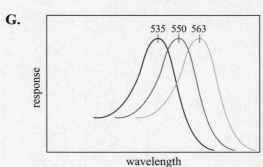

H.

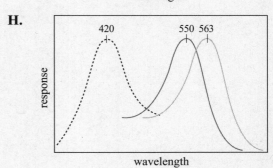

J.

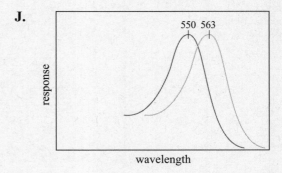

END OF TEST

STOP!

NOTES

NOTES

NOTES